THE AIRGUN BOOK

T·H·E
AIRGUN
B·O·O·K

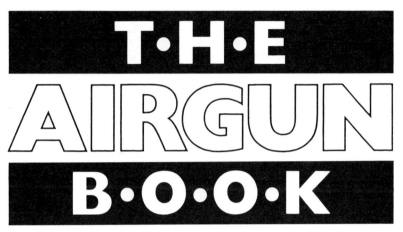

John Walter

The fully revised fourth edition of the classic one-volume guide to the world's airguns

ARMS AND ARMOUR PRESS
London ● New York ● Sydney

For Sue

First published in Great Britain in 1987 by Arms and Armour Press, Artillery House, Artillery Row, London SW1P 1RT

Distributed in the USA by Sterling Publishing Co. Inc., 2 Park Avenue, New York, NY 10016.

Distributed in Australia by Capricorn Link (Australia) Pty Ltd., P.O. Box 665, Lane Cove, New South Wales 2066, Australia

British Library Cataloguing in Publication Data

Walter, John D.
  The Airgun Book
  1. Air guns
  I. Title
  683.4   TS537.5

ISBN 0-85368-882-6

Key abbreviations and conversions

ACL: accuracy consistency limit.
e.g.: for example.
fp: one foot-pound — a measure of energy obtained by squaring the velocity (in fs^{-1}), multiplying it by the pellet weight in grains and dividing the answer by 450,240 (a constant arising from the fact that there are 7,000 grains in a pound and that the value of g, the gravitational constant, has been assumed to be $32.16fs^{-1}$). 1fp equates to 1.3558 joules.
fs^{-1}: one foot per second.
ft: one foot — 12in or 305mm.
gm: one gram — 0.03525oz or 15.432gn.
gn: one grain — 0.002286oz or 0.0648gm.
i.e.: that is.
in: one inch, 25.4mm.
ISU: International Shooting Union (see also UIT).
Joule (or J): a measure of energy. 1J equates to 0.7376fp (cf., German airgun energy limit of 7.5J).
kg: one kilogram — 2.2046lb, or 15,432.2gn.
lb: one pound — 16oz or 453.59gm.
m: one metre — 39.37in, 3.2808ft or 1.0936yd.
mf: manufacturer's claim.
mgp: mean grouping potential.
mm: one millimetre, 0.03937in.
na: not available.
nk: not known.
oa: overall length.
oz: one ounce — 28.2495gm or 437.5gn.
UIT: Union Internationale de Tir, the French name for the International Shooting Union (see ISU).
VCI: velocity consistency index.
VCL: velocity consistency limit.
yd: one yard — 36in, 3ft or 914.4mm.

Chronoscopes supplied by Skan Electronics.
Data processing by Susan Walter on Osborne, Amstrad and Commodore computers.

Designed by John Walter.
Origination by Service Twenty Four Ltd, Brighton.
Printed and bound in Great Britain by R.J. Acford Ltd, Chichester.

Contents

Preface and author's acknowledgement

A PERSONAL VIEW

This edition – the fourth of a series that began as recently as 1981 – departs considerably from its 1984-vintage predecessor not simply because of the passage of time, but rather because a change has occurred in the airgun scene.

When the very first airgun book was being compiled in 1980-1, sporting airguns included junior rifles intended to lead their purchasers upward to bigger and better things; and the phrase 'competition' allowed no other interpretation than 'paper punching', though the bell-target ringing leagues were still doggedly clinging to their traditions. During the 1980s, however, much of the impetus behind classical airgun target shooting has dissipated – possibly due to the supervision of ISU 10-metre shooting by the NSRA – and field-target shooting has grown immensely in popularity. The first competitions were enjoyable, and acceptably (but somewhat informally) organised. Consequently, the club scene, dormant since NARPA's disappearance, has blossomed once again and led to the formation of the British Field Target Association (BFTA).

In 1981, a good, powerful air rifle could be acquired for £55 (the price of the BSA Mercury); allowing for inflation at 7 per cent per annum, this would equate to a little over £82 in 1987. High-power sporters are still in this price bracket, as the Weihrauch HW35 and the Webley Vulcan II can be acquired for about £80-85, and the BSA Mercury Challenger – a more powerful and effectual gun than the Mercury III – will cost about £95 after some judicious shopping around. However, no-one wins a field target shoot's top prize with a gun of this class. Tuning, customization, silencers; sights costing several times as much as a standard gun; non-standard stocks; all these are inseparable from the championship guns, which can cost £800 – more, indeed, than the acme of competition rifle sophistication (cf., Walther LGR Match Universal and Feinwerkbau LG600 at £550-600).

That performance has improved is unquestionable; whether it is improving in direct relationship with the necessary capital investment is, however, less obvious. None of the largest manufacturers seems willing to mass-produce even the best of the privately-developed guns, which would undoubtedly reduce prices, and the reasons cannot simply be accountancy practices or licensing fees. Could it be that these companies sense a gradual contraction in the market and do not wish to invest too much too soon? And what has happened to the traditional progression from junior through intermediate to adult guns?

With the average sporting gun now costing perhaps £120-150, changes in the market-place are inevitable. The increased revenue potential of the industry, arising from higher priced products, probably masks a decline in the numbers of guns being made in Britain. And most of new guns being announced in blazes of publicity *are* expensive: the Galway Fieldmaster II is nearly £400; the Air Arms Shamal, another pre-charged pneumatic, will probably settle to nearer £450; the Saxby-Palmer Herald is priced at £350; the Air Logic Genesis will be £420-460, the Imperial Double Express is currently £550 and the Sportsmatch GC2 costs £850. These guns will often be kept for far longer than had they been part of the traditional buying chain, and, in due course, the average price of guns on the second-hand market must also rise appreciably. Good five-year-old HW35E Weihrauchs, for example, will now recoup their purchase price when sold second-hand!

One effect of the change in emphasis in the market place has been the undermining of the traditional junior airgun's position. Though the BSA Meteor and the El Gamo Cadet (ASI Apache) are still encountered in large numbers, the Milbros have gone; Crosman and Daisy junior guns are less popular now than they were; and even the cheap M&G Dianas are not selling in the quantities they once did. Of course, Mayer & Grammelspacher is in the throes of introducing a series of new guns, with inevitable dislocation, and time will be needed to restore retailers' faith in BSA after the company's collapse in 1986. Sales of the Crosman and Daisy guns have, admittedly, been weakened by continual changes in British agencies and — with the prices of the Spanish imports approaching comparability with the BSA Meteor — finding efficient low-cost junior guns is increasingly difficult. Though some of Italian and Chinese spring-piston guns (together with the Russian Baikal) are very cheap, their advantages are often illusory and their drawbacks can be severe enough to discourage a young airgunner.

The British airgun industry has to survive to fulfil large-scale demands, which (at the time of writing) it seems to be doing principally on the strength of export orders. Cottage industries customizing Weihrauchs are booming; but many small businesses are needed to equal the revenue-earning capacity of one large industrial concern. Even thirty one-man businesses cannot fill the gap left by the collapse of just one hundred-man company capable of true series production, and certainly fall well short of the employment generated by BSA, Webley & Scott and Milbro in their heyday.

Had the principal British manufacturers matched Weihrauch's trigger twenty years ago; had they clung to blueing instead of proffering baked-on paint; and had they not substituted amorphous hardwood for elegant walnut stocks, the story may have been so different. Perhaps the mass market would not have paid the necessary price but, in retrospect, it seems as though the British airgun makers followed the lead of others only when forced to do so — instead of being in the vanguard themselves. British airgunning may now be at a crossroads and a change of attitude must be induced in the public before the industry can be returned to a semblance of its former glory.

There are signs that even the German airgun manufacturers are finding life increasingly hard as a result of saturation in their home market, the effect of a strong Deutschmark and the effect in Britain of the Theoben Sirocco, the Saxby-Palmers, the Daystate Huntsman series and the Galway Fieldmaster. Hardly a month pases on the British airgun scene without the appearance something interesting, the Imperial Double Express, the Air Logic Genesis, the Air Arms Shamal and the Sportsmatch GC2 being notable recent examples. Virtually all of the new British guns could be mass-produced with no greater difficulty than a spring-piston system, but no-one seems willing to do so.

Indeed, the British seem to have temporarily lost the ability to translate prototypes to series production; in this connexion, the companies concerned would do well to heed the lesson of the Sinclair company, which persistently advertised products before they were ready and in the end fell foul of the law.

The British undoubtedly have the ideas to make a determined assault on the worldwide export markets, but have we the inclination to crystallise the dream?

Unfortunately, the status of the airgun – and, by implication, the airgunner – is scrutinised from the Home Office downwards through the RSPCA and RSPB, magistrates and police to 'concerned' journalists. A poll taken in the streets today would undoubtedly favour the anti-airgun faction. Airgunners seemingly forget that their sport *can* be regulated by the will of the majority in a democracy and that public opinion must be persuaded that airgunners, individually and collectively, are responsible adults. A single stupid but otherwise inconsequential act, or an ill-considered airgun magazine editorial, may do incalculable damage to our cause if it achieves public notoriety.

It is a proven fact that crime involving legally-held firearms is a minor fraction of that involving those held illegally; and that, therefore, most legitimate firearms owners are demonstrably law-abiding. This is as true of airgunners as it is of firearms certificate holders, but the image is tarnished when parents ignore the evidence of their children's vandalism, when supposedly reputable airgun dealers knowingly sell over-limit guns 'under the counter', and when legions of field shooters are turned away from shoots because their guns transgress a law that entered the Statute Books twenty years ago. As a result, a chapter on airgun law has been added to this edition; though by no means exhaustive, it goes further than the two laudable (but rather superficial) pamphlets commonly available and attempts to explain some of the most commonly encountered problems.

I have spent many thousands of hours analysing velocities obtained from a wide range of guns and pellets, and remain concerned that the Dangerous Airgun Rules in their present form make no concession to velocity fluctuations. There is no absolute guarantee that next year's pellet will not perform illegally in this year's gun, but though some progress has been made towards defining standard testing conditions, much has still to be done. I have no particular objection to a limit of 12fp, though the German 7.5 joules – only 5.53fp, incidentally – is too low to kill pests such as crows or large rats at anything but ultra-close range. But I hope that the Gun Trade Association, in its quest for 'workable' rules, realises that protection granted to the purchaser of an airgun is vital to goodwill. With the ready availability of chronography, the dealer should be able to look after himself! Plausible solutions to the problems will be found in the airgun law chapter. Unfortunately, to be effectual, they would need the co-operation and goodwill not only of the GTA, individual traders and the public, but also from the Home Office. Could even this be forthcoming in time...?

The compilation of this new edition has benefitted greatly from the co-operation of many manufacturers, distributors, customizers and consumers. In addition to the appended list, I would like to say a particular 'thank you' to Colin Greenwood, Editor of *Guns Review*, for his friendship and guidance through some of the pitfalls of the law, and for gritting his teeth while I delayed yet another 'Airgun Scene' article to work on this book; to Roderick Dymott, Director of Arms & Armour Press, for his enthusiasm and continued support;

ACKNOWLEDGEMENT

Malcolm and Sarah Cooper of Accuracy International; Bob Nicholls and Bill Sanders of Air Arms; John Stevens of The Airgun Centre; *Air Gunner* magazine; Gary Cobb, Editor of *Airgun News and Report*; John Fletcher, Editor of *Airgun World*; Dave Welham of Airmasters; Giacomo Cagnoni of Air-Match SRL; Reinhart Grassdorf of J.G. Anschütz GmbH; ASI; Ramón Hernaltes of Norberto Arizmendi SA; Martin Barthelmes of Fritz Barthelmes KG; Graham Barton of Battle Orders; the Benjamin Air Rifle Company; John Bowkett; Ken White and Ted Read of BSA Guns (UK) Ltd; L. Camilleri of L.J. Cammell (Merseyside) Ltd; Gerald Cardew of CARD; the Crosman Arms Company; David H. Lewis of the Daisy Manufacturing Company; Dieter Häge of Dianawerk; Frank Dyke & Co. Ltd; Eley Ltd; E. Micheli of Fiocchi Munizioni SPA; J.C. Casas of Industrias El Gamo SA; Lionel Leventhal of Greenhill Books; Joachim Görtz; Leslie Hewett Ltd; John Burns of the Home Office Forensic Science Laboratory, Huntingdon; Hull Cartridge Company; Colin Melluish; Colin Fisher of Milbro Caledonian Pellets Ltd; John Knibbs of P&J Springs; Hugh Earl of Prometheus Pellets Ltd; John and Bob Rothery of John Rothery (Wholesale) Co. Ltd; Royal Ordnance plc, Enfield; Roy Palmer and Colin Rowe of Saxby & Palmer Ltd; David Pickering of the Scalemead Arms Company; Michael Childs of Skan Electronics; Kensuke Chiba of the Sharp Rifle Company; John Ford of Sportsmatch; David Theobald and Ben Taylor of Theoben Engineering; Derek Bernard of Transmission Systems Ltd; Dave Pope of the Venom Arms Company; Peter Hoffmann of Carl Walther GmbH; John Knight of Webley & Scott Ltd; Hans-Hermann Weihrauch and Hans-Hermann Weihrauch, Jun., of Hermann Weihrauch KG.

Examining the bore. By courtesy of Dianawerk.

Milling the bifurcated air-cylinder extension of a barrel-cocker. By courtesy of Dianawerk.

to Dr Robert Beeman, for supplying information above and beyond the call of duty; to Colin and Teresa Hodgson of Sharpshooters Ltd, Eastbourne, for their time, trouble, coffee and premises (but not necessarily in that order); and to the members of Eastbourne Airgunners, who unwittingly expressed opinions that had much wider implications than they sometimes imagined.

To my parents, parents-in-law and long suffering wife Sue — who has put up with me and *The Airgun Book* for approximately the same period — all I can say is that there **is** life behind the pile of papers, photographs and instruction manuals... until the fifth edition.

John Walter
Hampden Park, Eastbourne, 1987

Introduction
Velocity, accuracy and performance

EXPERIMENTAL METHODS

The previous edition of *The Airgun Book* dwelt at length on the development of the ballistic pendulum and the chronograph (pp.49-51), together with the acceptable mathematical derivation of velocity and accuracy (pp.52-62). Despite interest evinced by airgun manufacturers who wished to find better ways of analysing the performance of their airguns, the system has yet to be widely accepted. This may be partly due to its apparent complexity, but also to its time-consuming nature; after all, it is far easier to measure the diameter of a five-shot group!

The widespread distribution of micro-computers gives many of the smaller manufacturers, gunsmiths and individual airgunners access to machines such as the Spectrum, the Amstrad or an IBM PC. For the purposes of this book, therefore, the analysis has been refined to suit electronic data processing and transferred to the Appendices. The methods by which the results are now being assessed are acceptable within the universally accepted statistical conventions.

It is easy to obtain velocity figures from SKAN or CARD chronographs, several patterns of which may be obtained for less than £200. Though offering fewer features than the best of the American Oehler or German Weinlich machines, the British examples are more than adequate for airgunners' purposes. The requirements are then no more than the time required to fire 25 shots and enter 25 figures in a statistical calculator or computer, plus the additional short period in which the latter sorts, calculates, displays and prints the answers.

Shooting for accuracy presents a greater problem. Though the method by which this is now undertaken was all but finalized for the Third Edition, too much time was still being spent adjusting each shot of five 5-shot series to a single 'group centre'. Eventually, an electronic graph-pad was connected to the computer and programmed to feed information directly into the memory without any time-consuming manual transcriptions.* Firing takes place on specially-printed targets, taking a constant aim-point but without adjusting the sights. Each target is then placed on the graph-pad, which is really no more than an electronic grid, and the centre of each individual shot 'entered' by means of a stylus. This automatically feeds the co-ordinates into the computer.

Once all 25 shots have been registered, the computer adjusts the figures to their 10-metre equivalent, calculates, displays and prints the mean grouping potential (mgp), assesses fluctuations and predicts the score on an ISU target.

Though there are plausible objections to the way in which the ISU target scoring is assessed – scores occasionally improve if the centre of the 25-shot group is not superimposed on the centre of the target – theory and practice

* The system eventually resolved into a Hegotron Robotics Grafpad 3 connected to a Commodore PC10 IBM-compatible computer, but ran initially (and quite happily) on an Amstrad CPC 6128.

These groups show how pellet changes affect accuracy. They were obtained from a 5.5mm Weihrauch HW77K firing (a) Scalemead Hustler, (b) RWS Superpoint, (c) BSA Pylarm, (d) RWS Diabolo and (e) Silver Jet. The 'total plots' of the 25-shot sequences are shown here approximately life-size. Group (f) was obtained from a 4.5mm Diana LG75U T01 firing H&N Match Select pellets, and (g) from the same gun with less impressive Hustler Match.

rarely deviate by more than a point or two in 100. However, the comparative insensitivity of the simpler graph-pads, the vertical resolution of which is often only about 0.3mm, introduces an additional approximation to the results. The older individual measurement method was sometimes capable of better accuracy, though this was often hidden in the difficulty of locating the true centre of each pellet strike — particularly in cloverleaf or one-hole groups.

The greatest asset of the graph-pad/computer link is the speed with which it can deduce results; instead of an hour or more to assess a single trial, the process now takes little more than two minutes to enter the 25 shots. The calculations are practically instantaneous, with the full print-out taking perhaps 30 seconds.

SCORING

An airgun barrel can be clamped in a fixed rest — such as the Pax Airguns bench, which is an excellent design — but, as this only gives a clue to the performance of the air-cylinder/barrel combination in an arbitrary environment, it bears little relationship to what may be expected in normal use. Pellet makers such as Dynamit Nobel regularly batch-test their match ammunition in this way and achieve groups whose diameters are little more than that of a single individual pellet. Tests of this type are necessary to establish whether the ammunition is capable of achieving a perfect score; and the capabilities of the marksman and his chosen gun, moreover, must be deliberately excluded.†

For the purposes of this book, accuracy trials were shot with the fore-hand on a sandbag rest. Despite the spring-surge and 'jump' of spring-piston guns, much of which clearly occurs before the pellet leaves the muzzle, the freehand method gave similar results to barrel-clamping; some guns even appeared to shoot more accurately. That 250×250 has never been achieved is simply due to the ammunition, which rarely reaches the consumer in the condition in which it was tested at the factory; apart from the individually packed match examples, pellets have usually been rattling about in transit or storage for some time. However, scores of 245×250 have been obtained from sporting guns and inherent performance deficiencies in guns or ammunition are easily detectable.

The manufacturers of top-grade target rifles generally reward marksmen who perform well with their guns — Feinwerkbau, for example, awards a silver pin for 520×600 and gold for 540×600. To put the accuracy of the best sporting rifles into proper context, the Webley Omega tried in 1985 would have attained

† The world air-rifle record currently stands at 'only' 595×600, so even gold medallists are incapable of perfection. Scores of 597×600 have twice been recorded, once in competition by Harald Stenvaag of Norway and once in the 1984 US pre-Olympic trials, both being achieved with Walther pneumatic rifles.

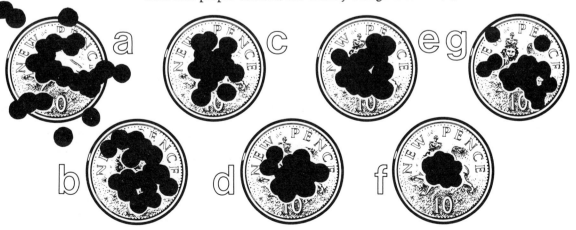

540×600 with BSA Pylarms, 529×600 with RWS Superpoints and 542×600 with RWS Diabolo pellets. The best scores achieved during testing equated to 591×600 with a second-hand Walther LGR and Eley Wasp pellets and a remarkable 585×600 with a Theoben Sirocco and specially selected RWS Superpoint pellets.

VELOCITY AND ACCURACY

It was once believed that consistent generation of velocity was essential to good airgun accuracy. However, the laggard perfection of the accuracy assessment system finally proved that direct correlation was unlikely. Occasionally, guns whose velocity indices bettered a praiseworthy 1 per cent shot wildly; others returned 1.5 per cent, 2 per cent or worse, yet produced cloverleaf groups. A cheap spring-piston Norica proved incapable of shooting 3cm groups at 10 metres, despite a velocity index as good as 0.57 per cent; on another occasion, an Airsporter that had regularly bettered 1 per cent shot poorly with a wide range of pellets. And all the time an old Weihrauch HW35, with a weak spring and a somewhat erratic action, was averaging more than 85×100 on the ISU target.

These anomalies were traced to the barrel of the Norica, in which a burr appeared to be scoring the pellets as they emerged from the muzzle. The BSA, conversely, showed no obvious manufacturing deficiencies until dirt was seen

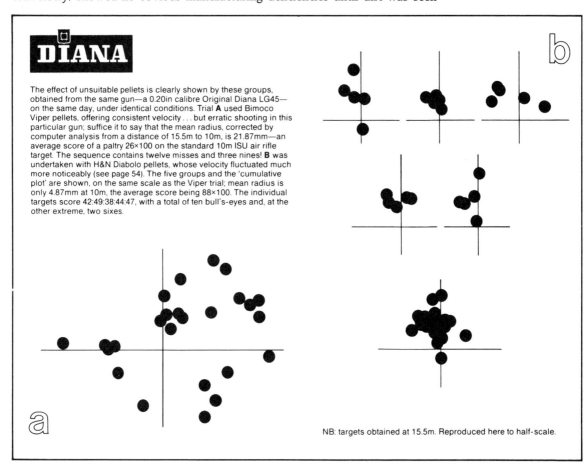

DIANA

The effect of unsuitable pellets is clearly shown by these groups, obtained from the same gun—a 0.20in calibre Original Diana LG45—on the same day, under identical conditions. Trial **A** used Bimoco Viper pellets, offering consistent velocity . . . but erratic shooting in this particular gun; suffice it to say that the mean radius, corrected by computer analysis from a distance of 15.5m to 10m, is 21.87mm—an average score of a paltry 26×100 on the standard 10m ISU air rifle target. The sequence contains twelve misses and three nines! **B** was undertaken with H&N Diabolo pellets, whose velocity fluctuated much more noticeably (see page 54). The five groups and the 'cumulative plot' are shown, on the same scale as the Viper trial; mean radius is only 4.87mm at 10m, the average score being 88×100. The individual targets score 42:49:38:44:47, with a total of ten bull's-eyes and, at the other extreme, two sixes.

NB: targets obtained at 15.5m. Reproduced here to half-scale.

to be preventing the loading tap seating properly; the rifle shot much better once it had been cleaned. The poor external condition of the Weihrauch belied its excellent bore, which proved more than capable of overcoming fluctuations in velocity.‡

Precisely what limits airgun accuracy may never be discovered without access to a research laboratory. Indeed, no adequate research into the ballistics of airgun pellets has yet been completed and too many modern claims are based on the traditional approach of *Hatcher's Notebook*, the British *Text Books of Small Arms* or ammunition-reloading handbooks. As most of these were based on experiments with artillery shells and rifle bullets, their relevance to diabolo pellets is questionable. In addition, Ingalls' Tables — the cornerstone of many airgun-pellet drop tables — are notoriously suspect at low velocities.

Part of the airflow over the surface of a conventional diabolo pellet may become trans-sonic when velocities exceed $850fs^{-1}$, though at $575fs^{-1}$ (accepted as optimal) little if any of the flow around a conventional pellet is affected. Once boundary flow becomes supersonic, drag increases radically before stabilising at a higher value; accuracy often deteriorates proportionately.* Consequently, super-power sporting airguns rarely shoot as accurately as those developing less than 12fp; for example, tests of high-power airguns, trans-sonic even with standard 0.22 pellets, have shown that they are rarely capable of grouping inside four inches at 40 feet. Power is undesirable unless compatible ammunition is available.

PELLET PERFORMANCE

Sufficient gyro-stability must be imparted to each pellet, but most manufacturers rifle their barrels similarly (indeed, several buy completed barrels from suppliers such as Lothar Walther) and serious mistakes are rarely made with rifling pitch.† However, a shooter must expect variations in azimuth (drift) when a pellet attaining $600fs^{-1}$ is compared with another developing $800fs^{-1}$ in the same gun. Differences of this magnitude are often obtained from light, fast moving Beeman Lasers and heavyweight H&N Barracudas. A trial undertaken in 1980 for Prometheus Pellets Ltd by the Royal Small Arms Factory, Enfield, showed that a 5.5mm H&N Match pellet hit nearly 49in below and 14.5in to the left of the aim-point at a distance of 109yd (100 metres), compared with 24in down and 1in to the right for the faster-moving Prometheus.‡

Assuming that a gun plays its part in generating the pellet-flight equations satisfactorily, uniformity of pellet shape is undoubtedly one of the most important factors governing airgun accuracy; minor fluctuations in pellet weight, conversely, severely degrade accuracy only if they disturb the centre of gravity in relation to the longitudinal pellet axis. Presenting an entirely flat-headed pellet to airflow will obviously create more drag than a roundhead, which will slip through the air more easily, and a smooth head will clearly be better than a rough surface. Yet all pellets of the same brand will only perform similarly if they are made so that variations in head shape, concentricity and surface finish are held to a minimum.

There are several popular cone points, and proprietary designs such as the hollowed-out head of the Beeman Silver Bear. No-one has yet published results of wind tunnel trials on these shapes, determined accurate drag coefficients* or assessed pellet performance in relation to range. That the flathead cuts clean holes in a 10-metre target is undeniable, but can a roundhead

‡ The difference in drop between pellets travelling at constant velocities of 500 and $600fs^{-1}$ across a gap of 50 feet is a mere 0.60in. Guns will easily group far larger than this, owing to the many other factors involved.

* The speed of sound is about $1,115fs^{-1}$ at sea level under 'normal conditions' — 15°C and an atmospheric pressure of 1 bar.

† However, the minor differences between the various rifling pitches may explain why some makers' guns shoot better at long range than others.

‡ The velocities were $587fs^{-1}$ and $705fs^{-1}$ respectively, fired from an Anschütz LG335. Though the Prometheus dropped less than its rivals when pitted against the H&N Match and the comparatively flat headed Champion Hunter (ostensibly a truncated cone-point), it is doubtful whether it would have struck above the RWS Superpoint or Silver Jet.

* This in turn influences the coefficient of form and the ballistic coefficient, on which predictions of velocity retention depend.

perform as well despite its poorer hole-punching ability? And is the cone-point really advantageous at 30 yards?

Though no proper ballistic coefficients are available – obtaining these conventionally and substituting them in Ingalls' Tables is risky – loss of velocity could be determined empirically and an equation of curve deduced for each type of pellet. This, in turn, would indicate what may be expected from a group of essentially similar pellets. However, the results can only be phrased in the most general terms, as the carrying properties of a pellet depend not only on its initial velocity but also on its sectional density (obtained by dividing the weight by the square of the pellet diameter). The heavier a pellet of given diameter, the better it retains velocity provided the same head-shape is retained. The 5.5mm RWS Superdome and H&N Barracuda pellets have much the same head shape, yet the former weighs about 14.5gn and the latter more than 21gn. As the Barracuda is almost half as heavy again as the Superdome, but offers the same cross-sectional area to the airflow, its sectional density is also 50 per cent higher. This promotes better retention of velocity and momentum; and, though the Barracuda emerges at an appreciably lower muzzle velocity than the Superdome (and has a higher vertex of trajectory), its maximum range is roughly comparable.

The correlation between sectional density and retention of velocity has been put to good use in the Sussex Sabo, whose bullet offers an effectual combination of shape, surface finish and weight. The Sabo is actually a sub-calibre projectile with a diameter of only 0.175in, once the plastic cage has been discarded at the muzzle. The value of a boat-tail is by no means established in subsonic velocity ranges, but the Sabo clearly retains its momentum better than virtually any other airgun projectile.

The Prometheus is a more conventional – and undeniably more convenient – combination of an alloy head/core and a synthetic skirt than the Sabo, and owes its effectual flight to a brightly polished ogival head and as streamlined a skirt as can be compatible with the raised sealing ribs. However, the use of a zinc-alloy core restricts the weight of the 0.22 pellet to 9.12gn and reduces sectional density. This is counteracted by unusually high velocity ($800fs^{-1}$ or more will often be achieved in standard 0.22 or 5.5mm rifles) and so the Prometheus, though decelerating rapidly, nonetheless performs well at normal shooting ranges.

At velocities of $800fs^{-1}$ or more, parts of the boundary flow over the Prometheus pellet's surface must be trans-sonic. However, the smoothness of the basic design minimises drag and the Prometheus is often unusually accurate once lead residue has been scrubbed from the rifle bore.

SUPER-POWER GUNS

Where ultra high-power airguns are concerned, already developing trans-sonic velocities with standard pellets, Prometheus may emerge at $1,150fs^{-1}$ or more; even in an 0.22 Ensign Magnum, capable of propelling the heavyweight Barracuda at only $700fs^{-1}$, Prometheus attained $985fs^{-1}$. At supersonic velocity, however, friction in the bore partially melts the pellet skirts, leads to a build up of plastic fouling at the muzzles of choked-bore guns and completely ruins accuracy. The problems have been solved by developing a harder skirt material, with which cloverleaf 40-foot groups can be obtained from most super-power guns in the 15-22fp energy ranges. Once 30fp is approached,

† During a recent independent
test of a Theoben Eliminator
producing energies up to 30fp,
undertaken by Theoben Engineering
and Prometheus Pellets Ltd, only
Titan Black pellets managed to group
properly at 40 feet.

however, only the heavyweight Titan Black performs properly. This is basically a heavy-core Prometheus, generating lower velocity but offering better sectional density and enhanced carrying properties at the expense of dispensing with non-toxicity. Unlike the diabolos, which perform very badly in this energy range owing to their basically subsonic body-shape, the Titan Black is much more like a conventional rifle bullet.†

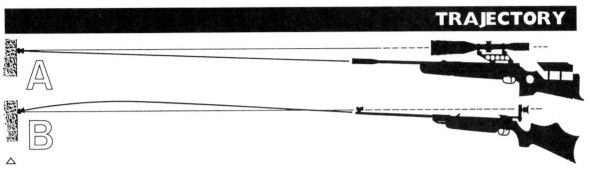

TRAJECTORY

Two possible trajectories, commonly encountered with sights mounted high above the axis of the bore. Case (a) is more usual in high-power guns at comparatively short ranges, while (b) suits low-power guns at medium distances or high power guns at long range.

The effect of changing to a different pellet-brand is important to airgunners, many of whom set their sights for a certain pre-determined distance. Virtually all the published pellet-drop tables assume the muzzle is horizontal and simply calculate the drop due to gravity once the time of flight to selected ranges has been determined. However, the gun is more usually sighted for ten or 30 yards and its muzzle is elevated at the instant of firing; the sight-axis also lies some distance above the axis of the bore; and, it is fair to say, the tables are often owe more to 'straight-line guesstimation' than true trajectory curves, which can only be obtained by highly sophisticated mathematics.

Assuming weights are roughly equal, ogival headed pellets seem to retain velocity best (a little better than cone-points), followed by roundheads with the flatheads lagging. However, individual flathead brands perform much less alike than may be supposed: a phenomenon that may be rooted in the degree of edge-chamfer.

There may be another insuperable obstacle to the provision of accurate pellet-drop tables. Trials to determine the ballistic coefficient of flat-head pellets were expected to provide comparable data from a 5.5mm-calibre Feinwerkbau Sport and a similar Weihrauch HW77. Though these guns developed practically identical muzzle velocities, the pellets were found to be performing markedly differently at 50 feet. The same problem occurred with an 0.177 BSA Mercury S and a 4.5mm M&G Diana LG45 developing 820-835fs^{-1}; and then in two target rifles, a Feinwerkbau LG300S and an M&G Diana LG75, at 575-580fs^{-1}. This was totally unexpected; though ballistic coefficients had been expected to vary with changes in velocity, the individual guns had not been expected to have any marked influence.

It is now suspected that the performance of an airgun depends more greatly on its pressure/time curve and barrel-length than had been realised. The velocity of a bullet fired from a rifle is controlled principally by the characteristics of the propellant and the weight of the power charge; in an airgun, velocity may depend more on the acceleration (or deceleration) acting on a pellet at the muzzle. Shortening an airgun barrel may materially affect performance; even though no difference may be seen at less than 20 metres, long-range shooting may even improve in cases where the pellet was decelerating because the barrel was too long (cf., possibly, Weihrauch HW35L and HW35E).

Performance of Original/Diana LG75U T01 with flathead pellets

mgp: mean grouping potential at 10 metres. ISU: score on International Shooting Union 10m rifle target, out of 100.

Bimoco Elite:	mgp 7.57mm	ISU 92.0
Champion Olympic Match:	mgp 5.37mm	ISU 96.0
H&N Match Select (ribbed):	mgp 5.62mm	ISU 94.8
H&N Match Select (plain):	mgp 3.89mm	ISU 98.2
Hustler Match (seated):	mgp 8.73mm	ISU 88.8
Hustler Match:	mgp 9.62mm	ISU 86.8
RWS Meisterkugeln (tin):	mgp 4.74mm	ISU 96.8
RWS Meisterkugeln (individual):	mgp 3.73mm	ISU 98.0
Stiga Match:	mgp 11.72mm	ISU 83.2
Stiga Match (seated):	mgp 5.33mm	ISU 95.2

The pellets with proprietary head shapes offer an interesting variety in performance. The Prometheus would shoot better at long range if it was of normal weight, while the sub-calibre Sabo performs well provided the sabot separates properly; the hollow-headed Beeman Ram Jet performs more like a flathead than a roundhead; while the differences between the Silver Jet and the RWS Superpoint (which has only one head-ring rather than three) owe more to the velocity-reducing effects of friction than any additional drag or interference contributed by the former's more massive head.

PELLET QUALITY

There is little discernible difference in the accuracy potential of unlike pellets of equal weight, length and diameter, provided they have perfectly formed heads of equal smoothness. The most expensive pellets tend to be the best made; consequently, Silver Jet, to name but one, often performs as well as standard RWS or H&N Match pellets at field-target ranges. Budget-price pellets are rarely made to the same high standards and casting flash, eccentric or damaged points, flaws in the alloy or crudely finished skirt ribs all degrade accuracy. Low-priced products such as the Italian-made Hustlers can rarely compare with Eley Wasps or RWS Diabolos even in the best gun. The exception seems to be RWS Hobby pellets, which are very competitively priced but still greatly favoured for field-target airgunning.

Comparing RWS Superpoint and H&N Pointed pellets reveals that the former has an unusually thin-walled smooth skirt and a brightly-polished conical nose with a well-formed point, while the latter has a strong ribbed skirt and a less precise point. To achieve optimal accuracy, only Superpoints with undamaged skirts should be selected, as they are very easily deformed in the tins. Conversely, though the sturdy skirts of the H&N pellets are rarely deformed in the same manner, the points should be examined before chambering lest they be sufficiently off-centre to degrade accuracy.

The merits and drawbacks of each individual brand of pellet may be hidden by the quirks of individual guns. Like all mass products, from cars to cameras, airgun parts are made within certain pre-defined tolerances. Though minuscule, these can have a disproportionate influence on overall performance. One rifle, for example, may have a bore diameter of 0.1775in while another may measure 0.1780; five ten-thousandths of an inch may seem insignificant, yet it can totally transform the shooting of a pair of supposedly identical guns. As a result, a hundred mass-produced airguns may contain five rogues and five offering above average performance; and no manufacturer is immune from this fluctuation.

Introduction
The law...and other problems

Though this section attempts to guide the airgunner in the existing laws, no warranty is implied or expressed in it that the guidance given is accurate. *The Law Relating to Firearms* by P.J. Clarke and J.W. Ellis, published by Butterworths, and *Gun Law* by Godfrey Sandys-Winsch are highly recommended – though somewhat heavy going – while the Home Office's *Gun Sense is Good Sense* and the Shooting Sports Trust's *Airgun Law* are also invaluable. The two pamphlets are supplied in the packaging of most British-made guns.

Though a spring-piston airgun may seem weak compared with even the 0.22in Short rimfire cartridge (which develops several times the 12fp limit), it nonetheless remains dangerous if handled carelessly. Though very rare indeed, accidental fatalities and serious injuries have testified that airgun pellets are potentially lethal if they penetrate the eye, or – in the case of children – if they strike where bones may still be relatively weak. Ironically, accidents are often caused by supposedly mature people who fail to unload a gun and then put it within reach of their children; or the proud possessor of a new gun, who shoots down his hall just as someone appears through a connecting doorway.

To minimize abuse, a legal obligation is placed on every airgun owner in an attempt to keep guns out of the hands of the very young or the unsupervised juvenile.

Children under 14:

☛ May not buy, hire, be given, otherwise receive or own an airgun or airgun ammunition of any type (it is also an offence for anyone to sell, lend or otherwise transmit an airgun or its ammunition to anyone under 14 except in the two situations described below).
☛ May not carry an airgun in a public place, even if it is covered.
☛ May only fire an airgun on private premises, and only when supervised by someone over 21. However, these rules do not prevent an 'under-14' using a fairground shooting gallery provided the calibre of the rifles does not exceed 0.23in (Firearms Act 1968, section 23).

Juveniles between 14 and 17:

☛ May not buy or hire an air weapon or its ammunition, though they may receive the items as a gift or on loan.
☛ May only carry an air rifle (but NOT an air pistol) in a public place provided it is securely covered in such a way that it cannot be fired.
☛ May not possess an air pistol unless shooting on private property or at an approved rifle range or shooting gallery.

The following additional rules apply to all airgunners, who:

☛ May not carry a loaded air weapon in a public place without lawful authority or reasonable excuse to do so. (Note: theoretically, it is permissible to carry an unladen gun uncovered in a public place provided the owner is over 17 – but it is stupidly provocative to do so, and laws or byelaws other than the Firearms Acts may be transgressed instead.) In section 56 of the 1968 Act, an airgun 'shall be deemed to be loaded if there is ammunition in the chamber'. Strictly, this means that a spring-piston gun is loaded in law even though the spring may not be cocked, and a pneumatic is loaded even though there may be no air in the reservoir. In one famous case, the Licensing Act 1872 was invoked against persons drunk in possession of a loaded airgun; in this, the judge accepted the definition of an airgun as a firearm under the terms of Section 57 of the 1968 Firearms Act, even though the intention of the Licensing Act 1872, when drafted, had been to refer specifically to a loaded cartridge gun.

☞ May not use an airgun on private land without the owner's permission, as this is tantamount to trespass. That there is no obvious evidence of ownership should be treated cautiously: virtually every piece of land, river, lake and reservoir in Britain is owned by a local authority or private individuals, while the remaining stretches of Common Land and 'public land' can generally only be used for specific purposes; to use them otherwise amounts to trespass. Land below the low water-line has no ownership, but the shore between this ebb point and the mean high-water line of 'spring and neap tides' belongs to the Crown. Entering land to which the public has no right of access is trespass, whether claims are displayed or not; and if there is a right of public access – to parks, bridleways, downland – the airgun may not be used at all except in very special circumstances (see above). It is also illegal to discharge guns in a cemetery or burial ground as defined under the Cemeteries Clauses Act 1847.

☞ May not possess (not necessarily just 'own') an airgun if the possessor has received any custodial sentence longer than three months. The prohibition period is five years from the conclusion of the sentence in the case of penalties shorter than three years, otherwise a life ban is attracted.

☞ May not shoot at any bird or animal (including those such as starlings, commonly regarded as vermin), unless 'authorized persons' within the terms of the Wildlife & Country-side Act 1981 or able to offer an acceptable reason (e.g., the humane killing of an animal so wounded by another person that it cannot be expected to recover). An authorized person is usually defined as the owner of the land, or someone to whom the owner's permission to shoot over the land has been granted.* The 'authorized person' must also be legally permitted to own an airgun under the provisions of the 1968 Firearms Act and its amendments.

* This may occasionally be invalidated by the Inclosures Acts.

Many species of British birds are protected by law, and may not be shot in any normal circumstances. The Protection of Birds Act 1954 lists the wild birds that can be killed or taken at any time 'by authorized persons' as: bullfinch†, cormorant, carrion and hooded crows, feral pigeon‡, greater and lesser black-backed gull, herring gull, jackdaw, jay, magpie, oyster-catcher†, rook, shag, house sparrow, starling, stock-dove and wood-pigeon. All others are offered some measure of protection within the 1954 act and the Wildlife & Countryside Act 1981, in addition to the proscribed seasons for so-called Game Birds (within which they may not be taken): bustard and wild turkey, 2 March to 31 August; grouse, 11 December to 11 August; partridge, 2 February to 31 August; pheasant, 2 February to 30 September; landrail, quail, snipe, teal, wigeon, wild duck, woodcock and all other (game) birds as defined by the Acts, 1 March to 1 August.*

† These may only be taken in certain parts of Britain as defined in Schedule 1 of the Act.
‡ That is, birds that have gone wild.

Certain British mammals of a size that could be taken with an airgun – e.g., the red squirrel or the pine marten – are also comprehensively protected and, in certain parts of the country, there may be prohibitions (under the Game Act 1831) on taking birds or animals on Sundays or Christmas Day. The discharge of airguns or tranquilizer dart-guns at larger animals such as deer, in an attempt to injure them or cause suffering, is prohibited by the Deer Act 1963 as well as the Wildlife & Countryside Act 1981, while shooting at cats or dogs is understandably governed by several laws in the animals' favour.

* However, the Protection of Birds Act 1954 extends differing protection to some of these species and would generally be taken to overrule the provisions of the Game Laws.

☞ May not normally discharge an airgun in the street, or within 50 feet of the centre of the carriageway, under section 140 of the Highways Act 1959. This provision is much more specific than widely claimed, as the Highways Act not only qualifies the conditions of dis-charge ('without lawful authority or excuse') but also specifies that an offence is committed only if 'in consequence thereof a user of the highway is injured, interrupted or endangered'. However, as the Firearms Act deems it illegal to have a loaded airgun in a public place, niceties in the Highways Acts rarely provide an effectual defence.

☞ May not own, without first obtaining a firearms certificate, an airgun classified as 'dangerous' by the Home Office, or capable of exceeding 12fp (6fp for an air pistol), as defined under the Firearms Act 1968 and/or the Firearms (Dangerous Air Weapons) Rules 1969.

The penalties for ignorance can be severe: 'carrying an air weapon with intent to commit crime' carries a maximum prison term of fourteen years, plus an optional fine, while shooting at (i.e., not necessarily hitting) a bird or animal can attract a £1,000 fine under the Wildlife & Countryside Act.

Current legislation is such a complicated tangle that many airgunners are regularly breaking the law while hunting, by ignoring protection granted to animals and birds, trespassing knowingly or unintentionally, or infringing such legal exotica as the Night Poaching Act 1828 – under which the taking of game animals and rabbits with the assistance of any 'gun, net, engine or other instrument' (e.g., a torch or flashlamp) may be prohibited.

Misuse of airguns is often the subject of emotive press articles and lobbying by bodies such as the RSPCA, but little need be done beyond enforcing the penalties that already exist. The 'anti-gun' articles generally overlook how rarely airguns feature in crime; in 1985, for example, only 89 of the 2,539 robberies in which firearms were used were undertaken with airguns and the proportion actually shows signs of decreasing (cf., 1976, 99 cases in 1,076). The proportion of animal cruelty that can be legitimately ascribed to pellet wounds is less than that caused by deliberate starvation or drowning, and the paint-spray aerosol contributes so much more to urban vandalism than the airgun. Admittedly, the airgun features more in criminal damage cases than any other class of firearm (93 per cent of the 3,977 cases reported in 1985) and also in 'violence against the person' (excluding homicide, attempted murder and acts endangering life), with 92 per cent of the 2,652 cases reported in 1985. Criminal damage is recorded if the value of the items concerned exceeds a mere £20; most prosecutions involving airguns, therefore, arise from broken windows or street lamps. 'Violence against the person', with airguns at least, is normally one juvenile causing another a minor injury. Put into proper perspective, while accepting that they should trouble responsible airgunners, these figures represent an insignificant part of the 3,426,000 offences recorded in 1985.

AIRGUNS AND POWER

Suggestions that airguns should be restricted further are indefensible, however well-meaning their intention: people die as a result of broken bottles, hammers or a kitchen knives, yet no-one of sound mind would restrict sale of tools or domestic cutlery. However, though regulatory laws certainly do exist to discourage misuse of airguns, the implementation of the Firearms (Dangerous Air Weapons) Rules 1969 is hindered by a failure to define the performance of an airgun realistically. It is one thing to state that an airgun should be treated as a firearm under the 1968 Act if it '[has been declared] capable of discharging a missile so that the missile has, on being discharged from the muzzle of the weapon, kinetic energy in excess, in the case of an air pistol, of 6 ft lb or, in the case of an air weapon other than an air pistol, of 12 ft lb'. But it is quite another to implement it fairly.

Though standard testing conditions have now been defined by the Home Office, concessions have yet to be made to inherent fluctuations in the performance of airguns – when the ammunition is changed, for example – or the effects of 'clearing' a gun by firing a specified number of shots before testing commences. As the generation of muzzle energy depends on so many factors, it cannot be regulated with hair-splitting precision.

To maximize advertising impact, unfortunately, many airgun manufacturers have tried to offer the 'most powerful gun within the limit' and pushed average velocities too high for safety. During testing for this book, and also for the companion *Airgun Shooting A-Z*, which goes into rather more detail, hundreds of trials have been fired while assessing many differing guns – new, second-hand, tuned or re-sprung – and a wide variety of ammunition. These

 LGR

suggest that no simple power-limiting statement can expect much success. The average performance fluctuation in a spring-piston sporting gun proved to be 0.75-1 per cent with average-quality pellets, though indices as low as 0.4 per cent of the average velocity have been achieved in isolated cases and poor-quality ammunition occasionally raises the value past three per cent. In the case of short-barrel pistols, however, the limits should be doubled: 2 per cent is praiseworthy, 3.5 per cent adequate and 5 per cent by no means unknown.

To illustrate the potential difficulties, a Webley Omega rifle was tested with 0.177in Eley Wasp pellets at a temperature of 64°F. The velocities were recorded on a SKAN Mk 5 chronoscope regulated in accordance with a master calibrated at the Royal Military College of Science, and the pellets, weighed individually on a Precisa electronic laboratory balance, varied from 7.24 to 7.49gn. The velocity index obtained in this trial was a highly satisfactory 0.61 per cent, the fluctuations being minimal (800.2-820.9fs^{-1}). However, owing to the greater diversity of pellet weights, energy variations of individual shots proved to be nearly three times greater — 10.42 to 11.16fp.†

Had this particular gun given an average energy figure of 11.90 instead of 10.67fp, for the purposes of argument, four of the 25 shots would have been over the limit assuming that the velocity index remained unchanged; at an

The single-stroke pneumatic Walther △ LGR has enjoyed a run of success at the highest level that has lasted for a decade. By courtesy of Carl Walther GmbH.

† The trial gun generated appreciably greater velocity than Webley's usual conservative claim (only 750fs^{-1}). 500 shots had been fired by the time of the trial in question and average velocity had dropped. However, even at the initial value of 833.6fs^{-1}, the gun was still quite legal.

average of 11.95fp, seven shots would have been illegal with another on the very limit itself. And yet this Omega is a notably consistent performer, certainly better than the average leather washered HW35.

In the late 1960s, The Home Office, having tested many HW35 rifles, decided that they were in need of certification. The leather washer allowed a certain amount of volatile lubricant to enter the air chamber on each cocking stroke and, until a state of equilibrium had been reached in which the amount of lubricant became constant for each shot, the Weihrauch almost always die-selled. Shot-energies would sometimes go way over the limit until the action settled down; when fresh lubrication was applied to the spring/piston assembly, the cycle often began again. Despite the efforts of David Hughes and the subsequent development of non-volatile lubricants, the reputation persisted for many years. Newer Weihrauch rifles — including the HW35 — have nylon pis-ton seals and the problem is now more that they are often pushed much too close to the limit. Of the dozen or more 5.5mm HW77 rifles tested on guns-miths' premises during preparatory work for this book, only one showed signs of exceeding 12fp with Eley Wasps. However, when they were tested with RWS Diabolo pellets, the situation was all but reversed. The new M&G Diana LG48/52 series appears to be precisely the opposite: generally under 12fp in 5.5mm, but sometimes much too powerful in 4.5mm.‡

Recently, the introduction of chronography by field-target shooting clubs has revealed many marksmen using illegally powerful rifles. Unfortunately, there is as yet no acceptable standard by which the various machines are calibrated. Chronographs vary greatly in performance and, while the best ones may offer an accuracy of ±2 per cent, the worst may be five per cent adrift; until this problem is resolved, therefore, those who resent the appearance of chrono-graphs at competitions will believe they have justification for complaint.*

Factors that may force airguns over 12fp — such as a long hot journey in the boot of the car — can be compounded by tuning. Many modified guns are available from reputable companies such as Airmasters or Venom, who aim more to improve consistency than to explore the margins of the limit. But it is also possible to buy tuning kits, such as Gunsport's Maximiser, or sufficient components to learn the rudiments at home. Most spring-piston guns, being mass-produced, may be improved by honing and specialist lubrication; the benefits usually include enhanced consistency, less spring noise and reduced vibration. A less desirable side-effect is increased power from an action that, in essence, has become more efficient. Weihrauchs are particularly susceptible to this process, partly because they already lie close to the limit and also because there is plenty of scope for improvement in the HW77 piston system.†

Of all the guns tested for susceptibility to changes in pellet-type, the pre-1986 BSA rifles seemed to be least affected. This is believed to arise from the gently tapered English-style chamber, which appears to be partially self-regulating.‡

The high-power pneumatics often shoot more consistently than spring-piston patterns developing comparable velocity and are less likely to give trouble when the average velocity approaches 12fp. However, the Sheridan and Sharp rifles are normally capable of prodigious energies and are not always restricted for the British market as well as they should be. This is particularly true of the Sharp Victory, which was withdrawn from Britain after no more than a handful had been sold. Some of the cheaper, cruder but otherwise comparable pneu-matics — such as the Spanish Setra — display the unusually capricious perform-ance that results from poor-quality valves.

Stages in the production of airguns: the drop-forge (1), the light machine-shop (2) and final assembly (3). By courtesy of Norberto Arizmendi SA and Dianawerk.

‡ In a letter to the author in May 1987, Weihrauch itself claimed that all guns had been chronographed before shipping. Yet velocities in excess of 640fs^{-1} with 5.5mm RWS Diabolo pellets have been obtained from a few guns.

* An interesting comparison with smallbore rifle shooting, where guns are minutely scrutinized to ensure they comply with regulations limiting weight, size and trigger-pull.

† The patentees of the Theoben Zephyr piston report that HW77 pattern is unusually slow-moving and that a few alterations can virtually halve the travel-time.
‡ The effect of the collapse of BSA Guns Ltd and its replacement by BSA Guns (UK) Ltd in 1986 is not yet known. Most Webley rifles made prior to 1985 also have gently tapered throats, but this is not true of the Omega. The Omega chamber seems suited to German-style pellets and performance can fluctuate appreciably when pellet brands are changed.

THE FUTURE?

The unwitting gun-owner found 'guilty' of transgressing the Dangerous Air Weapons Rules will have his expensive combination of rifle, optical sight, sling, silencer and fittings confiscated with little recourse to appeal. Unhappily, liability for supplying a supra-12fp airgun without the benefit of a firearms certificate is not defined specifically in law.* The onus should, I believe, lie with the manufacturer or the importer (if the gun originates outside Britain), whose duty of care to the purchaser is to ensure that the airgun as sold complies with the law. In the absence of Home Office or Proof House participation, and the far-from-universality of chronographing by retailers, it is difficult to see why this is not accepted as just. The Sale of Goods Acts may even allow the owner of a confiscated airgun to take action against a supplier, if the latter could be shown to have acted improperly in selling a product in which legal performance was warrantied by implication.

The Gun Trade Association is currently attempting to define standard testing conditions under which importers and retailers can be protected. Unfortunately, this will not spare much thought for the purchasers – who are often completely innocent, whereas suppliers avoid prosecution simply because the luckless individual cannot prove that the guns were performing illegally when despatched from the warehouse or passed over a counter! And yet there seems such a simple solution; the Firearms Act 1982, which regulates the distribution of replicas†, permits a defence of unwitting purchase and usually transfers onus to the retailer, importer or manufacturer in such cases. Surely this could be applied just as easily to an airgun?

If a purchaser could show that he had bought the gun in good faith, had neither tampered with the springs nor upgraded the gun other than by fitting a replacement factory spring, should he not be extended the protection granted to the replica collector? In most cases, the retailer and importer would also be protected provided they had not chronographed or lubricated the gun, action being taken over specific gun-models only after persistent transgressions‡; the only persons at risk, therefore, would be the customizers who, thanks to the widespread availability of chronography, would have a duty to check the power of their modified guns – and who, by virtue of the alterations, could not then claim a defence of innocence.

As the power of airguns does not fluctuate by tremendous amounts, the existing law should simply be rephrased so that the *average* of 25 shots should not exceed 12fp. Five shots should be fired to clear the gun immediately before the trial, and the temperature and humidity levels should also be defined within reasonable limits. With the availability of computerized assessment systems, and the comparatively low incidence of airgun-related prosecutions even under the existing law, this should not involve the Home Office Forensic Science Laboratory in any additional work. Indeed, a decrease may result...quite apart from a rise in airgunners' goodwill.

Though this procedure would probably lead to a slight increase in permissible power, there is no evidence to show that over-limit airguns feature so greatly in crime that they are in need of further restriction; indeed, airgun vandalism is generally the work of youngsters using the *cheapest* – by implication, low-powered – guns rather than the expensive precision shooting machines used responsibly by the growing number of field target enthusiasts.

* The Firearms Act 1968 places the onus on the gun-dealer if he knowingly sells an unlicensed airgun. With the widespread introduction of chronography in many shops, claims of ignorance by the owners of these particularly premises are no longer appropriate. If they or their employees (rather than the customer) undertake the tests personally, they could be held to be 'in possession' of a certifiable airgun. The mere act of handing it back to its owner would then be in breach of the law.

† Since the Firearms Act 1982 became law, new replicas (in addition to blank-firing guns) have to be approved by the Home Office before they can be sold in Britain.

‡ Persistent transgressions only affect a few brands, almost all of which originate outside Britain. In these cases, the importers would be prohibited from distributing the offending guns until action had been taken to reduce power. This can easily be done (for example) by modifying the spring, infinitesimally revising the transfer port or boring an additional hole in the piston-crown face.

The results of changing pellets are not particularly notable, increased power* rarely exceeding ten per cent of the mean energy figure. Consequently, the control system could be operated with a single standardized pellet and the effects of changing brands simply ignored. RWS Diabolo would, in my opinion, be as good a compromise as any: made in 4.5 and 5.5mm, offering consistent quality with minimal weight fluctuations in either calibre, these pellets are also likely to give higher than average energies. The British Field Target Association has recently recommended testing with RWS Superdome in 4.5mm and Eley Wasp in 5.5mm/0.22in, but these seem ill-chosen; the former is among the more likely to go over 12fp, while the latter simply keeps many marginally super-power large-calibre rifles below the limit. It may not be entirely coincidental that the most popular competition rifle is the 5.5mm Weihrauch HW77, which, apart from some of the conversions, usually develops greater energies with German-made pellets.

Only three things need to be done to honour the law while making life easier for everyone concerned: (i) allow the airgun purchaser a plea of innocence similar that permissible under the Firearms Act 1982, provided he can prove he has not tampered with the gun; (ii) change the Firearms (Dangerous Air Guns) Rules 1969 so that *average energy* should not exceed 12fp (6fp for a pistol) rather than any single shot; and (iii) nominate a single pellet type with which the Home Office tests will be undertaken. Then, at last, everyone – importer, retailer and purchaser alike – would know the obligations under which they are placed.

The product launch – in this case, of the BSA Buccaneer.

Research and development

Over the last twenty years, this has produced top-grade rifles in Europe, while American efforts have been devoted to the production of more efficient children's toys—though even this shows signs of changing, as Beeman enthusiastically promotes European-style sporting and target rifles. Sights have been greatly refined, until even the cheapest European guns offer fully-adjustable back sights, once restricted to better designs. Little progress has been made with the mechanics of the cheaper guns, though this is not true of the top-class sporting and target rifles. The BSA Meteor, the Webley Hawks and the Webley Victor are exceptions to this rule. The development of synthetic breech seals, particularly, has encouraged consistent performance.

Quality Control

Ensuring that output reaches a certain standard is an indispensable part of airgun production, and can be subdivided conveniently into functioning tests and examination of workmanship. The leading companies take great care to test fire their guns and may even provide a test target with each one, though whether this is a fair indication of quality can be disputed. However, it does prevent too many 'rogue' guns reaching the market. The task of airgun exporters is further complicated by differing national power restrictions, which place more emphasis on good quality control; otherwise, consignments of illegal guns could be delivered in error, and the whole marque could be banned as a result. Some lesser manufacturers apply less rigorous standards, and small batches of inferior guns are occasionally distributed elsewhere by intermediaries who fail to point out their defects. Increased enthusiasm, and the development of cheap testing systems, makes this 'dumping' process increasingly risky and the manufacturers' reputations can deteriorate greatly in a very short time. Unfortunately, problems are encountered in every manufacturing process and a small percentage of inferior guns will escape even the best-organised quality-control system; even some of the best guns will exhibit over-runs in the chequering or tiny blemishes in the blueing and internal finish.

Sights

Many components of low-priced sights are now made of plastic—including slide blocks, control discs and sometimes even the entire sight unit. This is not especially objectionable provided the sight is either well protected or easily replaced, and it often permits a good sight system to be fitted to a cheap gun. Some BSA sights are made of an exceptionally strong polymer called Kemetal, which is indistinguishable at a glance from metal alloy. British sights are often better designed than their German counterparts, although the latter are often better made. The Weihrauch back sights are very traditional, while neither the BSF nor the Feinwerkbau Sport patterns are especially efficient. The exception to the rule is Mayer & Grammelspacher, whose open back sights have usually been well conceived. American guns often feature the 'semi-buckhorn' or stepped-slider sight, but most of the rest of the world follows British or German lead.

The gun illustrated is a Webley Vulcan I. (Courtesy of Webley & Scott Ltd.)

Design and development TRENDS

Advertising and packaging

Much money has been invested in this during the past few years, particularly by British manufacturers whose guns are often supplied in expanded polystyrene boxes, accompanied by oil, pellets and even, in BSA's case, a small target holder. Many European manufacturers could learn a lesson from this, as their guns are often supplied in simple cardboard boxes. During the 1970s, manufacturers realised the importance of market research and advertising. Their approach has varied from the elegant, professionally advised ephemera used by BSA, Webley, Walther, Feinwerkbau, Anschütz and others, to the less sophisticated and more aggressive (but no less effective) approach of Sussex Armoury, Scalemead, Phoenix Arms, Daisy and others.

Quality

The last two decades, regrettably, have seen a deterioration in the quality of the materials used in airgun construction, and gunmakers have departed from traditional crafts in search of production expediency. The widespread introduction of automation and alloy and synthetic parts has been encouraged by cost-conscious management . . . and supported, it must be said, by equally cost-conscious clientele. Though the tendency to build guns 'down to a price' has been vigorously criticised, some alloy and polymer parts are actually stronger and more durable than the steel or gunmetal originals.

Barrel-locking systems

These have seen few radical changes in the past twenty years, despite the refinement of manufacturing techniques to include cold forming of rifling and extrusion of air cylinders. BSA, for example, has patented single-piece air cylinder and barrel-housing units, and now fits an extruded cylinder to the Airsporter S, applying no heat to the barrel during assembly. Few new locking systems have appeared, and most barrel-cocking guns still display a variation of the wedge-type Mayer Detent or its ball-operated derivative.

Air cylinder/piston assembly

This is one of the most vital features of airgun design, but one in which the last thirty years have seen little advance. The original BSA Airsporter of 1947/48 had an efficient but expensive conical-head piston, which has now been superseded by the flat-headed Power Seal design with a circumferential O-ring seal. Webley & Scott, after developing a copper-impregnated Polytetra-fluoroethylene (PTFE) piston ring seal for the Hawk and Osprey, obtained a provisional patent for a seal in which a neoprene O-ring forces out against the cylinder bore, braking the piston at the end of its travel. However, apart from the BSAs, Air Arms (using a similar piston to BSA), Webley and the makers of the principal recoilless target rifles, little has been done to improve piston design. The Weihrauch rifles used leather piston washers until the advent of the HW80 in 1981, but are now switching to nylon 'parachute' seals attached to the piston head. These have been claimed as innovatory, but the recoilless Mayer & Grammelspacher rifles have had similar seals for the last twenty years. Synthetic piston seals do not have the self-repairing quality of leather, though they undoubtedly perform more consistently over their shorter life-span. However, the leather breech seal, which was very prone to damage, has been overwhelmed by the nylon or rubber O-ring with beneficial results. The importance of the Theoben Sirocco gas-spring design should not be underestimated, but it is still too early to assess its impact.

Valves and air reservoirs

The development of air-tight seals has always provided the manufacturers of pneumatic and gas-powered rifles with major problems, though research in the last twenty years has resulted in systems that are practically leakproof. Much of the credit belongs to Crosman in the United States of America, Hämmerli and Walther in Europe, and Sharp in the Far East. The constant-power gas metering system of the Hämmerli 452 Single and 454 Master pistols is particularly impressive, and the Walther pneumatics, after many developmental problems, have been demonstrating the efficiency of their valves since the 1960s. The reintroduction of gas-powered target pistols, particularly the Walther CP2 and the Feinwerkbau LP2, plus the recent appearance of the Crosman Model 84 rifle (with its LCD pressure gauge), has re-established liquefied carbon dioxide as a credible propellant; however, it is notable that most manufacturers have abandoned the complexity of the Hämmerli and other constant-power metering systems in favour of a simple 'mass-pressure' charge intended to minimise the effects of firing fifty or so shots. At this point, the reservoir is still nearly full: topping it up returns the gun to its maximum velocity and the cycle can begin again.

Stocks and fittings

The design of stocks has been geared towards simplification in an effort to reduce hand-finishing; hand chequering, for example, has been superseded by the rolled or pressed variety on most guns other than the Weihrauchs, some of the BSF range, de luxe Webley and BSA rifles, and some of the products of the specialist manufacturers such as Theoben, Daystate and Galway. During the 1960s, the manufacturers of the competition rifles developed a stippling process, which is now commonplace; it gives an excellent grip, even if it looks out of place on a sporting gun. Wood remains the preferred stock material, though stable, warp-resistant synthetics are widespread on American BB guns. During the last year or two, Crosman and Daisy have introduced wood-stocked guns to compete (it is presumed) with the flood of European imports, and it will be instructive to chart their progress. The principal objection to synthetic stocks arises from shoddy appearance, though the satin-finish ABS butts supplied for the Milbro G5 Cougar pistol by TI Plasro was a notable exception. A few manufacturers can still acquire stocks of the highest quality from local supplies, but there has been a notable trend towards 'centralisation'—shown by the Italian beech stocks made by Sile SPA of Brescia and encountered on many British and German airguns. Apart from the four principal manufacturers of recoilless rifles, Weihrauch deserves special praise; yet there are ominous signs that even the low-price de luxe Weihrauch rifles are switching from European walnut to less interesting beechwood. Oil rubbed finishes have lost ground to acrylic melamine, polyurethane varnish and similar high-gloss synthetic material.

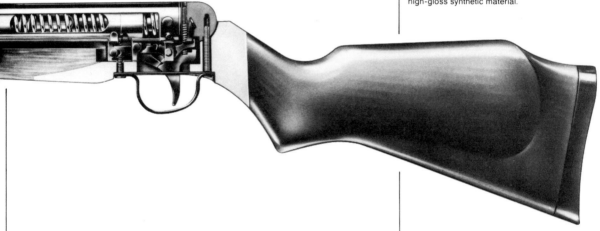

Trigger systems

The mechanical trigger attained its zenith long before the twentieth century, and it can be said that none of the airgun triggers of today, apart from the best of the competition airguns and the Weihrauch Rekord, approaches those fitted to some of the *Bolzenbüchsen* of the nineteenth century. Modern improvements are confined to the substitution of synthetic parts, which can be disconcerting, but the recent preference for precision-blanked parts is to be encouraged. The Feinwerkbau LP90 is the first commercially available airgun to be fitted with an electronic trigger, gaining favour in recent years on cartridge-firing Free Pistols such as the Hämmerli 152. It is too early to assess the potential impact of this design, or the relevance of electronics on the airgun scene.

Trigger guards

The traditional cast or forged guard is awkward to machine accurately, and so, as it receives many unavoidable knocks in use, many manufacturers prefer injection-moulded Acrilonitrile-butadiene-styrene (ABS) or similar trigger guards. These cheapen the appearance of a gun, but generally look better than the only alternative: an ugly stamped-steel strip, often left with unpleasantly sharp edges. Fortunately, Weihrauchs, BSAs and some other guns still display a traditional cast or forged guard.

Finish

Properly executed 'hot' blueing is still the best finish, but it is difficult to apply, and chemically applied 'cold' blue substitutes are rarely as durable. In addition, blueing needs care, as excessive moisture or humidity will cause damaging rust. Some airguns have exhibited electrostatic paint finishes (some Daisies), stove-enamelling (BSAs and others), baked-on epoxy coatings (Milbro Dianas) and an assortment of proprietary finishes. Modern BSA rifles have blued barrels and chemically blacked receivers, though stove-enamelling may be encountered on the trigger-guard block. The chemical finishes are often hard wearing and chip resistant, but the same cannot be said of paint.

Introduction
Operating systems

SPRING-PISTON GUNS

Terminology. Oddly, many differing attempts have been made to describe this type of operation. It is inappropriate to accept the clumsy (and misleading) term 'strike-pump', favoured by classical airgun scholars, though this at least hints that compression is part of the firing cycle. For the purposes of this edition, therefore, 'spring-piston airguns' has been substituted for 'spring-air gun'.

Origins. The principles of spring-air operation have been established since the end of the sixteenth century, the earliest known illustration appearing in a manuscript dated 1607. Despite its undoubted simplicity, however, the spring-piston airgun was almost immediately eclipsed by the reservoir pneumatic (see below) that offered appreciably greater power. Not until the middle of the nineteenth century was the 'gallery gun' revived in central Europe, which may have been insignificant had not the principles been taken to the USA during the great migrations from Germany, Austria and Bohemia during the 1850s.

A cutaway of the Webley Hawk Mk 1, a typical spring-piston design of the 1970s. By courtesy of Webley & Scott Ltd.

Though these European-inspired spring-piston airguns played a statistically minimal part in the post-1865 American airgun scene, they inspired Haviland & Gunn and Quackenbush to popularize the spring-piston airgun as a toy. The Haviland & Gunn butt-spring system was then the catalyst for the great advances made in twentieth-century Britain by George Lincoln Jeffries and BSA, who together elevated the status of the spring-piston airgun well beyond that of a toy. However, the large, powerful, efficient but expensive underlever-cocking Jeffries Pattern BSA tap-loaders were always supplemented by a range of cheaper barrel-cockers, mostly emanating from manufacturers such as Mayer & Grammelspacher, Oscar Will and Friedr. Langenhan.

After the intrusion of the First World War, spring-piston airgun production resumed in the 1920s and encouraged the wholesale participation of several new European manufacturers. This was not altogether ideal from the British viewpoint, as the Germans, initially banned from making firearms, used airguns to bolster an economy that had crumbled almost to nothing by 1923. By producing large numbers of guns at attractive prices, companies such as Mayer & Grammelspacher and Haenel soon established strong export markets to the detriment of British goods. The principal home successes during the period between the wars were minor modifications of the BSA-made Jeffries Pattern rifles, the superb Johnstone/Fearn Webley air pistols, and the expensive-but-efficient Webley Mark 2 Service rifle of 1933.

The Second World War effectively destroyed the European spring-piston airgun market for the second time in a generation, though the principal British companies soon re-established themselves after 1945. BSA developed the

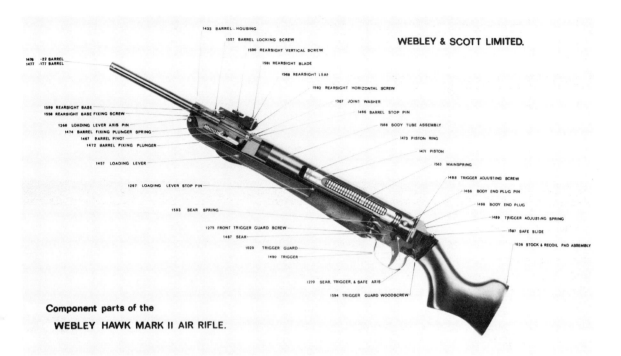

WEBLEY & SCOTT LIMITED.

1478 .22 BARREL
1477 .177 BARREL

1433 BARREL · HOUSING
1557 BARREL LOCKING SCREW
1590 REARSIGHT VERTICAL SCREW
1591 REARSIGHT BLADE
1568 REARSIGHT LEAF
1592 REARSIGHT HORIZONTAL SCREW
1367 JOINT WASHER
1466 BARREL STOP PIN
1568 BODY TUBE ASSEMBLY
1473 PISTON RING
1471 PISTON
1563 MAINSPRING
1488 TRIGGER ADJUSTING SCREW
1466 BODY END PLUG PIN
1469 BODY END PLUG
1489 TRIGGER ADJUSTING SPRING
1587 SAFE SLIDE
1639 STOCK & RECOIL PAD ASSEMBLY

1589 REARSIGHT BASE
1558 REARSIGHT BASE FIXING SCREW
1266 LOADING LEVER AXIS PIN
1474 BARREL FIXING PLUNGER SPRING
1467 BARREL PIVOT
1472 BARREL FIXING PLUNGER
1457 LOADING LEVER
1267 LOADING LEVER STOP PIN
1593 SEAR SPRING
1275 FRONT TRIGGER GUARD SCREW
1467 SEAR
1020 TRIGGER GUARD
1490 TRIGGER
1270 SEAR, TRIGGER, & SAFE AXIS
1594 TRIGGER GUARD WOODSCREW

Component parts of the
WEBLEY HAWK MARK II AIR RIFLE.

△ This cutaway BSA Scorpion pistol –
specially sectioned for the third
edition of *The Airgun Book* –
displays construction typical of
spring-piston designs.

Airsporter, introduced in 1948, while Webley persisted with its pistols and an adaptation of the Jeffries Pattern known as the Webley Mark 3. However, many smaller companies were unable to find more than a toehold in a market in which production of luxury goods was initially subordinated to clothing, food and furniture. Only Millard Brothers prospered, making copies of German Dianas on machinery bought cheaply from Mayer & Grammelspacher.

Once the German manufacturers recommenced operations in 1950-2, a familiar pattern repeated itself. Through solid workmanship, attractive prices and an eye to style, M&G Diana, Weihrauch, Falke and other guns began to attract export success. Whereas only one major new British airgun-making company (Milbro) was able to establish itself in the postwar era, BSF, Walther, Weihrauch and Föhrenbach were all new to airguns – having made camping equipment, firearms, firearms and bicycles, and conveyor-belt machinery respectively. Webley and BSA were forced increasingly into reliance on the traditional home and colonial markets for their success, but, with the gradual erosion of the British Empire, much of the previously captive export market also disappeared. Allied with the uniquely British denigration of indigenous products to the benefit of imports, and a seasoning of restrictive laws, this all but destroyed the British spring-piston airgun industry in the 1970s.

Though the short-lived emergence of Sussex Armoury appeared to reverse the trend in the late 1970s, Milbro went into liquidation in 1982 and BSA followed in 1986. Though BSA Guns has reappeared in a different form, Webley still battles away and Air Arms makes refinements of the original Sussex Armoury Jackals, much of the creative impetus now comes from a handful of small-scale experimenters and the limited output of the several specialist manufacturers.

It is more than ironic that while British guns sell so well in markets such as Sweden, where German products are all but unseen, the best selling airgun in Britain in 1960-85 was the German-made Weihrauch HW35/HW80 series. Though the current British predilection for field target shooting is having import-ant repercussions on sporting air-rifle design, it is a shame that so much of the work is based on the Weihrauch HW77, HW80 and HW85.

While the British spring-piston airgun industry languished, the Germans went from strength to strength until — in the mid 1980s — their home market also began to show signs of saturation. Success in the early phase (1950-70) was greatly helped by the differing national attitudes to the guns: in Britain they remained adult's toys, at best to be used for small-scale sporting use or bell-target ringing, whereas in Germany the airgun was a handy substitute for the greatly restricted smallbore rifle. Widespread enthusiasm for competition soon enabled the German manufacturers to monopolize their national target-rifle scene, and go on to conquer the worldwide market. The export volume was such that Westinger & Altenburger (Feinwerkbau) created a vastly successful business out of nothing other than an excellent design and a factory capable of making precision measuring equipment, while Mayer & Grammelspacher attained an annual output exceeding that of all the British manufacturers added together.

Distribution. The most widespread class, making up perhaps three-quarters of the British market, spring-piston airguns have a particular dominance for sporting purposes — though now being challenged by the pre-charged pneu-matic for field-shooting honours. The basic principles will be encountered in the smallest junior gun as well as the most expensive competition rifle.

Principal characteristics. Spring-piston airguns derive their power from a spring, which, compressed during the cocking stroke, is unleashed when the trigger is squeezed to thrust the piston down the air cylinder towards the transfer port. The greatly compressed air is forced through the transfer port, out behind the pellet and not only provides enough thrust to engrave the pellet in the rifling but also to start it on its journey up the bore to the muzzle. All spring-piston airguns have a characteristic pressure/time curve, each varying in detail. Disregarding proprietary spring, piston or trigger designs — few of which are obvious externally — the major differences concern the method of cocking. The third edition of *The Airgun Book* (pp.33-5) listed these, together with brief development histories.

1 – barrel-cocking (also known as 'break barrel'), in which the downward action of a pivoting barrel compresses the mainspring through one or more intermediate levers. This is the most popular of all spring-piston actions, being simple and easily made. Its only major disadvan-

tage is the accuracy-degrading effect of wear in the barrel pivot, which can reach major proportions if the barrel loosens. However, this problem has been known for many years and most responsible manufacturers offer adequate provision for adjustment.

2 – sidelever-cocking. This is a modern variant of the traditional underlever system (see 4) in which the cocking arm has been moved to the side of the action. During the last decade, the sidelever system has become more popular than the underlever largely because it is much easier to cock when prone and permits a more substantial stock. Unlike the underlever, which is ambidexterous, the sidelever can only be cocked satisfactory with one hand (forcing manufacturers to make two variants of each gun when they choose to do so). The sidelever and underlever both share the merits of a fixed barrel, incorporating greater strength, but are generally more expensive than otherwise comparable barrel-cockers and display more elaborate breech arrangements. Most sporting sidelever systems incorporate loading taps of varying degrees of sophistication, but a recent move towards the direct-loading breech, inspired by the competition rifles, is generally regarded as advantageous.

3 – lifting or pivoting barrel-cocking. This comparatively rare system is confined to pistols such as the Webleys and the Weihrauch HW45. It has the merits of simplicity, but sometimes has the disadvantage of exposing the barrel to unwanted strain. It may be confused with toplever action (6), but the latter has a fixed barrel in the frame.

4 – underlever-cocking. With a pedigree stretching back to Jeffries patent of 1904, the underlever system – though under threat from sidelever-cocking – still retains considerable popularity. Its advantage is its strength, though the lever system can be clumsy and complicated. Underlever-cockers are usually more expensive than barrel-cockers of comparable size and power, owing to manufacturing complexity. For many years, the Jeffries-inspired loading tap was all but universal, being sturdy and inherently safe. With the rise of direct-loading breech systems on the suppressed-recoil competition rifles, however, attempts have been made to adapt them for sporting use. Not all have been successful; for example, several of the early direct-loading breech systems (the Relum, some of the first Hämmerli sidelever designs) lacked adequate safety features. The popular HW77 is the best representative of the direct-loading genre, though the tap-loading BSA Airsporters have a much more elegant cocking system.

5 – lever-action cocking. This is now a trigger-guard lever action confined almost exclusively to Daisy BB Guns and the Erma ELG10. Owing to the limited mechanical advantage inherent in a lever that must suit a 'Winchester copy', power is always on the low side.

6 – top-lever cocking. Another comparatively rare system, this is confined to pistols such as the Barthelmes Jumbo. The advantages and disadvantages parallel side- and underlever-cocking systems (q.v.), but a top-lever can also foul a telescope sight.

7 – break-frame or break-butt cocking. Once popular, particularly in BB Guns, this is now very rare. The best known representatives include some of the pre-war Haenel pistols and the later British Acvoke.

8 – slide or pump-action cocking. Another of the inherently low-powered methods, even if an 'elbow pump' is incorporated, this is confined to BB Guns such as the Daisy No.25.

9 – telescoping barrel/air cylinder cocking. Once quite common, dating back to a pistol patented by George Gunn in the early 1870s, this is now confined to the Gat, the Schmidt HS9A and similar junior guns. Its simplicity commends itself to ultra-cheap production, but the change in the centre of gravity – and the jerk as the barrel flies forward on firing – inhibits accurate shooting.

10 – reciprocating-rod cocking ('push pull rod'). This is more commonly encountered as a means of charging a pneumatic, rather than cocking a spring-piston airgun.

11 – bolt-lever cocking. The poor mechanical advantage in this system, unless the lever is unacceptably long, limits its application to ball-firers such as the Anschütz LG275, the Haenel LG 310 series and the M&G Diana LG 30. Production is difficult, making bolt-action airguns appreciably more expensive than conventional rivals.

NB

Other systems – the previous edition of *The Airgun Book* identified six other categories: backstrap-lever cocking (12), pull-trigger action (13), thumb-cocked hammer (14), push-lever cocking (15), crank-wound cocking (16) and miscellaneous (17). None has much relevance to current spring-piston airguns.

'Sighting-in' – a vital quality-control △
function that prevents the
distribution of too many rogue or
ineffectual guns. By courtesy of
Dianawerk.

Principal strengths. The simplicity and ruggedness of the spring-piston system will assure its continued domination of airgunning. Apart from the understandable complexity of the suppressed-recoil guns and major structural failures encountered in sporting guns, which are rare, the most common problems are broken springs, ruptured piston washers or a failure of the seal between the transfer port and the breech. Few of these repairs are beyond the capabilities of owners with average manual dexterity, provided some suitable stripping information is available. Springs, seals and spare O-rings can usually be acquired from the manufacturer, the manufacturer's agent, specialist parts suppliers or a local airgunsmith.

Greatest weaknesses. The only major problems arise from the compression of the air in the split-second between squeezing the trigger and the departure of the pellet from the muzzle. The peculiar spring-surge and 'recoil' effects that characterize spring-piston airguns – particularly the high-power rifles – can contribute to sub-standard shooting, as can spring-induced vibration. Generations of airgunners, however, have proved that these reservations are more important theoretically than they are in practice. Though some brands display worse surge/recoil effects than others and it is often claimed that sidelever-cocking guns are especially prone to asymmetric vibration, the accuracy of the Air Arms spring-piston guns, the M&G Diana LG48 and LG52, the latest Webley Tracker/Viscount series and the Feinwerkbau spring-piston competition guns makes such doubts highly questionable. Manufacturing standards, rather than sophistication of design, are more likely to control the accuracy with which a spring-piston airgun will shoot.

The physical characteristics of the spring-piston system make recoil difficult to mask without unavoidably complicating the mechanism. Consequently, the twin-piston system used by the M&G Diana competition rifles and the sledge-type unit of the older Feinwerkbau guns are appreciably more complicated than the Walther-type pneumatics (q.v.).

Power generation. Spring-piston airguns may develop velocities across the entire useful range of the diabolo pellet (say 250-950fs^{-1}), and on into supersonics (i.e., above 1,115fs^{-1} under standard conditions). However, the accuracy of super-power guns is generally markedly poorer than those generating normal velocities unless special ammunition is available.

Consistency of shooting. Owing to the great diversity of price, construction and performance in this group, overall consistency predictions are impossible. However, the best of the sporting guns – not necessarily the most expensive – will return velocity indices bettering 0.75 per cent. Some have even exceeded 0.5 on trial with compatible ammunition, but usually only after extensive shooting-in. Spring-piston competition rifles are almost universally excellent. Claims that spring-piston airguns are inherently inconsistent, invariably made by champions of pneumatic systems, may be refuted; however, inexpensive multi-stroke pneumatics such as the Daisy 717 pistol or Crosman 2100 rifle often out-perform most basic spring-piston rifles in this respect (though inappropriate pellets or a poorly bored barrel may negate negligible shot-to-shot velocity fluctuations).

Principal manufacturers. See directory section.

Best buys:

☆ Webley Tempest (sporting pistol): compact, powerful and pedigree.

☆ Feinwerkbau LP90 (target pistol): the acme of spring-piston air pistol design, with an electronic trigger and proven efficacy at the highest level.

☆ El Gamo Falcón (junior pistol): well made, surprisingly powerful and competitively priced.

☆ Weihrauch HW77K (high-power fixed-barrel sporting rifle): a direct-breech loading underlever-cocking system, offering the accuracy of the HW77 rifle without its clumsiness.

☆ Air Arms Khamsin (thumbhole stock) or Camargue (Tyrolean stock): the best of the tap-loaders – expensive, but offering high power, good accuracy and excellent handling qualities.

☆ Webley Omega (barrel-cocking sporter): the excellent consistency, barrel-lock and safety system is sufficient to edge the cheaper BSA Mercury Challenger out of this position.

☆ BSA Supersport (junior high-power sporting rifle): a barrel-cocker offering an excellent combination of size, power and price.

☆ Feinwerkbau LG300S (target rifle): a suppressed-recoil sidelever-cocking gun, which can still compete efficiently at international level but is now cheaper than even the M&G Diana LG75.

☆ Haenel 312 (beginner's target rifle), an unusual sidelever-cocking recoiling design offering excellent features at a highly competitive price.

Well worth considering:

☆ Sporting pistols: BSA Scorpion, M&G Diana LP5G, Weihrauch HW45.

☆ Target pistol: El Gamo Target.

☆ High-power sporting rifles, barrel-cocking unless stated otherwise: Air Arms Bora and Mistral (sidelever), BSA Mercury Challenger, BSA Airsporter Stutzen (underlever), El Gamo Magnum, Feinwerkbau Sport, M&G Diana LG38, M&G Diana LG48 and LG52 (sidelever), Webley Viscount/Tracker series (sidelever), Webley Vulcan II, Weihrauch HW35, HW80 and HW85.

☆ Junior sporting rifles: BSA Meteor and Super Meteor, El Gamo Cadet, M&G Diana LG 24, Webley Air Wolf, Webley Victor, Weihrauch HW50.

☆ Target rifles: Anschütz LG380, M&G Diana LG75U T01.

☆ Junior target rifle: Anschütz LG335S.

Price brackets. Owing to the incredible diversity of spring-piston airgun design, these stretch from below £20 up to £875 or more for the most sophisticated of the target rifles.

PNEUMATIC GUNS

Terminology. There are now three principal classes of pneumatic – multi-stroke integral pump, single-stroke integral pump and independently pumped reservoir. The reservoir system is the oldest, but has only recently enjoyed a renaissance. The multi-stroke system is most common for all but competition shooting.

Origins. The concept of a reservoir airgun, charged by a separate pump, dates back to the seventeenth century. Though developed concurrently with the first spring-piston guns, the limited technology of the time was unable to gain sufficient power with a single stroke and the reservoir system triumphed. Though the styles of reservoir differed greatly – butt, barrel and ball patterns all having their champions – the method of operation was virtually standard. The gun was charged by hundreds of strokes of a sturdy pump until a pressure of several dozen atmospheres or more was attained. When squeezed, the trigger opened the air-valve to allow the confined air to expand behind the projectile, forcing it up the bore to the muzzle with appreciable power. The design of the valve usually allied with a comparatively short valve-opening period to give many shots from a single charging, even though velocity steadily dropped to a point where the reservoir was effectively exhausted.

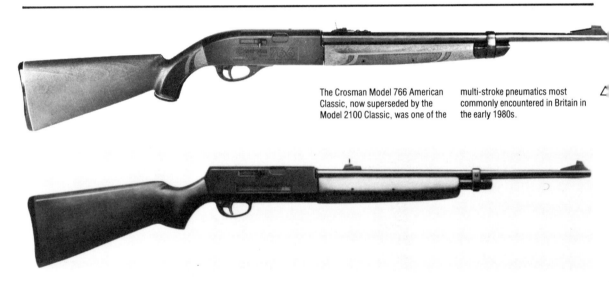

The Crosman Model 766 American Classic, now superseded by the Model 2100 Classic, was one of the multi-stroke pneumatics most commonly encountered in Britain in the early 1980s.

The delicacy and expense of the early reservoir systems inevitably restricted their use to noblemen's toys. Despite the comparatively high power of the best of them, compared with today's guns, the arduous charging process – which was not without danger to the pumper – ensured that the reservoir guns passed into history without ever achieving widespread distribution. The most successful was the Girandoni butt-reservoir rifle, adopted by Austrian sharpshooters in 1780, used with limited success as an assassination weapon but soon withdrawn once the predictable operating problems had become evident.

Though the English gunsmiths continued to make air canes, possibly the most popular pre-1900 expression of reservoir airgun design, the potential of the system lay dormant until Paul Giffard patented a modern-looking under-barrel reservoir with an integral pump (1862) and removed the dependence on

The Crosman Model 1 was an accurate and surprisingly powerful multi-stroke pneumatic with a Williams back sight. Rather strangely in view of its suitability for the British market, the last few guns were sold in the summer of 1987 and there are no plans to resume production. By courtesy of Crosman Air Guns.

a separate charging system. The Giffard gun had a longitudinally sliding handle protruding beneath the barrel; though not an instantaneous success, it inspired the later Benjamin system and, through this, the current generation of American-made multi-stroke pneumatic rifles.

Most US pneumatics are based on the original Benjamin, but the inconvenient straight-stroke ('linear') pump — which, according to old Benjamin catalogues was best operated by grasping the specially shaped pump handle between the feet — has been universally replaced by a swinging ('angular') lever beneath the fore-end. Only the Korean Ye-Wha air shotgun still embodies a linear pump.* The angular lever is undoubtedly easier to use, most examples being pivoted at the muzzle and compressing air into a reservoir-type valve on the closing stroke. Most rifles are 'dumpers' in which the entire contents of the valve-reservoir are released at once; however, the Benjamin 340 series will fire up to four shots per charging provided that more than eight pump strokes have been used.† Some of the Crosman rifles modified in Britain during the brief pneumatic boom of the late 1970s by Marshall, Whaley and others would also fire multiple shots.

* The Ye-Wha may now be out of production; at best, it is an obsolescent design.

† However, velocity declines appreciably and only the first two shots have any practical value.

Though the multi-stroke pneumatics remain very popular in the USA, the unnecessarily arduous charging process in relation to power generation has greatly restricted their success in markets dominated by the spring-piston airgun. During the 1960s, several attempts were made to develop a single-stroke charging system that would develop adequate power. The most successful of these was the Walther patent of 1962, which ultimately developed into the LGR competition rifle and has since inspired comparable competition guns from El Gamo, Feinwerkbau, Fiocchi, Air Match, FAS, Daisy and others. Unfortunately, very few successful high-power sporting rifles have yet been made on the principle, owing to the problem of compressing sufficient air into the reservoir with an acceptably easy cocking stroke. At the time of writing, only the British Bowkett rifle — and the Air Logic Genesis, which appeared just as this book went to press — has been able to overcome the engineering problems involved. Like so many of these developments, the Bowkett has been produced only in minuscule quantities.‡

‡ John Bowkett is now concentrating more on gas-powered guns for the US market, embodying a unique constant-pressure valve system.

The last five years have brought a surge of enthusiasm for independently-charged reservoir pneumatics. By far the most successful have been the Saxby-Palmer guns and their self-contained cartridges, each one an air reservoir in miniature, into which air is compressed from a separate pump. These cartridges are then loaded into the gun and six or more shots can be fired at precisely the same power by a conventional hammer or striker unit. As the Saxby-Palmers permit realistic rapid-fire practice, they have become popular for military or police training.

An alternative to the Saxby-Palmer system is provided by reservoir pneumatics such as the Air Arms Shamal, Daystate Huntsman, Galway Fieldmaster II or Sportsmatch GC2, all of which rely on large-diameter under-barrel tubes into which compressed air is fed either by a manual pump or from compressed-air cylinders offering a total of perhaps 3,000 shots before refilling. Modern reservoir pneumatics usually offer 50-100 shots from a single charge before deterioration in velocity becomes apparent. They are usually surprisingly simple and can often operate on carbon dioxide as well as compressed air. Their biggest drawback — apart from price — is the reliance on external charging in a market in which spring-piston airguns or pneumatics with integral chargers have been dominant.

Distribution. Single-stroke pneumatic rifles are popular for competition work, the Walther LGR series and the new Feinwerkbau Model 600 accounting for perhaps twenty per cent of sales. The multi-stroke pneumatic is now largely confined to plinking, high-power sporting guns no longer being in vogue. It is estimated that the pneumatics (all types) constitute less than a quarter of British airgun sales.

Principal characteristics. Pneumatics are almost always distinguishable by the pump-handle, pivot housing or air reservoir beneath or alongside the barrel. Virtually all the sporting guns rely on a separately manipulated bolt-type breech, though the convertible pellet/BB Guns often have supplementary gravity/magnetic feed and the target rifles generally feature tipping blocks. However, the Daisy Powerline rifles would not be readily identifiable as pneumatics were it not for the skeletal handle protruding ahead of the trigger guard. Similarly, the Walther LGR looks much like a sidelever-cocking spring-piston rifle and the Saxby-Palmer rifles resemble conventional firearms – particularly the Lee-Enfield and Parker-Hale Mauser derivatives, which once *were* firearms. Many of the lightly-made US-made guns include a larger number of synthetic parts than spring-piston guns of similar power. This is possible because of the lack of recoil and the absence of a powerful spring.

Principal strengths. Though pneumatics show few other advantages over the best of their spring-piston rivals, the lack of recoil in guns developing full sporting power (such as the Sheridan) is a great bonus. This is particularly advantageous in pistols, where pneumatics such as the Sheridan HC, the Crosman 1322/1377 and the Daisy 717 series are considerably easier to master than comparable spring-piston designs. In addition, the variable power levels of the multi-stroke guns can be matched to the environment – in a garage, for example, two pump-strokes may be sufficient for low-velocity practice.

Greatest weaknesses. The worst of these are undoubtedly the cumbersome and inefficient charging process of multi-stroke guns, the awkward and often taxing charging action of many single-stroke patterns, or the inconvenience of a independent charging system. Aficionados consider the elimination of recoil and spring surge worth the charging effort, which, in the Sheridan, is more than ten times that of the Weihrauch HW35, BSA Airsporter or M&G Diana LG 45. In addition, with exceptions such as the Sheridan and the highly desirable new Imperial Double Express, few of the multi-stroke guns are robust enough to encourage widespread sporting use. Most of the current Crosman and Daisy designs, for example, are intended for plinking. The compression of air into the valve-chamber with eight or more rapid pump strokes sometimes generates so much heat that excessively rapid fire may damage the valve beyond repair. Good though they are, the Walther, Feinwerkbau, El Gamo and other single-stroke pneumatic rifles are only intended for competition use; and the independently-charged reservoir guns are too expensive to find universal favour. The Saxby-Palmer system currently provides the best compromise in this group. However, the progress of the Air Arms Shamal and the Air Logic Genesis may be worth watching.

Power generation. The ease with which the multi-stroke pneumatics may be regulated between about 200 and 850fs^{-1}, depending on model, is often very useful. Only the Bowkett and the Air Logic Genesis will exceed 600fs^{-1} with standard 0.22in/5.5mm ammunition among the single-stroke designs, but most reservoir guns can be regulated to exceed 12fp.

Consistency of shooting. Despite claims that pneumatics are superior in this respect to the spring-piston guns, the best of each class performs similarly. It is rare that a properly shot-in Weihrauch HW35 performs markedly poorer than a Sheridan; equally, the M&G Diana LG75U T01 proved to be as consistent a performer as a Walther LGR. With the pneumatics, however, this performance can often be delivered for thousands of shots, whereas the spring of a conventional rifle will weaken or even fail entirely over the same period. Only in the lower-price brackets — and especially with short-barrelled pistols — does the consistency of the pneumatic show an obvious superiority.

Principal manufacturers. Multi-stroke guns with integral pumps — Crosman, Daisy, Imperial Rifle Co., Sheridan (also owns Benjamin), Sharp, Artes de Arcos ('Setra'). Single-stroke guns with integral pumps: Air Logic, El Gamo, Feinwerkbau, Walther, Daisy, Bowkett, FAS, Air Match, Fiocchi. Reservoir guns with independent chargers: Air Arms, Daystate, Galway and Sportsmatch (under-barrel reservoirs), Saxby & Palmer (separate cartridges).

Best buys:

☆ Saxby-Palmer Orion (sporting pistol): expensive but worth the investment for rapid-fire practice.

☆ Fiocchi-Pardini P 10 (target pistol): easy to cock, sophisticated and capable of winning international titles.

☆ Air Arms Shamal and Air Logic Genesis (high power sporting rifles). The Shamal is the first reservoir pneumatic to be made in large numbers by an established manufacturer, promising excellent performance and ready availability once series production begins; the Genesis, conversely, is the first single-stroke 12fp pneumatic to achieve series production.

☆ Feinwerkbau LG 600 and Walther LGR Match Universal (target rifles): expensive, though capable of the ultimate performance — 100×100.

Well worth considering:

☆ Sporting pistols: Sheridan HC, though developing more than 6 ft lb; Crosman 1322 and 1377, reliable despite low-cost construction.

☆ Target pistols: Daisy 747, a good beginner's target pistol at a very attractive price; Air Match 600 or FAS 604, Italian match pistols of proven pedigree.

☆ Sporting rifles: Sharp Ace, an enlargement of the Innova, bigger and offering better construction; Sheridan Model C, powerful but rather short for an adult gun and tiring to charge.

☆ Special rifles: Daystate Huntsman, Galway Fieldmaster II and Sportsmatch GC2, well made, but expensive and obtainable only in small numbers; Saxby-Palmer Lee-Enfield conversion, a unique combination of excellent construction and history.

☆ Target rifle: The El Gamo MC-Super offers excellent performance at a marvellous price, its only real competitor being the rarely seen Haenel MLG550. The Haenel is stronger and easier to use, but the El Gamo appears to be the more consistent shooter.

Price brackets. The multi-stroke pneumatics are the cheapest, rarely exceeding £100, though the Imperial Double Express retails at £550. A few cheap single-stroke guns can be obtained, mostly for junior use or plinking, but most are competition guns costing £300-£600. The prices of the reservoir pneumatics vary from £120 for the basic Saxby-Palmer Galaxy rifle to £850 for the Sportsmatch GC2. In addition, reservoir guns invariably need a separate pump, a special compressed-air cylinder or rechargeable cartridges.

GAS-PISTON GUNS

The prototype Theoben Sirocco (1) was an innovative design, though the earliest guns had much harsher shooting qualities than the current Zephyr piston-fitted Sirocco Classic (2). By courtesy of Theoben Engineering.

Terminology. The term 'gas-spring' has previously been used to describe this system, in which the conventional mainspring is replaced by a sealed gas-charge retained inside the hollow piston (or gas-ram) by a lip-seal mounted on a cylindrical dummy piston attached to the rear of the receiver. As this charge propels the piston unit up the air cylinder in much the same manner as a spring, 'gas-piston action' seems a more appropriate description.

Origins. The sole successful representative of this unique concept, the Theoben Sirocco rifle, was patented in Britain in 1982 by its designers, Ben Taylor and David Theobald. The inspiration for the Sirocco was apparently the gas-filled shock absorbers fitted to a Japanese motorcycle.*

Distribution. Being made by only one small manufacturer, Sirocco rifles have only captured a small portion of the market though – unlike some of the other British rifles – they are genuinely series-made. The gas-piston system has achieved a greater reputation than its comparatively limited distribution suggests. Innovations such as the Zephyr piston-head and the new inertia-type recoil suppressor, which improve what is already a potentially world-beating design, are proof that Theoben is still making rapid progress.

Principal characteristics. The Sirocco is scarcely distinguishable externally from its barrel-cocking spring-piston rivals, though it generally features special telescope sight mounts in which the clamp-ring bases are retained laterally in their dovetails.

Principal strengths. Owing to its construction, the Sirocco shares most of the praiseworthy features of the spring-piston guns, the only major difference being the substitution of a sealed gas charge for the spring. The substitution of compressed gas for the mainspring gives the Sirocco a notably fast action with none of the spring surge or vibration that characterize spring-piston guns. Firing the Sirocco – particularly when fitted with the patented Zephyr piston-head† – is much more like using a small-calibre rimfire rifle than a conventional airgun. The standards of manufacture are also high, with a custom stock, Anschütz barrels‡ on post-1984 guns, a sweet trigger and excellent blueing. The guns tested have all been among the most accurate of sporting airguns.

* The existence of a later Argentine design – briefly and ineffectually touted as the 'Shark' – caused patent problems in the Americas. As manufactured, the Shark was more a copy of the Sirocco than an embodiment of the original Argentine design!

† The channelled head of the Zephyr, which connects with the transfer port, reduces dead volume and suppresses piston rebound. Also found on Anschütz LG335 and Weihrauch HW77 rifles, customized by Theoben Engineering and The Airgun Centre respectively, it is an extremely effectual design.
‡ The earliest guns had Webley barrels, while Mayer & Grammelspacher examples appeared on 5.05mm guns made during the mid-1980s.

* To generate this power with a standard RWS Diabolo pellet would mean achieving $1,305fs^{-1}$ (4.5mm) or $985fs^{-1}$ (5.5mm). At these levels, few existing pellets offer much accuracy apart from the Titan Black.

Greatest weaknesses. Sealing the gas charge meant that the earliest rifles could not be serviced by their owners and that leaks, which usually arose through unauthorised tampering with the seals, could dent the Sirocco's reputation. However, the sulphur hexafluoride charge was replaced by nitrogen a year after production began, and it is now possible to strip, maintain and re-charge the gun from an air-pump without sending it back to the factory.

Power generation. The Sirocco generally develops either a little under or considerably in excess of 12fp. The super-power Eliminator can be regulated to deliver as much as 30fp.*

Consistency of shooting. The original gas charge was unusually susceptible to ambient temperatures. Power was highest in summer, but dropped markedly in the sub-zero depths of winter. Once nitrogen had been substituted, however, these fluctuations became no more noticeable than variations encountered in spring-piston guns. In addition, provided the seals perform efficiently, the gas system can give consistent shooting over tens of thousands of shots without deterioration.

Sole manufacturer: Theoben Engineering.

Price bracket: £220-£550, depending on model and, particularly, the grain of the walnut stocks.

Directory One
Air Arms to Weihrauch

AIR ARMS

NSP Development & Manufacturing Engineers, Hailsham Industrial Park, Diplocks Way, Hailsham, East Sussex BN27 3JF, England.

This Mistral AL features the standard auto-feeding system, the tube of which is visible above the barrel, together with an optional muzzle weight and special high sight mounts. By courtesy of Air Arms.

These rifles were originally Sussex Armoury Jackals. After the collapse of the Armoury in 1982, they were briefly marketed as 'NSP Sporters' – often with original 'Jackal' markings – but were then considerably refined and re-launched under the Air Arms banner. The third edition of *The Airgun Book* featured the wood-stocked Rapide, Supra and Woodsman, and the pseudo-military Combat, Firepower and Hi-Power. The wood stocks were completely revised at the beginning of 1985, greatly improving the handling characteristics, and improvements made in the action – including a sleeved ratchet and an improved cocking-lever catch – led to the current 'Mark III'. The rifles are now quite unlike their prototypes and perform well enough to have consolidated Air Arms' position in the British airgun industry. The Shamal reservoir pneumatic was announced in 1987, though only pre-production guns had been released at the time of writing.

Product range. Excepting the pneumatic, the guns all share a reliable tap loading sidelever-cocking action.

Assessment. The post-1985 guns are among the best made in Britain, being particularly light and handy yet delivering appreciable power. The wood stocked versions handle better than their ABS equivalents, though there is no detectable difference in performance.

Discontinued models: the Rapide, Supra and Woodsman were the predecessors of the Mistral AL, Mistral and Bora respectively. They differ principally in the clumsier stocks, the triggers and some minor parts.

Buying second-hand. There are appreciable variations among the components of the pre-1983 Sussex Armoury/NSP-marked guns, notably in the trigger system. Performance of the older guns, too, is rarely in the class of the modern ones; average power was lower, and Jackals usually shot less consistently.

SPRING-PISTON GUNS

The sidelever patterns

The standard action features a piston not unlike the BSA Power Seal type (q.v.); the barrel is supplied by Lothar Walther, though apparently Belgian on the original guns; the

SIDELEVER GUNS

Data: 4.5mm (excepting AL guns and Combat) and 5.5mm. Overall: 35.0in (Combat), 35.8in (Bora), 39.8in (Camargue, Mistral, Mistral AL), 40.6in (Firepower and Hi-Power), 40.9in (Khamsin). Barrel: 8.1in (Combat), 11.0in (Bora), 15.0in (others). Weight: 7.16lb (Combat), 7.28lb (Hi-Power), 7.72lb (Bora), 7.94lb (Camargue and Mistral), 9.04lb (Khamsin, with silencer). Features. A ratchet-type automatic sidelever safety; a two-stage trigger adjustable for travel and pull-weight. Power: 4.5mm Mistral: 856fs^{-1} with RWS Hobby (11.41fp). 5.5mm Camargue: 640fs^{-1} with RWS Hobby (11.02fp) and 610fs^{-1} with Eley Wasp (11.66fp). Reasonably strenuous to cock, but consistent and accurate.

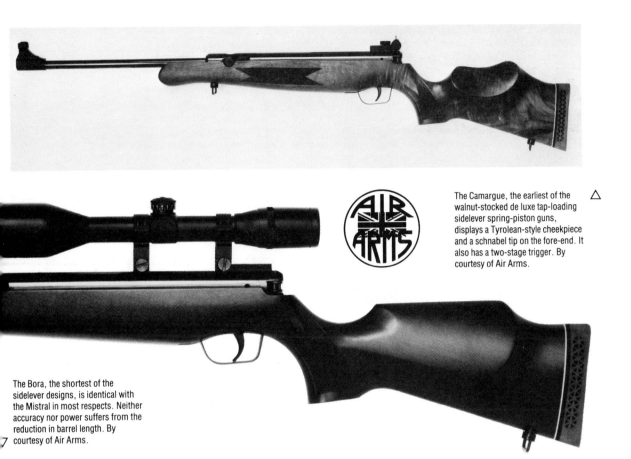

The Camargue, the earliest of the walnut-stocked de luxe tap-loading sidelever spring-piston guns, displays a Tyrolean-style cheekpiece and a schnabel tip on the fore-end. It also has a two-stage trigger. By courtesy of Air Arms. △

The Bora, the shortest of the sidelever designs, is identical with the Mistral in most respects. Neither accuracy nor power suffers from the reduction in barrel length. By courtesy of Air Arms.

mainspring and the ratchet safety device are sleeved to reduce noise; the latest two-stage trigger has a special wide-face sear; and the loading tap is retained by an allen-head bolt. The synthetic back sight (an optional extra on the latest guns) can be mounted at the extremity of the air cylinder above the trigger mechanism, its aperture element being used in conjunction with an open blade cast integrally with the alloy muzzle block.

Bora and Bora AL. Named after a wind that sweeps the Adriatic coast of Italy and particularly favoured for shooting in copses or undergrowth, the Bora has a barrel measuring a mere 11in. However, despite contributing to the considerable muzzle blast, this affects neither power nor accuracy. The elegant beech stock has a chequered pistol grip, a Monte Carlo comb, a well defined cheek piece and a ventilated rubber butt-plate accompanied by a thin white-line spacer. Originally made for Sharpshooters Ltd of Eastbourne, the Bora AL (or Sharpshooter) features the autoloading device,.

Camargue and Camargue AL. The famous wind of south-west France provides the name for the first of Air Arms' luxury guns, with a distinctive oil-finished Tyrolean-style stock of select French walnut contrasting with particularly noteworthy blueing. While the attempt at a schnabel tip may not be altogether convincing, and the stamped-strip trigger guard may do nothing for aesthetics, the Camargue remains a desirable and effectual airgun. The autoloading system is an optional extra.

Combat. The undistinguished injection-moulded black ABS stock of this gun, with sling anchor points on the butt and fore-end, is a legacy of pre-1982 days though the action incorporates the latest improvements in the trigger and piston train. The back sight now appears above the pistol grip, but the line of sight is really too low for comfortable shooting and riser blocks would have been advantageous. Owing to the provision of a dummy flash-hider on the ultra-short barrel, the front sight is mounted midway along the barrel and protrudes above the handguard. Resonance in the hollow stock presents a serious problem, but can be minimized by polystyrene foam infill.

Firepower. This variant of the Hi-Power (see below) displays the popular 1980-vintage autoloading system. The detachable magazine tube above the barrel will receive 25 to 35 pellets through the loading port, which is normally covered by a sliding rubber collar; actual capacity depends on the length of the pellet-body. When the loading lever is operated, the synthetic cut-off is cammed inward by the obliquely cut loading-tap base and allows one pellet to drop straight into the open breech. Sufficient pressure is applied to retain the second pellet and auto-feed takes place with a negligible effect on accuracy and none of the problems associated with mechanical systems such as El Gamo's (q.v.). The muzzle needs to be elevated slightly during cocking, allowing the pellets to run down the feed tube, before being returned to a horizontal position. In addition, the tap must be operated smartly to prevent misfeeding and care taken that the bell of a large optical sight does not obstruct the hand during the tap-stroke. Long-body pellets such as the Prometheus or flatheads with multiple head-rings rarely feed satisfactorily, and trouble will also be experienced with some flatheads. However, in the hands of an expert, the Firepower is one of the few fixed-barrel tap-loaders that can be fired fast.

The Hi-Power rifle combines the original Jackal-type ABS stock with the current sidelever system. The sights are, however, the most obvious distinction (cf, Sussex Armoury guns in Part Two). By courtesy of Air Arms.

Hi-Power. The standard long-barrel ABS-stocked gun lacks the simulated flash-hider and the conventional front-sight block enshrouding the muzzle of the Combat. Like the short-barrelled gun, and even the Firepower, the Hi-Power may be fitted with a dummy magazine. Its saleworthiness relies more on its pseudo-military appearance than advantageous performance.

Khamsin and Khamsin AL. The name of an Egyptian wind graces the best of the sidelever-cocking Air Arms rifles. The action is that of the Mistral, specially polished and blued, but the walnut thumbhole stock is most distinctive. An arrestor block, a silencer and sling swivels are standard on the Khamsin (but not on the other guns), as is the brass-plated trigger and trigger guard.

Mistral and Mistral AL. The standard Air Arms rifle is simply a long barrelled Bora, which it inspired. Neither power nor accuracy is improved in this way, though muzzle blast is reduced appreciably.

PNEUMATIC RIFLE

Shamal

Named after an Iraqi desert wind, this archetypal externally-charged pneumatic offers 50-60 shots from the large-diameter under-barrel reservoir. Like most of the rifles in its group, the Shamal incorporates a rotating cocking/loading bolt. The rifle is superbly

SHAMAL
Data: 4.5 and 5.5mm (5.05mm to follow in 1988), 44.3in overall with integral silencer, 22.0in rifled barrel, 7.75lb without sights.
Features. No safety; an adjustable trigger; and a combination rotating-bolt cocking/loading system.
Power, 4.5mm version, 795fs^{-1} with RWS Superdome (11.72fp). A super-power version can be supplied generating in excess of 20fp. Easily cocked, the action is very consistent and superbly accurate.

The Shamal reservoir pneumatic displays its elegant lines. Note the unusually high cheekpiece, well suited to the optical sight, and the integral silencer. By courtesy of Air Arms.

made, with an integral silencer, an excellent trigger, a comfortable European walnut stock, and a Lothar Walther barrel from which first-class accuracy will be obtained. Pre-production guns appeared at the beginning of 1987 and soon attained prominence in field-target shooting, to which their combination of accuracy, consistency and lack of recoil are especially suited. Once series production gets underway in the autumn of 1987, the Shamal will become the most readily obtainable — and thus the most influential — reservoir pneumatic.

ANSCHÜTZ

J.G. Anschütz GmbH, Jagd- und Sportwaffenfabrik, Postfach 1128, D-7900 Ulm/Donau, West Germany. British distributors: Frank Dyke & Co. Ltd, 1-7 Ernest Avenue, West Norwood, London SE27 0DG (some guns are also available from Gunmark).

Founded in Zella St Blasii in 1856, Anschütz has become one of the world's premier manufacturers of target guns since trading recommenced in 1950. Production of air rifles began with the LG275 ball-firer, but the company eventually graduated to the first of a series of successful semi-recoilless target rifles. The LG250, with its unique hydraulic damping system, made a sensational début in the 1966 World Shooting Championships in Wiesbaden. This success inspired volume production of the LG330 sporting rifle series from 1970, the introduction of the LG380 spring-piston competition rifle in 1981, and development of the brand-new Superair 2001 promised for 1988.

The original Anschütz recoil-suppressing mechanism, credited to Helmut Liebmann, was patented in 1958. This drawing, taken from DRP 1,111,064, shows that the two components of the piston/mainspring assembly moved in opposite directions. By courtesy of the Deutsches Patentamt, München.

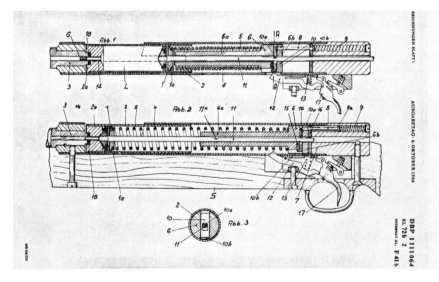

Product range: a small but select group of bolt-action ball-firing, barrel-cocking sporting, fixed-barrel spring-piston and pneumatic competition rifles.

Assessment: the Anschütz rifles are well made and offer excellent performance, though not always in the forefront of fashion.

Discontinued models: the original LG220 is rarely seen in Britain. The LG250 – the victor of Wiesbaden – was mass-produced in 1968-75 and is particularly sought by collectors, the quality of its construction, blueing and stock-finish being among the best (if not *the* best) of all competition rifles. It incorporates the Wild hydraulic recoil-suppressor, an unusually long action, and a distinctive muzzle rail along which the front sight can slide.

Buying second-hand: Anschütz rifles are well worth considering if they are in good condition – particularly the LG335 sporter, which may be acquired surprisingly cheaply. The LG250 is now considered more as a collector's than shooter's rifle; however, as it is still capable of holding its own in all but the highest-class competitions, the seals of the hydraulic buffer should be checked carefully before buying a used gun.

LG275
Data: 4.40mm (ball ammunition), 45.7in overall, 17.3in rifled barrel, 5.85lb.
Features. Automatic and manual safeties; a non-adjustable trigger; the detachable box magazine in the fore-end holds 6 or 12 shots.
Power: 379fs^{-1} with RWS-Punktkugeln Nr.9 (2.50fp). Awkward to cock, but quite consistent and accurate to 30ft.

SPRING-PISTON GUNS

LG275

This is now the only Western European descendant of the pre-war Haenel Sportmodell. Power is limited by poor mechanical advantage in the rocking bolt lever, but autoloading from the detachable box magazine is advantageous and the gun is surprisingly accurate at close range. In addition to good manufacturing quality – only the folded-strip back sight being something of an expedient – the LG275 has excellent safety features. Appreciably more expensive than most American rivals, it is nonetheless an outstanding 'fun gun'.

LG330 series

These three barrel-cocking sporting rifles (dating from 1970-1) are essentially similar, apart from size and power. Each offers outstanding constructional quality and finish, an effectual trigger and an automatic safety. The receivers are all grooved for optical sights, holes being drilled for an arrestor block and generally capped with small synthetic plugs.

LG330. Discontinued in 1983, the baby of the series offered lightweight construction and a very short butt. Guns made before 1978 had a simple back sight adjustable for elevation only; later examples, however, had the more sophisticated sight associated with the LG333. The last few made in 1982-3 also incorporated the LG333's long-butt stock.

Top to bottom: the LG275, LG333 (old style) and LG335 (pre-1986 model without the safety catch). By courtesy of J.G. Anschütz GmbH.

LG330 SERIES

Data: 4.5 or 5.5mm (LG333 currently in 4.5mm only), 42.9in (LG333) or 43.7in (LG335) overall, 18.5in rifled barrel, 6.88lb (LG333) or 7.45lb (LG335).

Features. An automatic safety on pre-1986 guns, or a semi-automatic catch on current production; the trigger is adjustable for pull-weight and travel.

Power: ➤ 4.5mm LG335S: 631fs^{-1} with RWS Diabolo (7.00fp), 582fs^{-1} with Eley Wasp (5.73fp). ➤ 4.5mm LG335: 767fs^{-1} with RWS Diabolo (10.34fp). ➤ 5.5mm LG335: 566fs^{-1} with H&N Match (10.44fp). The LG335S is comparatively easy to cock, but the full-power sporters are about average. Consistency is good; accuracy, very good.

LG333. The intermediate rifle was originally a larger LG330 with a longer butt and an adjustable tangent-leaf back sight. In 1986, Crosman began to market the LG333 as the Challenger 6300; as a result, the post-1987 rifle will feature the new sliding safety-catch and an LG335-style stock. The principal differences between the post-1987 LG333 and LG335, therefore, will be the detent-bolt barrel-lock, simpler back sight, and ramp-mounted hooded blade of the former.

LG335. Marketed in the USA as the Crosman Challenger 6500, the LG335 is greatly underrated in Britain. It is a moderately powerful but unusually accurate rifle with an elegant stock, a replaceable-element front sight tunnel and an additional barrel-lock. Pre-1979 rifles had a stamped-strip trigger guard and a sliding barrel-locking catch; newer patterns, however, have a more handsome stock, a better pivoting locking lever and a cast trigger guard. Several changes have been made to the trigger, which is now fully adjustable, and a sliding manual safety catch was added behind the receiver in 1986 to satisfy American demands. Perhaps because Anschütz is regarded as a maker of nothing but target air-rifles, the LG335 is often regarded — with no real justification — as inferior to the Weihrauch HW35 or Feinwerkbau Sport. A particularly efficacious custom version, with a Zephyr piston system, has been marketed in Britain by Theoben (q.v.).

LG335S. Originally a low-power derivative of the LG335 intended for the highly-restricted German airgun market, this has found wider favour as a basic target rifle. The reduced velocity minimizes recoil and makes better use of the ballistic properties of flathead diabolo pellets. The LG335S is usually encountered with the Anschütz Model 6706 diopter sight or the excellent Williams-made Model 6800.

The standard LG380, with the original plastic cheek piece — now replaced by a wooden version. By courtesy of J.G. Anschütz.

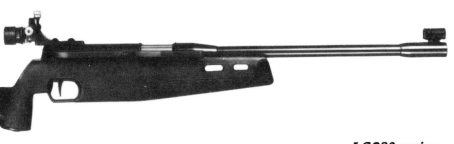

LG380 series

The perfected Anschütz spring-piston competition rifle, adapted from patents granted to Arthur Rau, Dieter Straube and others in 1973-9, was announced in 1981 and immediately gained a silver medal in the world championships. The mass/spring brake system allows the barrel and piston mechanism to slide back inside a fixed outer receiver, resulting in a short action and an easy cocking stroke. A world record of 1164×1200 was set in the women's team competition in the 1982 world championships in Caracas; a gold medal was gained at the 1984 Olympic Games and honours continue to be won at the highest level — including a gold in each of the 1986 world and European championships. The LG380 has gained a reputation for enviable accuracy and, indeed, may be the most accurate of all spring-piston designs. The rifle is immediately identifiable by its compactness and two slots cut laterally through the fore-end to combine optimal weight distribution with maximum fore-end depth. The stock profile is shared with the

The 'moving target' version of the LG380, the short-lived LG380LK, featured an extraordinarily shaped butt that may have inspired that of the new Air Logic Genesis (q.v.). By courtesy of J.G. Anschütz.

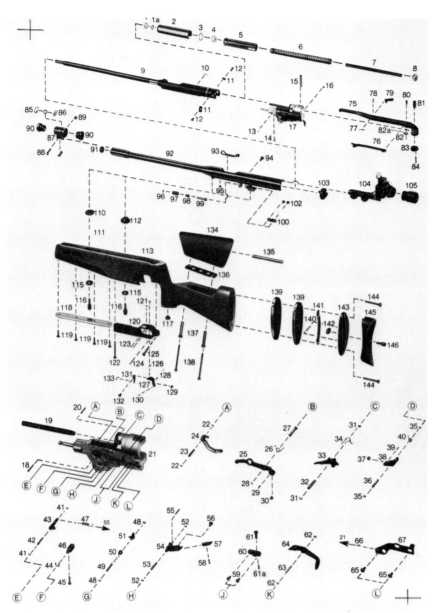

An exploded view of the LG380, a masterpiece of complexity that has a reputation for reliability and extremely good accuracy. Note the construction of the barrel, which slides back within the tubular extension of the receiver. By courtesy of J.G. Anschütz.

Anschütz's latest target rifle is the Super Air 2001, announced at IWA in 1987 and expected to enter production in 1988. This is a prototype; production versions may differ in detail. By courtesy of J.G. Anschütz.

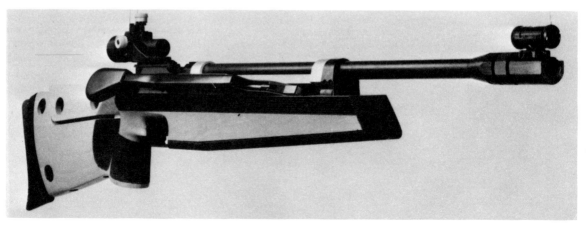

LG380

Data: 4.5mm, 42.1in overall, 20.3in rifled barrel, 10.80lb.

Features. Automatic piston and sidelever ratchet safeties; a comprehensively adjustable trigger.

Power: 601fs⁻¹ with RWS Diabolo (6.35fp). The cocking stroke is easy. Excellent consistency and accuracy potential.

Model 1807 smallbore cartridge rifle — useful for multi-discipline marksmen — and the unique adjustable cheekpiece can even be tilted to suit the individual firer. The cheek piece was originally synthetic, but this, like the optional walnut-finished beechwood stock, has now been substituted by walnut. A left-hand stock option is available to special order.

LG380 LK. In addition to the standard gun, small numbers of this moving-target competition rifle were made in 1983-6. It was distinguished by a skeletal mount for the obligatory optical sight, an odd-looking butt with a wooden butt-plate, a direct-action trigger and a raised cocking lever tip. The loading port faced the left side, as moving-target marksmen are encouraged to load with the left hand, and an optional muzzle extension (with an integral dry-firing device) could also be obtained.

PNEUMATIC GUN

Super Air 2001

Announced in 1987, and intended to enter mass production in 1988, this is Anschütz's answer to the Walther LGR and Feinwerkbau LG600 — an elegant single-stroke pneumatic rifle that promises outstanding performance. The Super Air has a free-floating barrel, a Feinwerkbau-type charging lever pivoted at the front of the receiver, and a wood stock with an adjustable cheekpiece. The stock of the prototype 2001 is most distinctively fluted immediately below the charging handle, has stippling on the pistol grip and fore-end, and large wheel-type adjustors inlet in the butt. No other details have been revealed at the time of writing.

marca registrada
cometa

BASCARAN

C. y T. Bascaran SL, Eibar (Guipúzcoa), Chonta-26, Spain.

The products of this small gunmaking company — which also makes rimfire cartridge rifles — are occasionally encountered in Britain, where they have been handled by Parker-Hale (1975-7) and David Nickerson (1981 to date).

Product range: barrel-cocking spring-piston guns only. Bascaran also makes 'Cometa' semi-roundhead diabolo pellets.

Assessment: the Cometa range has never been regarded as outstanding, poor quality causing Parker-Hale, for one, to lose interest. Like most Spanish-made guns, apart from the El Gamo Magnum, power is very low. However, the guns are sturdy and will give reasonable service if attention is paid to the interior of the air cylinder and the piston washer. In 1986, Bascaran introduced the first of the 'Marathons'; as one of these is being distributed by Crosman, quality has clearly improved.

Discontinued model: a large Cometa pistol was briefly sold in Britain (as the 'Lincoln Pistol') in 1983-5.

Buying second-hand: being essentially simple, the Cometa rifles have few inherent problems. However, parts are not easy to obtain and the guns do not keep their value particularly well.

SPRING-PISTON GUNS

Cometa series

Now sold in Britain as 'Lincoln Comets', these have been produced since the early 1970s. The three barrel-cockers differ only in their sights and stock arrangements, the piston train being common to all. The flat surface on the back of the air-cylinder plug is most distinctive.

Cometa V ('Lincoln Comet'). This is a simple design: trigger travel can only be adjusted roughly, the back sight originally had no lateral movement and the front sight was a plain bead. In 1985, however, the front sight became a hooded blade on a small muzzle ramp, and a fully-adjustable German-type spring-leaf back sight appeared. The cocking lever is articulated, there are dovetail grooves on the air cylinder and the short plain butt lacks a butt-plate. The current guns have a squared fore-end tip, earlier versions being rounded.

Cometa VI ('Lincoln Comet Deluxe'). Apparently merged with the Cometa V in 1985, this once had a deepened stock and a spring-leaf back sight.

Cometa VII ('Lincoln Super Comet'). A separate sear improves the trigger pull of this gun, though its action is still somewhat harsh. The front sight is a replaceable-element tunnel pattern (a muzzle-enveloping type has been fitted since 1985) and the improved butt features a shallow Monte Carlo comb. The black plastic butt-plate is accompanied by a thin ivory-coloured spacer.

Marathon series

These improved Cometas are rarely seen in Britain owing to their comparatively recent introduction. The most obvious innovations are the modernized stocks and the semi-automatic safety system.

Marathon-50. The junior gun is distinguished by an ultra-short butt; unlike comparable rifles offered by Arizmendi and El Gamo, however, Bascaran's has an acceptable distance between the pistol grip and the trigger. The Marathon-50 has a conventionally shaped stock with a low Monte Carlo comb, but lacks a butt-plate.

Marathon-100. An enlargement of the '50', this offers a better beech stock with a cheek piece and a fore-end that deepens ahead of the trigger guard. There is no butt-plate. The sights duplicate those of the current Cometa V.

Marathon-200. The top of the Bascaran range, the '200' combines the stock shape of the Model 100 with the refinements of the Cometa VII: a plastic butt-plate accompanied by a thin ivory-colour spacer and a replaceable-element front sight. The Marathon-200, which bears a superficial resemblance to the Feinwerkbau Sport, is currently being sold in the USA as the Crosman Model 3100. It has a good stock and exemplary sights for a gun of its type, but the trigger pull is usually very harsh.

COMETA

Data: 4.5 and 5.5mm. *Figures for Cometa V and VII:* 39.4 and 41.3in overall; 16.5 and 17.3in rifled barrel; 4.85 and 6.55lb.
Features. No safety catches; the trigger is either non-adjustable (Cometa V) or adjustable for travel only (Cometa VII). Power: about 575fs^{-1} with compatible ammunition (mf). Cocking effort is about average, but consistency and accuracy are uninspiring.

MARATHON

Data: 4.5 (all guns) and 5.5mm (Marathon-200 only). *Figures for Marathon-50, 100 and 200 respectively:* 33.5, 40.2 and 41.7in overall; 14.6, 16.5 and 17.3in rifled barrels; 4.40, 6.17 and 6.62lb.
Features. A semi-automatic safety catch; an adjustable-travel trigger. Power: 4.5mm Marathon-200: 591fs^{-1} with unspecified pellets (mf). Otherwise much the same as the Cometa.

The Bascaran Cometa V (1) and Cometa VII (2), alias the Lincoln Comet and Lincoln Comet de Luxe. By courtesy of David Nickerson (Tathwell) Ltd.

BENJAMIN

Benjamin Air Rifle Company, 2600 Chicory Road, Racine, Wisconsin 53403, USA. British distributor: Uttings Gun Company, 54 Bethel Street, Norwich, Norfolk NR2 1NR.

The Benjamin Air Rifle Company celebrates the centenary of Walter Benjamin's first airgun in 1987, though the intervening period has seen more than one

Benjamin
AIR RIFLE CO.

change of ownership. The first guns were made in Grand Tower, Illinois, until production switched to St Louis in 1899. The business was originally owned by Benjamin and Adolph Wissler, but passed to the Spack family on Wissler's death in 1927 and rose to become one of America's leading manufacturers of pump-up pneumatics. The owners of the Benjamin Air Rifle Company acquired a majority shareholding in Sheridan Products in 1982, consolidating production in the latter's Racine factory. By 1984, however, Benjamin had also acquired the production line for the British-designed Sterling spring-piston rifle and decided to build a brand-new factory. Moving from Missouri to Wisconsin – no small distance – enabled the company to rationalize production and only the 340 series rifles and the Model 130 pistol remain from the pre-1982 Benjamin range.

Product range: pneumatic and spring-piston airguns under the Benjamin, Sheridan and Sterling banners. Benjamin also makes the well-known Hi-Compression pellets, as well as the 0.20 Sheridan slugs.

Discontinued models: the Benjamin 132 and 137 pistols, essentially similar to the Model 130 described below, have been superseded by the 230 series. The ball-firing Benjamin 3100 and 3200 – tubular gravity-feed magazine derivatives of the 340 – have also disappeared.

Assessment: the rifles are strongly made, though the Benjamins are rather more traditionally styled than the Sheridans. The 340 series rifles are neither tremendously powerful nor especially accurate, but are surprisingly durable (even though the valve has a tendency to overheat during rapid fire). The Sheridans are renowned for their high power but have an arduous pump-stroke. The Sterling allies comparable power to the pneumatic Benjamins with the benefits of a single charging stroke.

Buying second-hand: the US-made Sterling has yet to be seen in Britain in large numbers, though Sheridan and Benjamin rifles have been distributed by Sussex Armoury, Scalemead and now Uttings. Care should be taken that British Sheridans are restricted to below 12fp, otherwise they require firearms certification. The pneumatics are strong and reliable enough, assuming the valve system is sound and no wear is evident in the pump-handle pivots.

MULTI-STROKE PNEUMATICS

Benjamin Model 130

This is the sole survivor of the pneumatic pistols introduced in 1942, since when millions have been made. The action is loaded after turning a bolt at the back of the receiver to expose the chamber. Made largely of parkerised brass, the 130 has an oval trigger aperture and a distinctively ribbed pump handle beneath the barrel. The guns have an affinity with the Crosman 1377 (q.v.), but are much more durable.

Benjamin 230 series

These replaced the older 130-series guns in 1984. The 232 and 237 have a chunky wooden pump-handle with a single longitudinal flute on each side, and high-ramp blade front sights on a distinctively triangular base. The receiver now tapers into the pump-handle housing, the earlier patterns being stepped.

Benjamin 340 series

These pneumatic rifles offer sturdier, more traditional construction than all their American rivals excepting Sheridan (which Benjamin owns). They are largely made of grey-green phosphated brass, with some stainless steel parts, and have American walnut stocks. Rather surprisingly, there are no butt-plates and an unsightly gap exists between the fore-end of the stock and the pump-handle. The standard back sight, too, is crude by European airgun standards. Though pumping the Benjamin is hard work, up to four shots can be fired from a single charge; however, only the first two will develop

MODEL 130

Data: 0.175in, 11.0in overall, 8.0in smoothbore barrel, 2.03lb.
Features. A manual safety catch; a non-adjustable trigger.
Power, twelve pumps: up to 443fs^{-1} with H-C pellets (mf, 4.09fp). Tiring to charge, though consistency and accuracy are average for a plinker of its type.

230 SERIES

Data: As Model 130, except 0.177 (237) and 0.22in (232), 8.0in rifled barrel.
Features. As Model 130.
Power, twelve pumps. ☛ Model 237: 418fs^{-1} with H-C pellets (mf, 3.64fp). ☛ Model 232: 315fs^{-1} with H-C pellets (mf, 3.14fp). Tiring to charge, but more accurate than the smoothbore Model 130 (q.v.).

340 SERIES

Data: 0.175 (340), 0.177 (347) or 0.22in (342), 35.4in overall, 18.5in rifled barrel, 4.73lb.
Features. A manual safety catch; the adjustable trigger is factory-set to about 4.2lb.
Power, twelve pumps. ☛ Model 347: 750fs^{-1} with H-C pellets (mf, 11.73fp). ☛ Model 342: 650fs^{-1} with H-C pellets (mf, 13.38fp). Tiring to charge, with no more than average accuracy.

satisfactory velocity. The trials rifle — a Model 347 — shot most consistently with an initial charge of eight pump-strokes and three additional strokes after each shot to top up the air reservoir.

Sheridan Model C

This pneumatic sporter was introduced as long ago as 1949, yet remains one of the world's leading designs by virtue of a programme of constant improvement; the present safety catch was added in 1963, for example, and a short synthetic handguard appeared above the breech in the mid 1970s. The Sheridan Model C is an aristocrat among pneumatics, combining first-class materials and chemically blacked 'blue' or satin-nickel finish with Missouri walnut stocks. Oddly, the excellent stock lacks a butt-plate and is rather short for an adult. The Sheridans also have an ineffectual spring-leaf back sight, but this can be replaced with the excellent Williams 5DSH aperture sight to capitalize on praiseworthy accuracy. The different models include: C, standard Silver Streak; CB, Blue Streak; CBS, Blue Streak with 4× telescope sight; CBW, Blue Streak with Williams aperture sight; CS, Silver Streak with 4× telescope sight; and CW, Silver Streak with Williams aperture sight. The 1976-vintage Model F, a low-velocity gas-powered Model C, may be obtained in the same diversity.

MODEL C
Data: 0.20in (5mm), 37.0in overall, 19.5in rifled barrel, 5.95lb.
Features. A manual safety catch and an adjustable trigger.
Power, eight pumps: 700fs^{-1}+ with Sheridan Diabolo (mf, 14.26fp). The guns sold in Britain are usually limited to less than 12fp. Very taxing to charge, but consistent and acceptably accurate.

In production for more than thirty years, the Benjamin Model 347 is a solid but somewhat traditionally styled multi-stroke pneumatic. By courtesy of the Benjamin Rifle Co.

SHERIDAN

Among the most powerful of the multi-stroke pneumatics, Benjamin's Sheridan Model C 0.20-calibre rifle is very popular in the USA, though much rarer in Britain. By courtesy of the Benjamin Rifle Co.

Sheridan Model HB

This 1983-vintage pistol is an 0.20-calibre adaptation of the Benjamin 130 series. Marketed as a pneumatic alternative to the gas-powered EB, the HB is a powerful and hard-hitting gun. Its most distinctive feature is the shaped wooden pump-handle, the underside of which flares out towards the trigger guard.

MODEL HB
Data: 0.20in (5mm), 12.0in overall, 9.4in rifled barrel, 1.69lb.
Features. A manual safety catch and a non-adjustable trigger.
Power, eight pumps: 400fs^{-1}+ with Sheridan Diabolo (mf, 4.66fp). Taxing to charge, average consistency and accuracy.

SPRING-PISTON GUNS

Sterling HR81 and HR83

This underlever-cocking spring-piston rifle was originally announced by the British Sterling Engineering Company in 1981. In the autumn of 1983, after a number of minor changes had been made to the trigger system, the Sterling was sold to Benjamin; production commenced in Racine early in 1986. The bolt-loading/auto-seating features had gained the HR81 a reputation as a consistent shooter, though oddly top-heavy construction and comparatively high weight did not endear it to British airgunners. The Benjamin-made version, however, has a Lothar Walther barrel, improved internal valving, a new safety catch and an improved cocking lever-lock. Most importantly, the old fixed front sight tunnel is now detachable and the open back sight has been moved

The Sheridan Model HB is a powerful 0.20-calibre multi-stroke pneumatic pistol adapted from the obsolescent pneumatic Benjamin 130 series and the gas-powered Sheridan Model E. By courtesy of the Benjamin Rifle Co.

▷

MADE IN U.S.A. BY

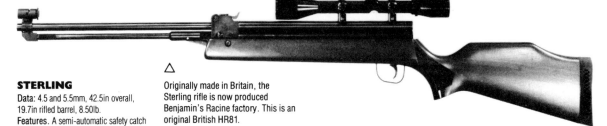

△
Originally made in Britain, the Sterling rifle is now produced Benjamin's Racine factory. This is an original British HR81.

STERLING

Data: 4.5 and 5.5mm, 42.5in overall, 19.7in rifled barrel, 8.50lb.

Features. A semi-automatic safety catch (US-made rifles only) and an adjustable trigger. [Note: this rifle will not fire a pellet with an open breech.]

Power: ☛ 4.5mm: 700fs⁻¹ with H-C pellet (mf, 10.22fp). ☛ 5.5mm: 600fs⁻¹ with H-C pellets (mf, 11.40fp). ☛ British guns tested in 1982-3 generated up to 668fs⁻¹ with 5.5mm RWS Diabolo (13.84fp). Cocking effort is about average, consistency and accuracy are very good.

from the breechblock to the sight rail. The standard Benjamin HR81 has an American walnut stock; the HR83, the luxury variant, differs principally in the style of the stock rather than the quality of the woodwork. Very similar to the original British luxury pattern, this has an unusually long pistol grip, with a sharp radius, cut chequering, a ventilated rubber recoil pad and additional chequering on the fore-end. Unlike the British HR81 and HR83, which were not identical, the Benjamin versions differ from each other only in the design of the stock. The excellent Williams FP aperture sight is standard on the HR83, but can be obtained as an option for the HR81.

BSA

* Originally applied to a BSA rimfire rifle introduced in the 1950s.

† 'Rise of the Piled Arms – the story of the Birmingham Small Arms Company' has been appearing in instalments beginning in the summer of 1984.

BSA Guns (UK) Ltd, Armoury Road, Small Heath, Birmingham B11 2PX, England.

1986 was a particularly traumatic year for BSA Guns Ltd. The company was liquidated, the firearms business sold and the airgun operations (re-styled 'BSA Guns [UK] Ltd') left to carry on alone. One immediate effect was a temporary shortage of the popular BSA rifles; by mid 1987, however, supply was returning to normal. The company continues to rely greatly on the Airsporter, Meteor and Mercury rifles – introduced in 1948, 1959 and 1971 respectively – plus the Scorpion pistol, though 1987 saw the launch of the powerful barrel-cocking 'Supersport' rifle.* Owing to its lengthy history, and an involvement with many types of military firearm, BSA exerts a peculiar fascination for the collector. The company's exploits have been covered in some depth in *Guns Review*† and by John Knibbs' outstanding history of the original underlever-cocking rifle; *B.S.A. and Lincoln Jeffries Air Rifles* is rapidly becoming the standard work on the subject and supersedes the information published in pages 86-7 of the third edition of *The Airgun Book*.

Product range: this currently consists of several versions of the Meteor, Mercury and Airsporter, plus the Scorpion pistol and the new Supersport rifle. Apart from the fixed-barrel Airsporter, BSA's guns are all barrel cockers, their breech design being a very distinctive patented design. One especially commendable feature of the BSAs – shared with Webley – is the expanded-polystyrene packaging which, together with a shooting kit (targets, a target holder and some pellets) and a brief explanation of airgun law, accompanies the guns and minimizes damage in transit.

Assessment. BSA rifles are strongly made and often exceed their maker's performance claims. The 'Power Seal' piston has performed well, all seals are synthetic and shooting is consistently accurate. Like most modern airguns, the finish is not what it was in earlier days; though BSA has made fewer concessions than some manufacturers to rolpins and synthetic parts, the finish on the standard models is not especially durable and the older trigger systems are not among the best. Conversely, the current stock shapes are infinitely superior to their clumsy predecessors and the open sights are well liked. The curved back-block design of the Airsporter and Mercury rifles, allied with the shallow-ground dovetail grooves, may inhibit mounting an optical sight: not all mounts are capable of gripping the groove satisfactorily, and the position of the back block some-times prevents adequate eye-relief being achieved.‡ The latest Airsporter Stutzen and Mercury Challenger, however, feature the new Maxigrip sight-rail.

Buying second-hand. Most of the guns are simple, with few basic faults, and soldier on for twenty years or more with no attention other than a periodic change of mainspring, piston washer or breech-seal. Weak points include the Meteor stock, which may split across the top of the pistol-grip, and the fore-ends of older Airsporters and the Meteors with one-piece cocking levers. The Meteor sear/trigger spring sometimes breaks, the sear/trigger contact in old Airsporters can be sufficiently worn to prevent safe operation, and spot-welded cocking-link brackets may occasionally break loose. When buying an old Airsporter, it also pays to check that the loading-tap is accurately aligned. Unfortu-nately, the demise of BSA Guns Ltd in 1986 was accompanied by a wholesale disposal of parts for the older guns and it is no longer easy to acquire spares.*

SPRING-PISTON GUNS

Airsporters

Despite pre-1950 origins – and by far the lengthiest pedigree of current British guns – the Airsporter has lost very little of its popularity even in recent years. The principal distinguishing characteristics are its fixed barrel, the manually operated loading tap and a unique underlever system contained entirely within the half-length fore-end. The current Airsporter VII, though mechanically identical to the Airsporter VI (1977-83), features an elegant Italian beech stock developed from those of the company's disconti-nued cartridge rifles. The air-rifle stock has a rounded fore-end, a Monte Carlo comb, a cheek piece and a comfortable ventilated rubber butt-plate. The old pivoting underlever locking-catch has been replaced by a longitudinally sliding pattern, similar to those on the Webley sidelevers, and the bridged fore-end is less likely to split than the older bifurcated patterns. The new stock handles incomparably better than its amorphous predecessor, though some mechanical advantage has been sacrificed in pursuit of superior aesthetics and the Airsporter VII is difficult to cock. The rifles are supplied with fully adjustable Kemetal polymer open back sights, with a choice of a shallow V or square notch, while a hooded reversible blade/bead sight graces the muzzle ramp.

Airsporter VII. The standard rifle has a plain beech stock with chequering on the pistol grip, two-piece barrel/cylinder construction, and the back sight immediately ahead of the loading tap.

Airsporter S II. The luxury version of the basic Airsporter made its debut in 1979, to be followed in 1983 by the Mark II. The specially selected oil-finished European walnut stock has cut chequering on the pistol grip and the fore-end; prominent fluting graces the tip of the one piece extruded cylinder/receiver assembly (into which the heavy barrel is threaded); the sights are diecast rather than synthetic; and the back sight is mounted noticeably further forward of the loading tap than on the standard rifle.

The graceful Airsporter I featured, among other things, a cone-head piston and a loading tap that opened automatically as the cocking lever was retracted.

▷

‡ Among the most efficient mounts is the Sportsmatch monoblock pattern, which has a rearward overhang specially for Airsporter and Mercury rifles.

* Suitable Air Force, Ox, Titan or similar mainsprings may be fitted, and other parts can be acquired through specialists such as P&J Springs.

AIRSPORTER

Data: 0.177 and 0.22in. *Figures for Stutzen, S Carbine, Airsporter VII and S II respectively:* 39.2in, 40.5in, 44.3in or 44.7in overall; 14.0in, 15.8in, 18.5in or 19.5in rifled barrels; 7.71lb, 7.83lb, 8.09lb or 8.54lb.
Features. No safety; the trigger is adjustable for travel and pull-weight.
Power. ☛ Airsporter VII, 0.177: 742fs^{-1} with RWS Diabolo (9.67fp) and 767fs^{-1} with Eley Wasp (9.94fp). ☛ Airsporter VII, 0.22: 565fs^{-1} with RWS Diabolo (9.90fp) and 581fs^{-1} with Eley Wasp (10.62fp). ☛ Airsporter S II, 0.177: 791fs^{-1} with RWS Diabolo (10.99fp) and 830fs^{-1} with Eley Wasp (11.64fp). ☛ Airsporter S II, 0.22: 610fs^{-1} with RWS Diabolo (11.54fp) and 602fs^{-1} with Eley Wasp (11.40fp). Difficult to cock, but consistent and acceptably accurate. S-models usually perform better than standard guns.

△ The Airsporter VII, dating from
1983, exhibits greatly refined stock
contours.

† The standard open sights may be
fitted to special order.

Airsporter S Carbines are provided by shortening the standard barrels by about 4in
(10cm). This change has no appreciable affect on performance; though muzzle blast is
somewhat more noticeable, the result is a handier gun.

Airsporter Stutzen. This short-barrel gun, derived from the Centenary Rifle (see
below), made its debut in 1986. It has no fixed sights†; instead, an efficient Maxigrip
optical sight ramp with an integral arrestor plate appears above the air cylinder ahead of
the back block. The gun has a full-length stock with a contrasting schnabel tip, sling
swivels appearing under the butt and on a barrel band protruding through the fore-end.
The Stutzen handles particularly well, but lacks some of the grace of the Airsporter S II.

Centenary Rifle. A thousand of these distinctive rifles was made in 1982, commemor-
ating the registration of the Piled Arms trademark in 1881. The European walnut stock
of the Centenary Rifle has a rosewood schnabel tip, cut chequering on the fore-end and
pistol grip, an attractive gold/black plastic pistol-grip cap and a ventilated rubber butt-
plate. The legend BSA PILED ARMS CENTENARY 1982 – ONE OF ONE THOUSAND appears atop
the air cylinder and serial numbers run from C01 to C1000. Each rifle was accompanied

by a special 4×40 telescope sight, a Canadian MacGregor rifle case and a certificate of authentication. The elegant contours of the three-quarter length stock and the improved underlever catch were subsequently adapted for the Airsporters VII and S II.

Mercury series

Originally introduced in 1971, the barrel-cocking Mercury shares the Power Seal piston, trigger system and general construction of the Airsporter. The patented barrel/barrel-block and detent-lock system parallels that of the Meteor, though the articulated cocking-lever mechanism has an intermediate laminated section between the link and the piston, and the trigger components are anchored securely in a massive close-form forged alloy housing. The Mercury is often a little more powerful than the standard Airsporter, but has sacrificed the solidity of its fixed-barrel prototype in pursuit of simplicity.

Mercury IV. Introduced in the summer of 1983, replacing the third pattern of 1978, the improved, lightened and greatly refined lacquered beech stock of this gun extends to the front of the barrel block. The Mark IV was displaced by the Challenger (q.v.) in 1986.

Mercury S II. The luxury version of the standard rifle displays a heavy barrel, a one-piece extruded air cylinder permitting increased power, and a walnut stock with chequering on the fore-end in addition to the pistol grip.

Mercury S Carbine. This is identical with the full-length 'S' rifle, but has the barrel cut by 4in (10cm) to improve handiness without reducing velocity or compromising accuracy. Only a handful was made in 1986.

Mercury Challenger. Introduced in 1986, this differs from the Mercury S II principally in the design of the butt – which has slightly differing pistol-grip radii and a more precisely cut cheekpiece – and the omission of chequering from the fore-end. However, it has the Maxigrip optical sight ramp, with integral arrestor plate, and full S-level power.

MERCURY

Data: 0.177 and 0.22in. *Figures for S Carbine, Mercury IV, and Mercury S II/Challenger respectively:*
40.6in, 43.5in or 44.5in overall; 15.6in, 18.5in or 19.4in rifled barrel; 6.95lb, 7.12lb or 7.34lb.
Features. As Airsporter.
Power. ☛ Mercury IV, 0.177: 752fs⁻¹ with RWS Diabolo (9.94fp) and 772fs⁻¹ with Eley Wasp (10.07fp). ☛ Mercury IV, 0.22: 587fs⁻¹ with RWS Diabolo (10.68fp) and 598fs⁻¹ with Eley Wasp (11.21fp). ☛ Mercury S I, 0.177: 767fs⁻¹ with RWS Meisterkugeln (10.95fp) and 814fs⁻¹ with Eley Wasp (11.20fp). ☛ Mercury S II, 0.22: 606fs⁻¹ with Eley Wasp (11.51fp). Appreciably easier to cock than the Airsporter, but offering very similar power and often more accurate.

The Mercury IV (1) and Mercury S II (2) both display better-shaped stocks than their predecessors, greatly improving handling characteristics.

Sometimes known simply as the 'Challenger', the BSA Mercury Challenger is a refinement of the Mercury IV with the Maxigrip sight rail and a modified stock. By courtesy of BSA Guns (UK) Ltd.

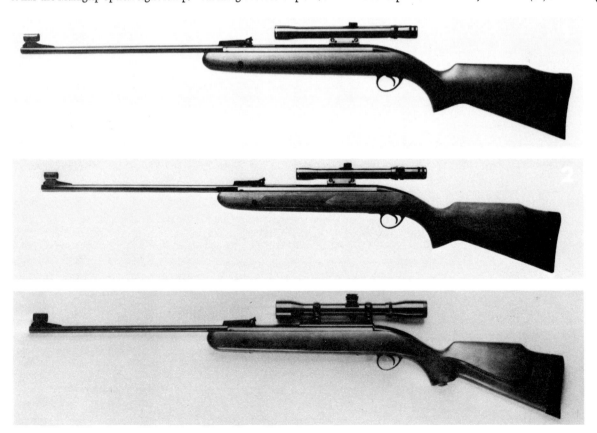

△ The standard Meteor VI is a popular junior gun. The Super Meteor is similar, but has a deeper fore-end and a ventilated rubber butt-plate.

METEOR

Data: 0.177 and 0.22in. *Figures for standard and Super versions respectively:* 42.1in or 43.5in overall, 18.5in rifled barrel, 6.03lb or 6.95lb.
Features. No safety; the trigger, set at between 4-6lb, is adjustable only for travel.
Power. ☛ Super Meteor VI, 0.177: 668fs⁻¹ with RWS Diabolo (7.84fp) and 700fs⁻¹ with Eley Wasp (8.28fp). ☛ Super Meteor VI, 0.22: 525fs⁻¹ with RWS Diabolo (8.55fp) and 518fs⁻¹ with Eley Wasp (8.41fp). Easy to cock, consistent and accurate.

‡ Patented by Josef Veselý and Roger Wackrow in 1962.
* BSA used to allow Meteors out of the factory provided they reached the minimum acceptance velocities (512fs⁻¹ in 0.22) and remained legal. This meant that the power of occasional guns could rival the larger Mercury.

† Patented by Roger Wackrow, Robert Cranston and Harold Jones in 1973 (British Patent 1,423,153).

SCORPION

Data: 0.177 and 0.22in, 15.7in overall, 7.8in rifled barrel, 3.48lb.
Features. A semi-automatic safety and a hammer-pattern trigger system, adjustable for travel and pull-weight (3-5lb).
Power. ☛ 0.177: 564fs⁻¹ with BSA Besa (5.48fp). ☛ 0.22: 413fs⁻¹ with RWS Diabolo (5.29fp). The action is difficult to cock — even with the separate cocking extension — but powerful, consistent and acceptably accurate.

SUPERSPORT

Data: 0.177 and 0.22in, 43.8in overall, 18.5in rifled barrel, 7.2lb.
Features. A manual safety lever and an adjustable trigger.
Power. 0.22: 664fs⁻¹ with RWS Hobby (11.86fp). Export versions mas exceed 15fp. Comparatively easy to cock, the Supersport is consistent and accurate.

Meteor and Super Meteor

This is another BSA rifle design with a healthy pedigree, dating back to 1959. An unsophisticated barrel-cocker, its most distinctive feature is the detent-bolt of the barrel locking system and a non-enveloping barrel/barrel block joint.‡ The current Meteors have the Power Seal piston and an articulated cocking-lever with a smoother stroke than its predecessors. The Kemetal sights are identical with those of the Airsporter (q.v.). However, the Super Meteor's back sight can be moved to the extreme rear of the receiver and the notch-plate replaced with a small peep element befiting a rudimentary junior target rifle.

Meteor VI. This replaced the Mark V (1979-83), differing principally in the greatly refined stock contours. The gun has a plain butt with a simple butt-plate, but is very popular and among the best buys in the junior category. It is large enough even for a small adult and generates greater power than most junior rifles emanating from Germany and Spain.*

Super Meteor VI. This offers the same basic construction and identical power as the standard Meteor. The major difference concerns the butt which, on the 'Super' version, has a low Monte Carlo comb, a cheekpiece and a ventilated rubber butt plate. The enhanced handling is well worth the extra expense.

Scorpion and Shadow

Work began on BSA's only fully-exploited pistol design in 1972, the first guns reaching the market in October 1973. Problems with the power of the 0.22 version – which exceeded the 6fp limit – then delayed full-scale production until 1977. Virtually a lightweight rifle, the Scorpion is the most powerful spring-air pistol made in Britain. The barrel/barrel block construction, detent system, sights and piston train are shared with the Meteor, but the hammer-type trigger unit is unique to the Scorpion and its derivatives.† The pistol is large, heavy, difficult to cock and awkward to strip. However, it remains remarkably popular in spite (perhaps because) of its impressive appearance. At the SST Show in London in April 1984, BSA displayed a Scorpion with a cut-down Buccaneer stock as the 'Shadow Carbine'. This project has been shelved temporarily; and the much larger Buccaneer was restricted to the German and other restricted markets until production ceased in 1986.

Supersport and Supersport Custom

Launched in the USA at the beginning of 1987, but not available in Britain until the middle of the year, the latest BSA rifle is very keenly priced and intended for the high-power/low price bracket. The Supersport clearly has an affinity with the Meteor, though it has an entirely new large-diameter air cylinder and a nylon piston head with a scraper-ring. The adjustable trigger system is also completely new, and a manual safety catch – primarily intended for the American market – appears (rather oddly) on the right side of the breech. The standard rifle is rather light for its power, demonstrating appreciable spring-surge and recoil effects despite being a consistent and accurate shooter. The plain ambidexterous stock offers a rubber butt plate, but little else of distinction. Alternatively, the Supersport Custom offers a special walnut stock, the Maxigrip sight-rail, a heavy barrel, and a better power/weight combination – as well as better handling qualities and a metal two-stage trigger that can be adjusted down to a few ounces.

Introduced in 1973 and shown here in its carbine-pattern stock (as the 'Shadow'), the Scorpion is the most powerful spring-piston pistol made in Britain. By courtesy of BSA Guns (UK) Ltd.

BSA's latest barrel-cocking rifle, the Supersport, is a powerful design bearing some external resemblance to the Super Meteor — though internally utterly different. The Supersport Custom features a walnut stock, the Maxigrip sight rail and greater weight than the standard gun. By courtesy of BSA Guns (UK) Ltd.

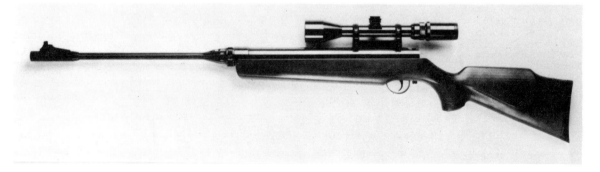

VS 2000 and VS 2000 Custom

Announced in a blaze of glory at the 1985 SST Show, the VS 2000 project was suspended after no more than a few prototypes had been made. The gun is not a BSA design, but a product of the team that developed the Sterling rifle (q.v.). The classic curved back-block lines have gone, to the detriment of appearance and quite losing the instantaneous identification with this particular manufacturer. The guns are sidelever-cockers with a unique rotating pellet magazine immediately ahead of the air cylinder.

VS2000

Data: 0.177 and 0.22in, 46.1in overall, 16.0in rifled barrel, 8.95lb.

Features. An automatic sidelever ratchet safety, an adjustable trigger and a nine-shot disc magazine.

Power. ☛ 0.177: 850fs^{-1} (mf). ☛ 0.22: 625fs^{-1} (mf).

The Most Powerful Pneumatic Rifle In The World!

CROSMAN PELLS—Rounded nose, spool shaped ungreased. Manufactured exclusively by us. $1.75 per thousand. Beware of substitutes, they will not furnish accuracy and power.

Here's How The Automatic Dodo Targets Work

Shoot this one

Then this one

Now hit the target and both Dodos spring up automatically

The Repeater

This Crosman Silent .22 is the only high powered repeating pneumatic rifle in the world. Its twenty shot magazine is an outstanding feature. It is 36 inches long; weighs 6 pounds, has walnut stock and forearm, pistol grip, steel cyanide hardened butt plate, round deeply rifled barrel, improved sights (peep or open sight optional) and exclusive pyra-steel valve, giving lifetime service.
Priced at only.......$12

THE MOST AMAZING GUN EVER INVENTED FOR TARGET SHOOTING AND SMALL GAME

Although it uses no powder the Crosman silent .22 has deadly accuracy and tremendous power. It will give you more real pleasure and enjoyment and is of more practical value than any other .22 you can buy. Because it has all the advantages of .22 powder guns combined with six features that no firearm possesses, it is the ideal rifle for target shooting and small game hunting.

The Single Shot

The highest powered pneumatic rifle in the world. It is 36 inches long; weighs 6 pounds, has walnut stock, pistol grip, steel cyanide hardened butt plate, round deeply rifled barrel, blade front sight and rear peep sight, and exclusive pyra-steel valve, giving lifetime service.......$10

EXCLUSIVE CROSMAN FEATURES

NOISELESS—It won't disturb the neighbors or scare game away.
NO RECOIL—No lame shoulders after using a Crosman Silent .22. It doesn't kick.
NO CLEANING—No fussing with oily rags. When you finish shooting just lay it away.
ADJUSTABLE POWER—This feature makes the Crosman ideal for indoor or outdoor shooting.
NO BULLET SPLATTER or ricochet. A safe gun for both target and field work. Shoot it in the living room.
LOW COST AMMUNITION—Near ly 5 shots for a cent. The saving in ammunition soon pays for the rifle.

CROSMAN ARMS COMPANY
INCORPORATED
ROCHESTER, N. Y.

△ Crosman has a long involvement with pneumatics, this advertising leaflet dating back to the 1940s. Note the auto-resetting 'Dodo' target.

◁ An unusual design with a nine-shot manually indexed magazine originally developed by the London Scottish Rifle Company, the VS2000 is BSA's first sidelever-cocker. At the time of writing, its future is very uncertain. By courtesy of BSA Guns (UK) Ltd.

* Several attempts to achieve this have been made by Daisy, Winchester and others, but never with conspicuous success. However, Crosman appears to have pinned its hopes on Anschütz airguns, which are not distributed in the USA in any great numbers by organizations such as Beeman's; consequently, the company may yet succeed where the others have failed.

Crosman Air Guns, Routes 5 & 20, East Bloomfield, New York 14443, USA. British distributor: Crosman Air Guns, P.O.Box 5, Portishead, Bristol.

Crosman originated in the early 1920s when William A. McLean, chauffeur to the owner of the Crosman Seed Company, developed a pneumatic rifle (US patent 1,512,993 of 1924); a gun company was formed to exploit McLean's and a number of other designs, but, after a promising start, its fortunes declined during the 1930s and it was sold to Philip Y. Hahn in 1940. Ironically, Hahn had left Crosman a decade previously. A variety of gas and pneumatic guns has been made since 1945, though it is on the latter that Crosman's current British reputation rests. The Coleman Corporation acquired the majority of the shareholding in 1971 and has since energetically promoted design and development of improved guns; in 1986, as part of the reconstruction programme, the company finally moved from its old Fairport factory.

Product range. Owing to rivalry between Crosman and Daisy (q.v.), whose markets overlap greatly, new designs are introduced regularly. Indeed, many are directly comparable and each innovation by one company usually results in a counter-move by the other. Consequently, many of the guns described in the Third Edition are no longer in production. Crosman still pursues its traditional pneumatic and gas-gun markets, with such innovative products as the A☆I☆R☆17 pneumatic, the 338 Auto (based loosely on the Walther P-38) and the Z-77, which has an affinity with the Uzi submachine-gun. Ultra high-quality competition guns – the gas-powered Model 84 Olympic rifle and the Crosman-Skanaker pistol – have also been developed alongside attempts to establish European spring-piston airguns on the American market.* Apart from the Bascaran-made Model 3100, better known as the Marathon-200, the barrel-cockers are marketed under the Challenger brandname: the Model 6100 is the M&G-made RWS Model 45, the 6300 and 6500 being the Anschütz LG335 and 333 respectively.

Discontinued models: the powerful Model 1 and Model 766 American Classic multi-stroke pneumatics, though small numbers of the former were still available in Britain at the time of writing; the once-popular telescoping-barrel-cocking M1 Carbine; and several of the gas-powered guns, including the Model 73 Saddle Pal and the comparatively unsuccessful M1861 Shiloh revolver.

Assessment: the Crosmans feature diecast and synthetic components to improve cost-effectiveness. Though they are durable enough for the American market, they are regarded as somewhat frail in Europe owing to their plastic furniture and baked-on finish. Despite their somewhat toylike appearance, however, the Model 2100 Classic and the Model 2200 Magnum can develop power up to the British limit: generally, Crosman pneumatics are more powerful than their Daisy equivalents.† Triggers are not always inspiring, but the guns are recoilless and shoot quite well.

Buying second hand. Unfortunately, Crosman rifles have been distributed in Britain by several agencies – Sussex Armoury, Scalemead, now Crosman itself – and obsolete spare parts are difficult to obtain. Provided there is no evidence of valve-seal leaks, and no serious wear in the pump system, the Crosmans will usually deliver acceptable performance even when some years old.

▷ The Model 760 (1) and the similar, but now obsolete Model 761 (2) are both multi-stroke pneumatics. The current guns feature hollow rather than solid synthetic butts and lighter construction than their otherwise similar predecessors. By courtesy of Crosman Air Guns.

† However, the new Daisy single-pump Power Line 900 is appreciably more powerful than the competing Crosman Model 781.

Three typical Crosman pneumatics: the multi-stroke Model 66 Pumpmaster, together with the single stroke Models 781 and A☆I☆R☆17. Note the loading clip immediately beneath the pseudo-military gun. ▽

PNEUMATIC GUNS

A☆I☆R☆17

This interesting multi-stroke pneumatic smoothbore is based – very loosely – on the US Army's standard infantry rifle, the M16. The most obvious features are a butt with a separate pistol grip, a fore-end extended upwards until it all but envelops the barrel, a carrying handle, raised sights, a simulated flash-hider, and a dummy 'magazine' which doubles as a reservoir for the pellets. The A☆I☆R☆17 is derived from the Model 781, sharing the single-pump action and the four-pellet Firepow'r clip (cf., Daisy Snap Shot system). It is a shame, perhaps, that the receiver shape is not more faithful to the M16, but the A☆I☆R☆17 has nonetheless sold spectacularly in the USA.

Model 66 Powermaster

This multi-stroke pump gun is basically a combination of the discontinued Model 766 American Classic and the still-current Model 760 (q.v.). It can fire BBs or pellets interchangeably, the former from a gravity/magnetic feed magazine. The rounded synthetic fore-end and pistol-grip display moulded chequered, while the black plastic butt-plate, pistol-grip cap and fore-end tip are accompanied by white spacers. The Model 66 has a ramp-mounted open front sight blade and a crude, but typically American, stepped-slider back sight.

Model 760 Pumpmaster

The five millionth example of this highly successful multi-stroke pneumatic left the production lines in 1986 – merely twenty years after its inception, and a tribute to its

A☆I☆R☆17

Data: 0.177in (BB or pellet), 36.8in overall, smoothbore barrel, 3.06lb. Features. A manual safety crossbolt; a non-adjustable trigger; a 21-shot magnetic/gravity BB tube on left of breech with a 195-shot BB reservoir in the 'magazine'; the 4-shot Firepow'r pellet clip.
Power: 450fs⁻¹ with Copperhead BBs and 437fs⁻¹ with RWS Hobby (2.97fp). Easily charged, the action gives good consistency and adequate accuracy.

MODEL 66

Data: 0.177in (BB or pellet), 38.5in overall, rifled barrel, 3.87lb. Features. Generally as A☆I☆R☆17; the BB feed-tube holds 18 balls and the BB reservoir is in the pistol grip. Power. Three pumps, 428fs⁻¹ with RWS Hobby (2.85fp). Twelve pumps, 690fs⁻¹ with RWS Hobby (7.41fp). Otherwise as A☆I☆R☆17, though requiring multiple pump-strokes to achieve greater power.

1

2

adequate performance at an ultra-competitive price. The gun shares its dual BB/pellet capability action with the newer Model 66, but features simpler construction and plainer Croswood furniture. The fore-end has a single longitudinal groove on each side to facilitate grip, while the butt has chequering moulded into the pistol grip. Like virtually all other Crosman pneumatics, the Model 760 is a bolt-cocker. Several variants have been made, including the gaudily 'gold-plated' Model 760 XL and a wood-stocked 761. The current 'Pumpmaster' name was adopted in 1983.

Model 781

Crosman's first single-pump design appeared in 1984 to compete against the Daisy 850 series, its action fed from a four-shot Firepow'r clip or – alternatively – a magnetic/gravity feed BB magazine. The gun is a smoothbore, which understandably limits its accuracy at anything other than short range, and the brown Croswood furniture has a distinctly slab-sided look.

Model 788

Sometimes known as the '788 BB Scout', and dating from 1977, this junior multi-pump pneumatic will only fire BBs. Power befits its limited role and small size. The straight-wrist butt and simple fore-end are Croswood synthetics, a bolt cocking/loading system is used, and the open front ramp is accompanied by a stepped-slider back sight.

Models 1322, 1377 and 1388

The Crosman pneumatic pistols have enjoyed great popularity in Britain owing to their power, accuracy, absence of recoil and outstanding value for money. They all offer sturdy construction, apart from the standard synthetic grips; cock by retracting the large bolt at the rear of the pump-system tube; and load by rotating and retracting the breech cover. Once a pellet has been placed in the feed trough, returning the breech cover pushes the pellet into the barrel. The circular trigger guard became oval in 1981, and the trigger/valve system was refined in 1983 to give a better pull. The front sight is an open blade mounted on the nosecap, while the back sight, mounted behind the breech cover, may be adjusted vertically by means of a large slotted-head bolt. The most recent guns also have a reversible sight-plate giving a choice of an open notch or a small peep.

Model 1322 Medalist. Claimed to be the most powerful 0.22-calibre pneumatic pistol made‡, this variant may just exceed the British limits in its American form.

Model 1377 American Classic. The Crosman pistol most commonly encountered in Britain, this may also slightly exceed the British limits – though reduced-power guns sold in the UK usually comply with the law. The 1377 is difficult to distinguish externally from the 1322 apart from the bore diameter and the differing brandnames on the pump cylinder above the grips.

Model 1388 Super Stock Combo. This 1377 variant features a skeletal shoulder stock whose grainy matt-black finish contrasts oddly with the smooth brown fore-end; the 1300 series would undoubtedly look much better if the stock, fore-end and standard pistol grips were all black.

MODEL 760

Data: 0.177in (BB or pellet), 36.0in overall, smoothbore barrel, 3.06lb.
Features. Generally as Model 66.
Power, ten pumps: 670fs^{-1} with Copperhead BBs and 630fs^{-1} with Copperhead pellets (mf). Otherwise as Model 66.

MODEL 781

Data: 0.177in (BB or pellet), 34.8in overall, smoothbore barrel, 2.87lb.
Features, power: comparable with A☆I☆R☆17.

MODEL 788

Data: 0.175in (BBs only), 31.5in overall, smoothbore barrel, 2.43lb.
Features. As Model 760 except that the BB feed-tube holds 20 balls; no BB reservoir.
Power, ten pumps: 500fs^{-1} with Copperhead BBs (mf). Otherwise as Model 760.

‡ This is only true of American-made guns, as the reservoir-type British Daystate Competa, for one, can be set to exceed the Crosman's power by a considerable margin.

MODELS 1322 AND 1377

Data: 0.177in (Model 1377) and 0.22in (Model 1322), 13.6in overall, 9.7in rifled barrel, 2.44lb (2.75lb with stock).
Features. A manual safety crossbolt and a non-adjustable trigger.
Power, ten pumps. ☞ Model 1377: 560fs^{-1} with Copperhead pellets (mf). Guns sold in Britain in the early 1980s, however, were often much less powerful. ☞ Model 1322: 433fs^{-1} with RWS Diabolo (5.95fp). Tiring to charge (though less so than the Benjamin or Sheridan pistols), but consistent and accurate.

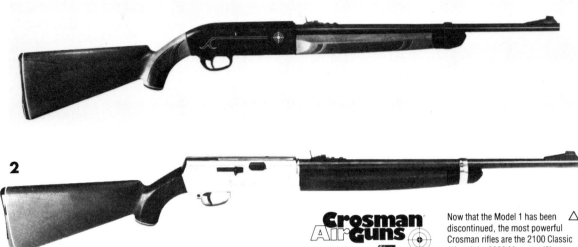

2

Now that the Model 1 has been △ discontinued, the most powerful Crosman rifles are the 2100 Classic (1) and the 2200 Magnum (2).

Model 2100 Classic and 2200 Magnum

These are Crosman's most powerful multi-pump pneumatics, offering power that is comparable with the European spring-piston guns in the company's current range — albeit at the expense of ten pump-strokes instead of one. Both guns have bolt loading-cocking systems, synthetic furniture with chequer patterns moulded into the fore-end/pistol grip, and straight-comb butts; both also have black-finish receivers with distinctive white-filled decoration. The Model 2100 will fire BBs or 0.177-calibre pellets interchangeably, the former singly or from the gravity/magnetic-feed magazine, while the Model 2200 is restricted to 0.22-calibre pellets. Both guns have standard Crosman open ramp and stepped-slider sights, but can be fitted with optical sights or the Crosman Model 411 Target Sight Kit.

MODELS 2100 & 2200
Data: 0.177in (2100) and 0.22in (2200). 39.0in (2200) or 39.8in (2100), 21.0in rifled barrel, 4.78lb.
Features. A manual safety crossbolt and a non-adjustable trigger. The Model 2100 has a 17-shot gravity/magnetic BB feed-tube and a 200-ball reservoir in the pistol grip.
Power. ☛ Model 2100, three pumps, 518fs^{-1} with RWS Hobby (4.18fp); twelve pumps, 795fs^{-1} with RWS Hobby (9.84fp). ☛ Model 2200, ten pumps, 558fs^{-1} with RWS Diabolo (9.65fp). Tiring to charge, but consistent and acceptably accurate.

DAISY

Daisy Manufacturing Company, Inc., P.O.Box 220, Rogers, Arkansas 72757. British distributor: SSM International, Tedstone Wafre, nr Bromyard, Herefordshire HR7 4PY.

Daisy began life as the Plymouth Iron Windmill Company, whose initially profitable operations declined in the mid 1880s until a cheap spring-piston airgun was distributed as a premium item. Designed by Clarence J. Hamilton and protected by US Patent 320,297 of 1888, this gun was so successful that windmill production had ceased by 1890! The Daisy Manufacturing Company was created in 1895, growing rapidly under the direction of three generations of Houghs — Lewis, Edward and Cass — until it produced more guns than all its rivals combined. The total production of the legendary Daisy No.25 pump-action BB Gun, designed in 1913-15 by Charles F. Lefever, has alone approached twenty million. The company's post-1945 history is rather tortuous. In 1958, Daisy moved from the Michigan town of Plymouth to Rogers, and control passed from the Houghs to the Murchison Brothers in 1960. The Murchisons sold out to the Victor Comptometer Corporation in 1967 and Daisy was merged with James Heddon's Sons Company four years later. Daisy became an independent operating division within Victor Leisure in 1974; but,

Daisy®
FIRST IN AIRGUNS.

by 1978, the entire organization had become part of the Kidde Group. A consortium headed by Cass S. Hough finally regained control in 1983 and the company reverted to its original name.

Product range: until the 1970s, Daisy was best known for a series of comparatively unsophisticated BB Guns, regarded in Britain as toys, but then introduced an effectual multi-stroke pneumatic known as the Power Line 880*. The success of the Power Line series has now changed the company's image appreciably. Though the Power Line rifles have all been small, light and made largely of diecastings, they were distributed in some numbers by Milbro, Sussex Armoury and Scalemead before disappearing again in the mid 1980s. It is unfortunate that distribution in Britain has been so erratic, because the latest products have much to offer. Particularly noteworthy are the Models 920 and 970 – revisions of the 922 and 917, with wood stocks – and the Model 747 target pistol, which offers outstanding performance in its class. The Model 953 target rifle is also noteworthy, though at a severe disadvantage to the sturdy Haenel 312 in Britain. In addition to its own products, Daisy has flirted with Feinwerkbau spring-piston guns and Japanese Sharp pneumatics, but without conspicuous success; currently, the El Gamo MC-Super and Expomatic (Power Line Models 126 and 130 respectively) are being marketed under the company's banner, along with an assortment of 'Soft-Air' guns (q.v.). Several gas-powered guns are also being made, including the Beretta-lookalike Power Line 92.

Discontinued models. The competitiveness that exists in the US BB Gun market – and, in particular, the rivalry between Daisy and Crosman – means that products come and go with monotonous regularity. The following have been deleted since 1984: Model 41, a nickel-plated variation of the Model 790 (q.v.); Model 179, the well-known spring-actuated Colt Peacemaker-style BB revolver; PL790, the last surviving model of the once popular S&W Model 79G gas-powered pistol (made by Daisy, 1980-5); PL845, PL850 and PL851, the company's first single-stroke pneumatic rifles; PL822, PL881, PL882, PL917 and PL977 Target, the older multi-stroke pneumatics; PL925 and PL930 (the Sharp Innova and Ace); and the venerable Model 1894 Winchester-clone BB Gun. Most of these were described in the previous book, pp.96-101.

Assessment: the Daisy guns are cleverly made, with great attention to detail and packaging (e.g., the improved Snap Shot 5-pellet clip or the current Pistolpaks). Though the guns incorporate a large number of diecast and synthetic parts by European standards, they work well.

Buying second-hand: owing to the desultory distribution in Britain, Daisy products are currently uncommon. Apart from the valve units (and the tendency for plastic stocks to crack), the worst feature is the excessive wear in some of the alloy-to-alloy surfaces once the protective paint finish has worn away. In addition, as Daisy has made regular changes to the triggers and magazines of the BB Guns, spare parts are not always easy to acquire.

SPRING-PISTON GUNS

The BB Guns

These can be considered under a single heading, although the four survivors differ greatly in detail.

Model 95 Wood Stock. This lever-action repeater, derived from the discontinued Model 99 Champion in 1962, features the Heavy-Duty (HD) frame and action. The hardwood butt has always had a straight wrist, while the original synthetic fore-end was replaced by a more appropriate wooden pattern in 1983. Magnetic BB feed was added in 1977. The sights comprise a ramp-mounted blade and an open adjustable spring-leaf with a V-notch.

Model 105. Formerly known as the M105 Pal or M1105, this adaptation of the Models 33 (1934-59) and 102 Cub (1960-78) is a light-frame junior BB Gun with the standard gravity/magnetic feed and fixed sights. The current guns have an all-metal receiver/barrel unit, with a 'gold' Daisy transfer on the right side, and also feature a short butt.

* Known as the Power King until c.1974, but then altered – presumably because of infringement of a non-gun trademark.

BB GUNS

Data: 0.175in. *Figures for M105, M111, M95 and M1938 respectively*: 29.8in, 34.3in, 35.2in or 35.4in overall; smoothbore barrels; 1.60lb, 1.80lb, 2.20lb or 2.40lb.

Features. A manual safety crossbolt and a non-adjustable trigger. The gravity/magnetic feed magazines hold 400 (M105), 650 (M111, M1938) or 700 BBs (M95).

Power: 275-330fs^{-1} with Daisy BBs, depending on model. These guns are easily cocked, but consistency and accuracy are no better than adequate.

Model 111 Western Carbine. Dating from 1963, this features the standard gravity/magnetic feed and an adjustable stepped-slider back sight instead of a fixed open notch. The receiver displays gold paint-filled decoration, the butt and fore-end being synthetic. Guns made in 1983-6 had a chequer-pattern moulded into the fore-end, and a straight chequered wrist on the synthetic butt; the 1987 version, however, looks more like an enlarged M105 with a plain hardwood butt and no fore-end.

Model 1938 Red Ryder. Reintroduced in 1972, though originally dating from 1940-54, this BB Gun has a stained semi-pistol gripped hardwood butt displaying a mounted cartoon cowboy and RED RYDER formed by his lariat. The fore-end is also hardwood, while a sling ring and a leather thong lie on the left side of the diecast receiver. A compass and sundial were added to the butt during 1984, but the gimmickry was short lived and current guns have reverted to the original plain style.

Two Daisy BB Guns: the Model 95 Woodstock (1), once made with the synthetic fore-end shown here, and the Model 111 Western Carbine (2). By courtesy of Daisy.

The Daisy 188 is an underlever-cocking BB pistol, popular but offering neither power nor exceptional accuracy. It is, however, a good trainer or 'fun gun'. By courtesy of Daisy.

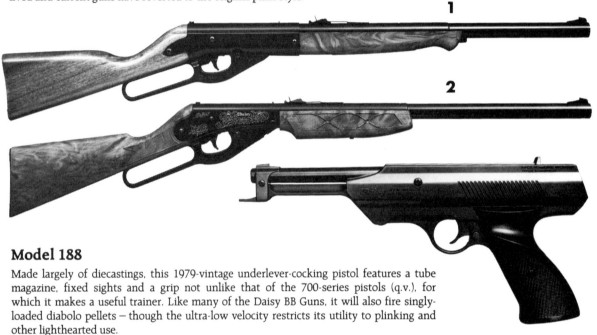

1

2

Model 188

Made largely of diecastings, this 1979-vintage underlever-cocking pistol features a tube magazine, fixed sights and a grip not unlike that of the 700-series pistols (q.v.), for which it makes a useful trainer. Like many of the Daisy BB Guns, it will also fire singly-loaded diabolo pellets – though the ultra-low velocity restricts its utility to plinking and other lighthearted use.

PNEUMATIC GUNS

Power Line 717, 747 and 777

Daisy's attractive, effectual and competitively priced pneumatic target pistols – the PL717 and PL722 – made their debut in 1978. Sales of the large-calibre PL722 were so disappointing that it was withdrawn in 1982, but the PL717 proved to be a great success.

PL717. This pistol offers remarkable performance at a very low price, providing excellent target practice. The pump lever lies on the left side of the receiver, below the barrel, cocking and loading being effected by a rotating bolt whose flattened handle lies on the right side of the breech above the grip. The front sight is a wide blade, the back sight being a clever fully-adjustable synthetic open notch controlled by large slotted-headed screws. The PL717 does not have the manufacturing quality of the FAS AP604 or the M&G Diana LP6G – the cheapest European match pistols – as many parts are made of lightweight alloy and the finish is not especially durable. However, it is less than half the price of the LP6G and can easily attain 90×100 on ISU pistol targets. The Daisy is truly recoilless, has a fixed trigger set at 3.5-5lb, and is comparatively easy to charge. Currently, its value is challenged only by the spring-piston El Gamo Target (q.v.).

PL747. This is a more recent version of the PL717, introduced in 1986. The principal improvements are the fitting of a Lothar Walther barrel and a trigger adjustable between 1 and 3lb. The PL717 and PL747 are otherwise difficult to distinguish externally. Each

MODEL 188
Data: 0.175in, 11.7in overall, smoothbore barrel, 1.70lb.
Features. A manual safety crossbolt and a non-adjustable trigger; 24 BBs can be held in the feed-tube.
Power: 215fs^{-1} with Daisy BBs (mf).
Easy to cock, adequately consistent and acceptably accurate.

PL717 SERIES
Data: 0.177in, 13.3in overall, 9.2in rifled barrel, 2.87lb.
Features. A manual safety crossbolt; a non-adjustable trigger appears on PL717, but is adjustable for pull-weight (1-3lb) on PL747 and PL777.
Power. ☛ PL717: 392fs^{-1} with Daisy Bullseye Match (2.55fp) and 383fs^{-1} with RWS Diabolo (2.58fp). ☛ PL722: 308fs^{-1} with RWS Diabolo (2.94fp) and 298fs^{-1} with Eley Wasp (2.78fp).
Comparatively easy to charge; outstandingly consistency and very accurate.

The Power Line Models 717 (1) and 777 (2), together with the essentially similar 747, are among the world's best single-stroke pneumatic target pistols in their price groups. By courtesy of Daisy.

MODEL 840

Data: 0.177in, 36.8in overall, 18.8in smoothbore barrel, 2.25lb.
Features. A manual safety crossbolt, a non-adjustable trigger, and a 350-shot gravity/magnetic feed BB magazine.
Power: 277fs^{-1} with RWS Hobby (1 pump) but 323fs^{-1} with *two* pumps (supposedly a single-pump design!). Otherwise generally as Daisy BB Guns (q.v.).

Daisy's one-stroke pneumatic Model 840 is made almost entirely of synthetic material, apart from the barrel and some of the breech components. Velocity is low — but still sufficient to cause a nasty wound at short range. By courtesy of Daisy.

▷

PL747 is tested in a machine rest to ensure that it can group no worse than 0.40in ctc at 25 feet (maker's figure). The pistol will also accept the No.800 Point Sight provided a suitable adaptor is used.

PL777. Claimed to be "America's only Olympic class air pistol", the PL777 is a refinement of the PL717 with an improved trigger — later used in the PL747 — and a better back sight. The guns have palm-rest style walnut grips and a Lothar Walther barrel; accuracy is such that the acceptance standard from the machine rest is 0.20in ctc or better at 25 feet. Theoretically, therefore, the gun can score 100×100 on an ISU target.

Model 840

This little rifle, introduced in 1978, is one of the world's best-selling single-stroke pneumatics. It will fire diabolo pellets or BBs interchangeably, the latter being fed singly or from the internal magazine. The diecast receiver features a straight-pull cocking/loading bolt, while the furniture is injection-moulded plastic. The current guns feature a small raised mount for the Point Sight or a telescope, but pre-1986 guns had an unsuitably rounded receiver.

Power Line 850 series

The original PL850 (introduced in March 1981) was a single-pump pneumatic, but it has been replaced by the PL900. The PL953 match-shooting derivative is also considered separately. The series now contains only the new PL856 and PL860 multi-pump pneumatics which, unlike the 880-series guns, have a conventional fore-end pump handle of the type associated with Crosman. Whether this offers the efficiency of the longer skeletal type is debatable, though the PL856 and PL860 are only slightly less powerful than the PL880 and PL922. The guns fire single diabolo pellets and BBs, or can feed from a gravity/magnetic BB magazine. They are identical externally, apart from the furniture. The PL856 has a plain woodgrain synthetic butt, with a pistol grip and a straight comb, together with a longitudinal grasping groove on the fore-end; the PL860, however, has integrally-moulded chequering on the fore-end and pistol grip, a Monte Carlo comb and a white spacer accompanying the black plastic butt-plate.

PL850 SERIES

Data: 0.177in, 37.4in overall, 18.8in rifled barrel, 2.75lb (PL856) or 3.6lb (PL860).
Features. A manual safety crossbolt, a non-adjustable trigger, and a 100-shot gravity/magnetic feed BB magazine.
Power, ten pumps: 650fs^{-1} with Daisy BB and 630fs^{-1} with Daisy Diabolo (mf, 6.59fp). Reasonably easily charged, very consistent and acceptably accurate.

Power Line 880 series

Introduced in 1972 as the 'Power King', these were the first Daisy guns to feature a multi-stroke pump unit and chambered diabolo pellets rather than BBs. They have particularly elegant lines, with most of the pump lever hidden in the fore-end and only the skeletal operating handle protruding ahead of the trigger guard. The diecast alloy receivers have integral rails for optical sights, while the ramp-mounted front sight blade is accompanied by a typically American 'stepped slider' back sight. Daisy's constant-pressure triggers are generally crisper than their Crosman rivals, but the bolt handles are much too short to give adequate leverage during the cocking/loading stroke. Consequently, the rifles handle German 5.5mm diabolos better than English-style 0.22 types. The rifled barrels give acceptable accuracy, though the guns rarely shoot in the same class as the better European spring-piston guns.

PL880. Introduced in 1972, this gun features a black finish, a plain fore-end and optional BB/pellet feed. BBs are contained in its gravity/magnetic-feed magazine.

Power Line rifles include (from top to bottom) the Models 856, 2860, 900, 1880 and 1917. The 1880 and 1917 are simply optically sighted but otherwise standard 880 and 917 respectively, the 2860 is an 860 fitted with the Daisy Point Sight, and the Model 900 is a single- rather than multi-stroke pneumatic. The Models 900 and 917 both utilize the Snap-Shot clip system.

By courtesy of Daisy.

POWER LINE®

Daisy®
FIRST IN AIRGUNS.

PL920. This 1986-vintage 0.22-calibre adaptation of the PL922 feeds from a single-shot adaptor or the ingenious five-shot Snap Shot clip. The clip holds up to five diabolo pellets, which are pushed into the breech by the bolt-head after each shot has been manually indexed.† This fascinating idea would benefit from more precise construction, for, though the design is not deficient in any way, synthetic execution causes feed difficulties. The principal distinguishing characteristics of the PL920 are the hardwood butt and fore-end. However, though the new butt is undoubtedly more durable, it has lost the subtle elegance of the original plastic version.

PL880 SERIES

Data: 0.177in (PL880, PL970) and 0.22in (PL920, PL922), 37.7in overall, 20.6in rifled barrel, 4.50lb, or 5.20lb with wood butt/fore-end.

Features. Generally as PL850 (q.v.); PL920, PL922 and PL970 feature the 5-shot Snap Shot clip.

Power, ten pumps. PL922: 481fs^{-1} with RWS Diabolo (7.17fp). Note: Daisy claims appreciably higher figures. Otherwise generally as PL850.

† It seems possible that the auto-indexing Snap Shot clip currently fitted to the PL900 may be adapted to the PL920 and PL970 in due course.

PL922. More successful than the 0.177-calibre PL917, with which it was introduced in 1978, the 0.22-calibre PL922 differs from the PL920 principally in the design of the synthetic stock and fore-end. Both are integrally chequered, the butt-plate and pistol-grip cap being accompanied by thin white spacers and a decorative white-edged black diamond being inset in the fore-end sides.

PL970. Introduced in 1986, this is simply a 0.177-calibre version of the PL920. It shares the new hardwood stock and the Snap Shot clip loading system.

Power Line 900

Daisy's latest pneumatic is a single-pump 0.177-calibre rifle delivering lower velocity than the multi-pump PL970, but with an auto-indexing Snap Shot clip system. Developed from the PL850 and PL851 − introduced in 1981-3 but now discontinued − the PL900 is immediately identifiable by its one-piece synthetic stock and the rounded skeletal pump-handle protruding ahead of the trigger guard.

Power Line 953

Introduced for the 1984 sales promotion, this variation of the PL850/851 (and, indirectly, a progenitor of the PL900) is a moderately-priced competition rifle capable of competing effectively against much more expensive designs. The single-pump PL953 can be identified by its distinctive muzzle weight, on which the replaceable-element tunnel pattern front sight is mounted; it also has a full length hardwood stock and the diecast Daisy No.5899 Precision Rear Target Sight at the back of the receiver. The current guns are fitted with Lothar Walther barrels, have single-stage triggers with a pull of about 4.5lb, and are rejected if they fail to group within 0.38in ctc at 25ft from the machine-rest.

PL900
Data: 0.177in, 38.4in overall, 20.6in rifled barrel, 4.3lb.
Features. As PL880 (q.v.), with the 5-shot auto-indexing Snap Shot clip.
Power: 545fs^{-1} with Daisy Diabolo (mf, 4.93fp). Reasonably easily charged, but otherwise with much the same performance as the PL850.

PL953
Data: 0.177in, 38.9in overall, 20.9in rifled barrel, 5.08lb without sights.
Features. Generally as PL900 (q.v.), but with aperture sights.
Power: 480fs^{-1} with Daisy Diabolo (mf, 3.82fp). Otherwise as PL900.

DIANA

Dianawerk, Mayer & Grammelspacher GmbH & Co. KG. D-7550 Rastatt/Baden, Karlstrasse 34, West Germany. British distributors: Frank Dyke & Co. Ltd, 1-7 Ernest Avenue, West Norwood, London SE27 0DG ('Original' brand guns acquired directly from M&G). Leslie Hewett Ltd, Upton Cross, Liskeard, Cornwall PL14 5BQ ('RWS Diana' brand guns bought from Dynamit Nobel). John Rothery (Wholesale) Co. Ltd, Bedford Road, Petersfield, Hampshire GU32 3AX. ('Diana' guns imported from German wholesalers).

* The early history of the company may be found, in some detail, in *Guns Review*, September-October 1983 and March 1984.

One of the world's largest manufacturers of spring-air guns, Mayer & Grammelspacher claims origins stretching back to 1890.* The original production machinery was purchased by Millard Brothers shortly after the end of the Second World War and installed in a new factory in Scotland. This was originally believed to have been the result of chicanery, but it has since been discovered that one of the Millard family visited the M&G plant in 1947 as part of the Allied investigation team and the purchase was probably a simple commercial transaction at a time when the Mayer family needed money. An important side-effect of the purchase of the machinery, much of which was obsolescent, was that M&G was forced to re-tool when the authorities allowed production of cork-firing toys and junior guns to recommence in 1950. Most of the pre-1939 rifles reappeared in the early 1950s, the successful re-establishment of the 'Diana' line permitting the company to begin research that culminated in the Giss Contra-Piston system recoilless spring-air guns.

Product range. Many of the guns with pre-1939 origins have recently been superseded and the range now consists of barrel-cocking pistols and rifles, a single underlever-cocker and a number of sidelever-cocking match and sporting rifles. There are also three 0.22 LR rimfire target rifles to enable multi-discipline marksmen to change codes with a minimum of trouble. This is an unusual trend; M&G has always been an airgun maker, whereas most of its German rivals – including Anschütz, Walther and Weihrauch – were originally firearms makers.

Assessment: M&G's airguns are widely distributed in Britain. They are usually strongly made, but incorporate more stampings than some rival German designs. Unfortunately, the principal guns introduced in the 1970s were complicated (and difficult to strip) and simpler more cost-effective designs have appeared in the 1980s; there has also been a foray into brightly-coloured stocks, which may not be entirely to British tastes.

Discontinued models. Four old junior rifles – LG15, 16, 22 and 23 – were covered in the third edition of *The Airgun Book*, together with the larger LG25, LG27 and LG35; some of these are still being marketed under the RWS brand (qv). The break-barrel target rifles of the LG60 series (LG60, LG65 and LG66) have also disappeared.

Buying second-hand: the older Dianas are widely seen in Britain. They are all sturdy, apart from the plastic back sight fitted to some of the smaller guns, but spare parts are in short supply. Excepting the LG45 series, few of the pre-1980 guns develop much power. However, most Dianas are consistent, accurate performers and those with the ball-sear have a unique trigger action. The Giss-system barrel-cocking target rifles (particularly the perfected LG66) are well worth considering at the right price.

The standard Diana LP5G, a conventional spring-piston gun with an unusually lengthy pedigree. By courtesy of Dianawerk.

The latest version of a pre-war design – the Diana LP5GS pistol with an optical sight and a ribbed muzzle weight. By courtesy of Dianawerk.

A stock-shaping machine. Note the master pattern in the centre and the four identical copies. By courtesy of Dianawerk.

The recoilless Giss system double-piston LP10 is the company's finest target pistol. By courtesy of Dianawerk.

SPRING-PISTON GUNS

Diana LP5G and LP6G

The LP5G barrel-cocking pistol traces its origins back to 1933, but was reintroduced in June 1958 and the current raked-grip form dates from November 1978. Despite its taxing cocking stroke, the LP5G is popular for sporting use, being acceptably powerful, well finished and robust enough to withstand misuse. The LP5GS, released in November 1984, is a standard LP5 with a 1.5×15 telescope sight and a ribbed cast-alloy muzzle weight. The LP6G and LP6GS are similar to the relevant variants of the single-spring LP5G, but incorporate the GCP action. The principal recognition features are the transverse controller-cog housing through the receiver above the grips and the knurled receiver end-cap. The LP6G also has a replaceable-element synthetic front sight unit, rather than the fixed hooded blade of its conventional near-relation. The LP6M, a special match-shooting variant, has the open front sight and cocking sleeve associated with the LP10 (q.v.), as well as adjustable walnut grips.

Diana LP10

One of the earliest challengers to the Feinwerkbau LP65, the GCP-system LP10 dates from August 1974. Among its distinguishing characteristics are the rotating synthetic barrel shroud, which carries the auxiliary barrel weight and protects the hand during cocking. The fully adjustable walnut palm-rest grips are among the finest available, and a curious annular eccentric sleeve around the rear of the receiver can be used to clamp the thumb web. The trigger is superb, and the micro-adjustable open back sight is complemented by an ingenious rotating post front sight with which the image-width can be infinitely adjusted between 2.5 and 4mm. The gun is phosphated. It is unusually large, but shoots well owing to the absence of recoil and the position of the bore, which is virtually an axial extension of the firer's arm.

LP5 AND LP6

Data: 4.5 or 5.5mm, 15.7in overall, 7.1in rifled barrel, 2.81lb (LP5GS).
Features. No safety; the trigger is adjustable for travel only.
Power. ☛ 4.5mm, 410fs^{-1} with RWS Hobby (mf, 2.63fp). ☛ 5.5mm, 358fs^{-1} with RWS Hobby (3.45fp). Quite taxing to cock, but consistent and accurate.

LP10

Data: 4.5mm, 16.1in overall, 7.1in rifled barrel, 2.84lb without auxiliary weights.
Features. An automatic safety: a comprehensively adjustable trigger.
Power: 440fs^{-1} with RWS Diabolo (3.03fp). Taxing to cock, but consistent and extremely accurate.

Introduced in 1984, the first of the new-generation Diana barrel-cocking rifles were (1-3) the LG24, LG26 and LG34.

By courtesy of Dianawerk.

▷

LG24

Data: 4.5mm and 5.5mm, 41.7in overall, 17.3in rifled barel, 5.92lb.
Features. A semi-automatic safety catch; a trigger adjustable for travel only (standard guns).
Power. ☛ 4.5mm, 575fs^{-1} with RWS Hobby (mf, 5.18fp). ☛ 5.5mm, 388fs^{-1} with RWS Diabolo (4.68fp). The cocking stroke is easy; consistency is average, but accuracy is quite good.

Diana LG24 series

This, the first of a new series of simplified guns, made its début in March 1984. It has a nylon piston seal, a semi-automatic safety system adapted from the LG45 (q.v.) and a plain pistol-grip stock. To economize, the popular M&G mounting ramp for optical sights has been replaced by grooves milled into the top of the receiver, and the separate butt plate has been abandoned. The standard LG24 now represents M&G's idea of a junior gun — just another example of the trend towards increasing sophistication in this class. In addition to guns supplied to Webley & Scott (as the 'Air Wolf', q.v.), which have different sights, several other variants have been sold in Britain – including the '24SH', intended for fairground use, and the '24D'. The former has fixed sights and a sturdier-than-normal stock, while the latter has the ball-sear and sight rail.

Diana LG26

This enlargement of the LG24 (q.v.) offers essentially similar construction but slightly greater power. The 'butt plate' consists simply of grooves cut directly into the wood to improve grip against the shoulder: a production expedient that begs damage to the toe. Some of the guns made for export have apparently featured the ball-sear and the sight rail (see LG24).

Diana LG28

The LG28 is the smallest of three new luxury sporting rifles, differing from the LG26 – which it resembles in size and general construction – principally in quality and reversion to a ball-sear trigger system. The beech stock has a partially chequered pistol grip, a low Monte Carlo comb and the rubber butt-plate is accompanied by a white spacer plate. The distinctive metal back sight was developed for the LG35S (now discontinued), but the front sight is a replaceable-element tunnel instead of a ramp-mounted blade.

LG26
Data: 4.5 and 5.5mm, 42.9in overall, 17.3in rifled barrel, 6.17lb.
Features. As LG24.
Power. ☞ 4.5mm: 656fs^{-1} with RWS Hobby (mf, 6.73fp). ☞ 5.5mm, 541fs^{-1} with RWS Hobby (7.87fp). Otherwise as LG24.

LG28
Data: 4.5 and 5.5mm. Otherwise as LG26 except weight – 6.80lb.
Features. A LG24-type safety; a trigger adjustable for pull-weight and travel.
Power: as LG26.

LG30
Data: 4.4mm (ball), 43.3in overall, 18.5in rifled barrel, 7.27lb unladen.
Features. Manual and automatic safeties; a 125-shot tube magazine; a trigger adjustable for travel only.
Power: About 410fs^{-1} with RWS-Punktkugeln Nr.9 (2.96fp). Strenuous to cock, the action is only moderately consistent. Accuracy is quite good at short range.

The second batch of new barrel-cocking M&G Dianas was announced in the autumn of 1985. The LG28 (4), LG36 (5) and LG38 (6) differ from the previous group in the restitution of the ball-sear and (in most cases) the sight rail. The stocks offer cheek pieces, butt-plates and better quality; and, on the latest LG38 at least, a diecast trigger guard has replaced the old stamped strip. By courtesy of Dianawerk.

Diana LG30

This idiosyncratic adaptation of the Schmeisser bolt-action system features shot-counters suited to shooting-gallery use. The bolt lies well forward over the fore-end, rather than immediately ahead of the trigger (as in the original Sportmodelle) and a tube magazine extends forward beneath the barrel. The hardwood stock seems to have inspired that of the LG45 (q.v.) and all the major metal parts are phosphated.

LG34

Data: 4.5mm and 5.5mm, 45.3in overall, 19.5in rifled barrel, 7.39lb.
Features: as LG24.
Power. ☛ 4.5mm, 919fs⁻¹ with RWS Hobby (mf, 13.32fp). ☛ 5.5mm, 689fs⁻¹ with RWS Hobby (mf, 12.77fp). 'Full power' guns will exceed the British 12fp limit. Cocking effort and consistency are average; accuracy is good.

Diana LG34

The largest of the trio of simplified guns dating from March 1984 is basically an enlarged LG24 (q.v.), with which it shares its basic construction. The LG34 retains the synthetic back sight and sight-mounting receiver grooves of the LG24 and the laterally ribbed 'butt-plate' of the LG26, though a British-market 5.5mm variant will be encountered with the traditional M&G sight ramp above the receiver. It also provides the basis for the brightly coloured 'Sport 1000' model, with black, blue, red, yellow or white stocks — each decorated with diagonal twin-line DIANA SPORT transfers and supplied with matching gunslips. Unfortunately, these stocks are no more than standard beechwood with a thick acrylic paint coat; unlike synthetic stocks, in which the colour runs through the material, they mark relatively easily.

LG36

Data: 4.5 and 5.5mm. Otherwise as LG34 except weight — 8.01lb.
Features: as LG28.
Power: as LG34.

Diana LG36

This enlargement of the LG28 (q.v.) appeared in 1986. The increased power is obtained by fitting a more powerful spring, the lengthened barrel contributing virtually nothing to the generation of extra velocity. The LG36 — a sturdy, but somewhat plain gun — is as yet rarely encountered in Britain.

LG38

Data: generally as LG36 (q.v.).

Diana LG38

Introduced at the IWA show at Nürnberg in the Spring of 1986, the LG38 is a deluxe '36' with a refined walnut stock with a hog's back comb, a more precisely defined cheek piece, cut chequering on the pistol grip and a plastic pistol-grip cap/spacer combination. The brown rubber butt-plate, ventilated rather than solid, is accompanied by white and black spacers; and the familiar sight-ramp lies above the receiver. The powerful LG38 is clearly intended to compete with the Weihrauch HW80 and HW85, and its progress will be watched with interest.

LG45

Data: 4.5, 5.05 and 5.5mm, 45.5in overall, 20.5in rifled barrel, 7.97lb.
Features. A semi-automatic safety catch and an adjustable trigger.
Power. ☛ 4.5mm, 828fs⁻¹ with Eley Wasp (11.59fp). ☛ 5.05mm: 756fs⁻¹ with H&N Diabolo (12.49fp). ☛ 5.5mm: 611fs⁻¹ with RWS Diabolo (11.58fp). The export pattern will exceed the British 12fp limit by 10-15 per cent. The guns are arduous to cock, but very consistent (once shot-in) and extremely accurate.

Diana LG45

This appeared in 1978, when M&G realised that the power of the 'S' series guns had fallen behind its rivals. The famous ball-sear was replaced by a more conventional trigger system, in which a sliding semi-automatic safety protruded from the back of the receiver. This safety unit was initially confusingly marked, displaying a white dot when set (protruding) but nothing when ready to fire. Guns numbered above about 245000, however, display a white encircled 'S' in an aperture on the rear left side of the receiver when the safety is applied — or a red dot when ready to fire. The back surfaces of the new safeties display 'N' (neuer Art or 'new pattern').

Diana LG45. Remarkable for its plain ambidexterous beechwood stock, the standard gun has a one-piece cocking lever that necessitates a long slot in the fore-end. The pistol grip has neither chequering nor cheek piece, though the ventilated rubber butt-plate helps to improve the handling characteristics. The LG45 inherited the sturdy LG35S-type back sight, but the synthetic replaceable-element front sight tunnel-block is held only by a combination of friction and splines on the muzzle. As this unit may loosen during firing, to the detriment of accuracy, some rifles display a conventional hooded blade fixed to the muzzle dovetail by a threaded bolt.† The basic LG45 was briefly sold in the USA as the 'Beeman 250' and a hybrid combining the LG45 action with an LG35S-pattern stock is marketed as the RWS 45 (q.v.) or the Crosman 6100 Challenger. The true LG45 can be recognised by its distinctive stock design, deep angular trigger guard (which will admit even the largest gloved finger) and the crossbolt through the stock immediately above the trigger lever.

† It is probable that the folded-sheet back sight of the LG48 series will now be fitted to the LG45.

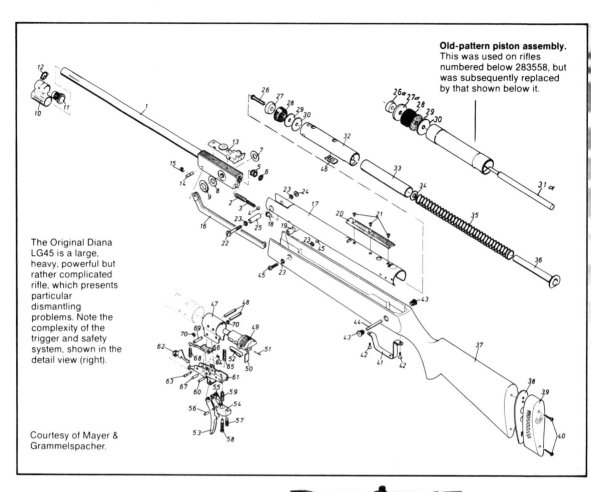

Old-pattern piston assembly.
This was used on rifles numbered below 283558, but was subsequently replaced by that shown below it.

The Original Diana LG45 is a large, heavy, powerful but rather complicated rifle, which presents particular dismantling problems. Note the complexity of the trigger and safety system, shown in the detail view (right).

Courtesy of Mayer & Grammelspacher.

△ A large, powerful and popular sporter, the LG45S features a muzzle weight and an optical sight. By courtesy of Dianawerk.

Diana LG45S: this lacks fixed sights, but has a detachable muzzle weight/cocking grip, and sling swivels on the barrel and butt.‡

The LG45 has not gained the acceptance expected in Britain, despite its sweet trigger, pleasant shooting characteristics and acceptable power. On the debit side, the big M&G Diana is clumsy for field work and greatly benefits from shortening the barrel (which has no appreciable effect on power or accuracy); the detent-lock is almost always very stiff when new; the angled breech face necessitates care during loading; and the cocking stroke requires some strength. It is also a difficult dismantling proposition, owing to the complexity of the trigger.

Diana LG48

The LG48 is the first sidelever-cocking M&G sporting rifle, clearly influenced by the LG75 (q.v.) but with only a single piston. The rifle has a direct-loading breech, with a toothed safety bar beneath the action that can be disengaged during cocking by pressing the thumb-catch on the left side of the breech. This bar blocks the return of the breech-sleeve while the pellet is being inserted. The gun has a remarkably easy cocking

‡ These guns have been designated '45S', '45SB' and '45SBS' in Britain (being supplied with no sights, 4×20 and 4×28 optical sights respectively). These terms appear to have originated with Frank Dyke & Co. rather than Mayer & Grammelspacher, to whom all three 'variants' are simply LG45S.

LG48

Data: 4.5 and 5.5mm, 43.3in overall, 17.3in rifled barrel, 8.84lb.
Features. Automatic, semi-automatic and 'ratchet plate' safeties; and an adjustable trigger.
Power: as LG52.

stroke considering that it will attain prodigious velocities. It has a plain beechwood stock with a rubber butt-plate, and a cunningly folded metal back sight inspired by that of the LG45; the open front sight, however, is mounted on a short ramp and can be moved longitudinally to adjust the point of impact without touching the back sight elevation. A traditional M&G sight-ramp appears on the rear of the receiver. At nearly nine pounds, the rifle is something of a handful, but it is very accurate and shoots remarkably consistently in its unrestricted form. As the rifle was originally designed to generate high power, which it does with ridiculous ease, the standard sub-12fp adaptations are not as satisfactory. As the piston stroke is unusually long, 'lock time' is greater than most spring-piston guns and a forward surge is usually notable. The phenomenon seems to affect the 4.5mm LG48 more than the 5.5mm version; and, in addition, the latter is actually easier to cock. Owing to the solidity of the basic design, together with the scope for improvement, the LG48 and LG52 appeal greatly to the British customisers. No sooner had the gun appeared in Britain, therefore, than the Venom Trophy 52 and Venom Lazer 52 were being successfully marketed.

The replacements for the underlever-cocking LG50 are the powerful LG48 (1) and LG52 (2), differing principally in their stock designs. Note the unique front sight, which slides longitudinally on the muzzle ramp, and the short sight radius. By courtesy of Dianawerk.

Diana LG50 T01

This adaptation of the underlever-cocking LG50 (originally introduced in May 1952) superseded the unattractively angular LG50S in September 1981, but is itself being phased out during 1987-8. The ball-sear trigger has been replaced by the more conventional LG45 type, with its distinctive sliding safety block, and the elongated cocking lever – which improves mechanical advantage – protrudes some way ahead of the three-quarter length stock. The sights are shared with the LG45, the back sight appearing ahead of the loading tap to give an unusually short sighting radius. The earliest LG50 T01 had an S-style butt with a massive angular cheek piece, a Monte Carlo comb and chequering on the pistol grip; however, this was soon superseded by a plain pattern based on that of the LG45. Despite its weight and general air of solidity, and though it remains a favourite with champions of fixed-barrel guns, the LG50 T01 is generally less powerful than the LG45.

LG50 T01
Data: 4.5 and 5.5mm, 45.1in overall, 19.1in rifled barrel, 8.33lb.
Features: as LG45.
Power. 4.5mm, 771fs^{-1} with RWS Hobby (9.31fp). 5.5mm: 584fs^{-1} with RWS Diabolo (10.57fp). Otherwise as LG45.

LG52
Data: generally as LG48. The LG52 is often slightly heavier, owing to different stock-wood.
Power. 4.5mm British pattern, 802fs^{-1} with RWS Superdome (11.93fp). 4.5mm export pattern, 1,016fs^{-1} with RWS Diabolo (16.16fp) and 966fs^{-1} with Eley Wasp (15.77fp). 5.5mm British pattern, 603fs^{-1} with RWS Superdome (11.77fp). 5.5mm export pattern, 755fs^{-1} with RWS Hobby (mf, 15.33fp). Surprisingly easily cocked, but with a very long stroke; the action is consistent and accurate.

Diana LG52

This is no more than an LG48 (q.v.) with a heavier barrel, a deluxe walnut stock, chequering on the pistol grip and fore-end, and an improved rubber butt-plate with white/black spacers.

Diana LG75

The first of these sidelever-cocking GCP-system rifles – derived from the barrel-cocking LG60, LG65 and LG66 – appeared in August 1977 after their predecessors failed to challenge Feinwerkbau and Walther. The LG75 has a fixed barrel and a directly accessible breech, but is complicated even by target gun standards owing to its double piston assembly and highly sophisticated trigger. Despite being appreciably cheaper than its rivals, the LG75 initially failed to make much of an impact at the highest level; in 1983, however, radical improvements were made to the design of the stock. The addition of an adjustable cheekpiece, a detachable hand-plate beneath the fore-end ahead of the trigger (LG75U version only) and a revised butt-plate system elevated the LG75 to a point where it can compete successfully at the highest level.

LG75 T01. Formerly known simply as the LG75, the original rifle has a deep squared walnut stock with three shallow cutaways in the fore-end to reduce weight, a blued receiver, a phosphated barrel and conventional competition sights. The most commonly encountered micro-adjustable back sight is the Diopter 75, but this is gradually being superseded by the improved Diopter 82.

LG75 T01 HV. Intended for marksmen who prefer to shoot head-up, the sight line of this variant is raised by auxiliary blocks.

LG75U T01. This features the greatly revised 1983-pattern stock, riser blocks being fitted as standard.

LG75K T01. Similar to the 'U' version, this is intended for moving-target competitions. It has an optical sight, a detachable muzzle weight, a wooden butt-plate and a raised cocking-lever tip. Apart from these features, and the omission of the hand-plate beneath the fore-end, it is otherwise practically identical with the 75U T01.

Match 1000. A variant of the LG75 T01 can be obtained with a plain beech stock; this, in turn, provides the basis for the eye-catching Match model, which has transfer-decorated black, blue, red, yellow or white stocks to accompany the Sport 1000 (LG34, q.v.).

LG75

Data: 4.5mm, 43.7in overall, 18.9in rifled barrel, about 10.75lb with sights.
Features. Automatic and sidelever-ratchet safeties and a comprehensively adjustable trigger.
Power: 600fs^{-1} with RWS Diabolo (6.32fp) and 587fs^{-1} with Eley Wasp (5.82fp). Easily cocked, unusually consistent and extremely accurate.

Three versions of the popular fixed barrel Giss-system recoilless Diana rifle: the standard LG75 (1), the LG75U T01 with its very distinctive stock (2), and the LG75K T01 moving-target gun (3). By courtesy of Dianawerk.

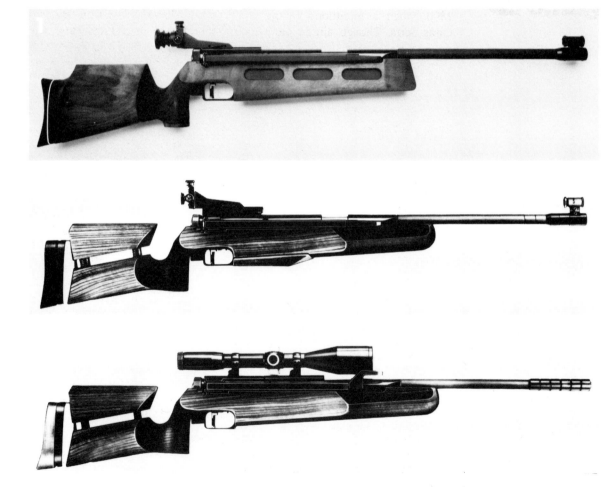

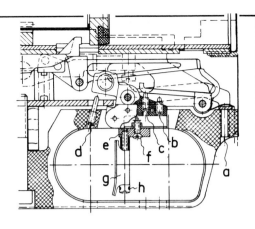

DIANA

Right: in common with all top-class target rifles, the LG75 has an adjustable trigger. Screw A controls the weight of the first pull; B controls the weight of the second pull; D is the trigger stop; F locks the trigger stem E, which moves laterally once the screw has been loosened; and G controls the angle of the trigger blade. Screw C is a factory adjustment only.

Courtesy of Mayer & Grammelspacher.

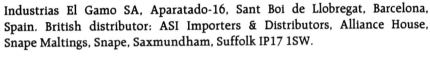

EL GAMO

Industrias El Gamo SA, Aparatado-16, Sant Boi de Llobregat, Barcelona, Spain. British distributor: ASI Importers & Distributors, Alliance House, Snape Maltings, Snape, Saxmundham, Suffolk IP17 1SW.

The premier airgun-maker in the Iberian Peninsula, El Gamo claims origins in 1890, when a munitions-making company was founded by Don Antonio Casas Serra. Though airgun production did not begin until 1960, extremely rapid prominence has been achieved by producing, in the words of the current catalogue, 'medium-high quality at medium-low price'; by 1980, guns were being exported to fifty countries and the work force of about 125 was making 200,000 guns annually. The astute foundation of a subsidiary in Brazil (Gamo Armas e Muniçoes Ltda, Avenida Sertório, Porto Allegre) has ensured that El Gamo guns are also widely distributed in South America.

Product range. A series of barrel-cocking spring-piston guns, ranging from the smallest of junior guns to a comparatively high-powered Magnum sporter, is complemented by the first truly recoilless single-stroke pneumatic rifles to be made in Spain. There are also several underlever-cocking pistols, and a new pneumatic ball-firer called the PR-15. Three of the rifles — the Cadet, Expo and 361 — and the Falcón pistol are offered as shooting kits (Equipos de tiro) which, in the case of the Expo and the Mo.361, may also include optical sights, target holders, targets and pellets. Interestingly, airgun targets are known as 'dianas' in Spain — an interesting commentary on the penetration of Mayer & Grammelspacher into an earlier market! El Gamo also makes several types of diabolo pellet.

Assessment: the El Gamo guns are invariably sturdy and well made, though they feature an appreciable number of synthetic parts. Performance is not generally up to the best of the British and German-made guns, though the company has made great strides to improve quality in recent years. The MC Super has proved popular in competition shooting owing to its comparatively low price, though its action is quirky compared with the Feinwerkbau LG600 or the Walther LGR.

Discontinued models: several obsolescent or comparatively unsuccessful designs have now disappeared, including the barrel-cocking semi-recoilless sporting rifles known as the Statical* and Stamic (single-shot and magazine-feed respectively); a predecessor of the Modelo 361 known as the 45-S-61; a larger version of the Expo 200 called the Modelo 300; and the junior David and DS barrel-cockers.

* At the time of writing, small quantities of the Statical were still available in Britain from the distributor's stocks.

Buying second-hand: the older rifles are regularly seen in Britain, having been distributed by ASI since the late 1960s. Apart from the distinctive Gamo 68 and Gamatic (the 'Paratrooper' and 'Paratrooper Repeater'), the most commonly encountered gun is the Expo 200. This has been sold here under several tradenames, including Rangemaster and Sniper. Though parts for the pre-1980 guns are not always easy to obtain, the El Gamo airguns are generally simple and require little attention.

SPRING-PISTON GUNS

Cadet-S

Introduced in 1979, this gun shares the fully adjustable sights, receiver, piston and barrel with the Expo 200. The hardwood stock has a Monte Carlo comb, a rounded pistol grip, a squared Expo-style cheek piece and a very distinctively grooved fore-end. Unfortunately, the distance from the pistol grip to the trigger is much too far for many of the junior airgunners for whom the Cadet is clearly intended. The gun cannot be mistaken for any other in the El Gamo range owing to its small size.

CADET
Data: 4.5mm, 37.0in overall, 15.6in rifled barrel, 4.56lb.
Features. A semi-automatic safety lever and a travel-adjustable trigger.
Power: 544fs^{-1} with RWS Diabolo (5.20fp). The Cadet is easily cocked, but the detent is often stiff; acceptably accurate and moderately consistent, the action is prone to dieselling when new.

The Cadet (1), known in Britain as the ASI Apache, and the larger Expo (ASI Sniper, bottom) are El Gamo's principal junior air rifles. By courtesy of Industrias El Gamo.

Center

Dating from 1973, this underlever-cocking spring-piston pistol is one of the most popular in its class, and offers surprising quality for its price. The blued air cylinder, barrel and cocking lever contrast attractively with the black crackle-finish frame, which has a unique pivoting grip. The Center also has an ingenious laterally swinging 'floating' loading port, efficiently sealed as the piston flies forward provided it is properly repositioned in the breech (the absence of a breech locking catch being one of the gun's poorer features). The back sight is fully adjustable and the front sight blade is protected by a hood.

CENTER
Data: 4.5mm, 14.9in overall, 7.1in rifled barrel, 2.83lb.
Features. No safety; the trigger is adjustable for travel only.
Power: 429fs^{-1} with RWS Diabolo (3.23fp). Reasonably easily cocked, adequately consistent and accurate.

Expo series

These are the current versions of a gun introduced as long ago as 1965, and offered in Britain under a selection of tradenames (e.g., Rangemaster and Sniper). Several variants have been made; the earliest had rounded stocks, later more fashionably squared, and fore-end grooving was added in the early 1980s. The latest guns have a safety adapted from that of the Cadet (q.v.).

Expo-S: though sharing the same basic Cadet action, this has an appreciably longer barrel and air cylinder and will develop greater power. The lengthened butt has a separate plastic butt plate, the fore-end is deeper and the curiously unattractive synthetic trigger guard slopes downwards towards the barrel. Like the Cadet, the Expo-S has a clearly graduated adjustable spring-leaf back sight and a fixed front sight blade mounted on a hooded ramp. It is justifiably popular in Britain and El Gamo has made consider-

EXPO
Data: 4.5 or 5.5mm, 41.2in overall (older guns, 40.5in), 17.7in rifled barrel, 5.51lb.
Features. A semi-automatic safety appears on Expo-S; the trigger is adjustable. The Expomatic has a magazine tube above the air cylinder.
Power. 4.5mm: 595fs^{-1} with RWS Diabolo (6.22fp). 5.5mm: 465fs^{-1} with RWS Diabolo (6.70fp). Otherwise generally as Cadet (q.v.), though more powerful.

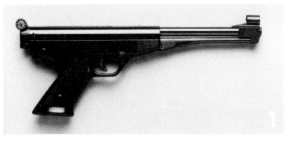

Center

The El Gamo underlever-cocking pistols are very popular in Britain; the Falcón (1) is a simplified version of the Center (2), with a plastic grip/frame, while the Target is a variant of the Center with a match-type adjustable grip and a refined trigger. By courtesy of Industrias El Gamo.

able effort in recent years to improve its quality; however, its power is less than that of the BSA Meteor.

Expomatic: practically identical with the Expo, this has a magazine tube above the air cylinder from which a mechanical elevator feeds pellets into line with the bore. Experiments suggest this system can damage the pellets during its cycle, with a measurable deterioration of accuracy and velocity, but the guns are fast to cock/load and great fun to use.

Falcón and Falcón R-20

The Falcón is basically a simplified Center (q.v.), sharing a similar underlever-cocking action and the distinctively floating laterally-swinging loading port. However, a one-piece synthetic grip/frame has been substituted for all-metal construction. The sights are shared by both pistols, but the Falcón has a fixed rather than articulated grip. It is sturdy, shoots pleasantly and offers surprisingly high power without an unduly arduous cocking stroke; like the Center, however, the Falcón's loading port is too narrow to accept particularly long-body pellets and the occasional flier may result from the imprecise seating of the loading block in the breech. The R-20 is a 1986-vintage modification of the single-shot underlever design with a tube magazine in the left side of the barrel — paralleling the bore — and a laterally-feeding injector. It can only fire ball ammunition.

FALCÓN

Data: 4.5mm, 2.82lb, otherwise as Center (q.v.).
Features. A manual safety crossbolt; a trigger adjustable for pull-weight (1.8-5.3lb); and a 20-ball magazine alongside barrel (R-20 only).
Power: 439fs^{-1} with RWS Hobby (3.02fp) and 393fs^{-1} with Eley Wasp (2.61fp). Otherwise generally as Center.

The Gamo-68 (1) and Gamatic (2) are among the most popular of the Spanish-made airguns seen in Britain, largely owing to their unusual appearance. The pistol grip

undoubtedly aids shooting and the autoloading system (3) certainly permits rapid firing with compatible pellets. By courtesy of Industrias El Gamo.

GAMO SERIES

Data: 4.5 and 5.5mm, 38.0in overall, 17.7in rifled barrel, 6.37lb.
Features. A manual safety (Gamo-85 only), plus an adjustable (Gamo-68) or non-adjustable (Gamo-85) trigger.
Power. ☛ 4.5mm Gamo-68: 571fs^{-1} with RWS Hobby (5.11fp). Otherwise generally as Expo (q.v.).

Gamo series

The original Gamo-68 caused something of a sensation when it first appeared in Britain owing to its unorthodox pseudo-military design. Though many of the parts are shared with the Expo (q.v.), the provision of a separate pistol-grip on the crackle-finish frame distinguishes the Gamo from other guns. The trigger originally featured three screws at the back of the guard to adjust the travel and pull-weight (the screw nearest the butt locked the pull-weight adjustor).

Gamo-85. This has a new trigger system with a button-type safety catch behind the trigger on the left side of the frame, the standard Expo 200 sights, an alloy fore-end/pistol grip unit and a synthetic butt with a rubber butt plate.

Gamatic: known in Britain as the 'ASI Paratrooper Repeater', this combines the action of the Gamo-68 or 85 with a tubular pellet magazine above the air cylinder. An elevator feeds pellets into line with the barrel each time the action is cocked. The system is effectual, though prone to damaging weak-bodied or sharply pointed pellets.

Ranger. Not yet seen in Britain, this is a variant of the Gamatic with a side-folding rod-type stock. It appears to lack the safety catch, but is otherwise similar to the standard guns.

Hunter

The latest El Gamo sporting spring-piston rifle, introduced for the 1987 season, is mechanically a Magnum (q.v.); however, it is fitted with a muzzle-weight and a 1.5×15 telescope sight on the barrel block. The combination looks not unlike the Webley Vulcan II Teleskan system, the lengthy eye-relief being required by what is basically a pistol sight. Sling swivels are standard fittings on this gun.

HUNTER
Data: 4.5 and 5.5mm, 45.7in overall (with muzzle weight), 8.05lb. Otherwise as Magnum.

Hunter is a version of the Magnum with a barrel weight and a pistol-type 1.5×15 optical sight above the barrel block. This assures satisfactory eye relief, while isolating the sight from the effects of wear in the main barrel pivot. By courtesy of Industrias El Gamo.

Magnum

This 1983-vintage design gave El Gamo a powerful and attractive gun with which to compete on the worldwide export market – and, perhaps, fight off the penetration of northern European guns into Spain. The Magnum possesses a sturdy, well finished beechwood stock with a cheek piece, a short high Monte Carlo comb, a rubber butt plate accompanied by a white spacer-plate and a plastic pistol-grip cap. The latest guns have stippling on the pistol grip, but earliest examples were plain. The sturdy all-metal back sight developed for the Statical has been retained, there is a manual safety system and an adjustable trigger. Sling swivels may be encountered on the barrel and under the butt, but are no longer standard. The Magnum is advertised as "one of the world's most powerful and accurate rifles", which is misleading: it is undoubtedly the most powerful gun currently made in Spain, but tests of several guns have indicated that they are less powerful that the standard BSA Mercury IV.† Interestingly, the piston system of the new BSA Supersport rifle bears a considerable resemblance to the Magnum's, though developing much greater power.

Modelo 361

Dating from 1979, when it replaced the essentially similar 45-S-61, this popular barrel-cocking spring-piston gun can be considered as an adult-size Expo with a longer air cylinder and a more conventionally rounded stock. More than a million 45-S-61 and Mo.361 rifles have been made since 1961.

Model 600

This modernized 361 has the Statical's sturdy all-metal back sight and a hefty stock based on the Expo-S style – longitudinally grooved, with the unattractive synthetic trigger guard. However, though the 600 is appreciably larger than the Expo, and has a longer air cylinder, the piston stroke and power generating capacity apparently remain unchanged. These guns sell well in greatly restricted markets such as Germany, but it is hard to see them attaining great success in Britain now that the Hunter and Magnum offer so much more. A modified version known as the 600-S, with the Magnum-type trigger and safety system, is available in Spain.

MAGNUM
Data: 4.5 and 5.5mm, 43.9in overall, 17.7in rifled barrel, 7.88lb.
Features. A manual safety catch and an adjustable trigger.
Power. ☛ 4.5mm: 726fs^{-1} with El Gamo Magnum pellets (mf). ☛ 5.5mm: 546fs^{-1} with RWS Diabolo (9.24fp) and 515fs^{-1} with Eley Wasp (8.31fp). Reasonably easily cocked, the Magnum is acceptably consistent and quite accurate.

† The standard BSA Mercury is conservatively listed by the manufacturer at 550 and 750fs^{-1} (0.22 and 0.177in respectively), while the BSA Mercury S, the Webley Omega and the Weihrauch HW77 – to name but three – generate appreciably more. This is noted not to denigrate the Magnum, which offers good performance at a highly attractive price, but merely to place it in its proper context.

MODELO 361
Data: 4.5mm, 43.7in overall, 17.7in rifled barrel, 7.01lb.
Features. No safety; the trigger is adjustable for sear engagement only.
Power: 591fs^{-1} with El Gamo pellets (mf). Otherwise as Expo.

MODELO 600
Data: 4.5 and 5.5mm. Otherwise generally as Mo.361, apart from the Magnum-type safety system on 600-S and slightly greater weight.

Modelo 900

Introduced in Spain in 1987, but as yet unseen in Britain, this appears to combine the action (and trigger guard) of the Magnum series with a fluted stock similar to that of the Modelo 600 (q.v.).

Target

Introduced in 1986, this variant of the Center (q.v.) is intended specifically for target shooting. The action of the two pistols is practically identical, but the Target has an adjustable palm-rest style wood-grain plastic grip and a greatly improved trigger system with which its performance – at the price – is quite unbelievable. In its group, only the single-stroke pneumatic Daisy Model 717 offers anything like competition, and the El Gamo is appreciably more sturdy.

TARGET
Data: 4.5mm. The trigger is comprehensively adjustable. Otherwise generally as Center (q.v.).

The Modelo 600 combines an enlarged Expo-type stock with a Magnum-type trigger, but is rarely encountered in Britain owing to its comparatively low power. By courtesy of Industrias El Gamo.

The Target pistol is a minor variant of the popular Center (q.v.), with a beneficially modified trigger that can be adjusted longitudinally and a competition-style synthetic grip.

An interesting and well-made autoloading single-stroke pneumatic, the El Gamo PR-15, despite firing only ball ammunition, promises to become a popular 'fun gun'. By courtesy of Industrias El Gamo.

◁

The Super (or MC-Super) remains the only Spanish target air-rifle capable of successfully challenging northern European designs. Designed in Sweden and perfected in Barcelona, the gun is an accurate and consistent-shooting single-stroke pneumatic with a unique compensating chamber and a manually retracted breech sleeve. By courtesy of Industrias El Gamo.

In addition to the rifles, El Gamo makes a wide range of pellets, target boxes and accessories, part of which is shown here. By courtesy of ASI.

SINGLE-STROKE PNEUMATICS

Contest

Incorporating the single-stroke pneumatic action designed by the Swedish engineer Sigge Olofsson, and patented in October 1982, this sporting derivative of the MC Super lacks the power necessary to dispatch anything but small vermin. The compensating-chamber principle differs completely from the Walther the El Gamo rifle may otherwise have been expected to resemble. The MC (Mono-Compresión, single-stroke charging) valve opens under the power of its own spring when pressure on the trigger retracts a supporting bar. The Walther striker is undoubtedly more effectual, but the Spanish version works adequately enough and certainly avoids any let-off jump. The breech sleeve must be opened manually after the charging lever has been retracted and closed before the charging stroke is completed. This is inconvenient, but the rifle has a sweet trigger action and the overall impression is one of considerable satisfaction.

PR-15

The latest El Gamo pistol is an excellent single-stroke pneumatic with an integral tube magazine for ball-shot. It is made largely from die-castings, to offer, according to the 1987 catalogue, 'maximum power in minimum space to reduce size'. It has a smooth two-stage trigger, an adjustable back sight and opens to load in much the same way as the FAS or HW45. Closing the breech automatically feeds the next ball into the breech. Though representing an interesting departure from El Gamo's previous products, it is a shame that the PR-15 cannot also fire diabolo pellets – not only to enhance its appeal but also to capitalize on the accuracy of the pneumatic system. However, it is believed that a pellet-firing variant is under development.

Super or MC-Super

Spain's first true target rifle shares the Mono-Compresión single-stroke charging system with the Contest (q.v.). The principal distinguishing characteristics are a deep competition-style stock, with extensive stippling on the pistol grip and under the fore-end, an

CONTEST
Data: 4.5mm, 43.4in overall, 17.7in rifled barrel, 10.14lb.
Features. An automatic trigger safety and a comprehensively adjustable trigger.
Power: 588fs^{-1} with RWS Diabolo (6.07fp). Awkward to charge, the mechanism is supremely consistent and offers excellent accuracy.

PR-15
Data: 4.50mm (ball only), 9.1in overall, 6.9in barrel, 2.15lb.
Features. A manual safety crossbolt; a non-adjustable trigger; and a tube magazine.
Power: 361fs^{-1} with El Gamo ball ammunition (mf). Moderately easy to charge, the PR-15 shoots very consistently.

SUPER
Data: 4.5mm, 10.62lb with sights. Otherwise as Contest.
Power: 591fs^{-1} with RWS Diabolo (6.14fp).

‡ The prototypes and pre-production MC-Super guns were fitted with Feinwerkbau sights, but production guns feature a Spanish-made copy.

adjustable butt plate sliding vertically in a dovetail, and fully adjustable aperture sights.‡ The excellent trigger is adjustable longitudinally within the guard, as well as for pull-weight and travel. Though the general construction of these rifles is inferior to their German rivals, they are so competitively priced that their progress must be watched with interest. Tests indicated that they shoot as consistently as the Walther LGR and Feinwerkbau LG300 series, though the charging stroke is much more taxing than the latter's.

The Super (or MC-Super) remains the only Spanish target air-rifle capable of successfully challenging northern European designs. Designed in Sweden and perfected in Barcelona, the gun is an accurate and consistent-shooting single-stroke pneumatic with a unique compensating chamber and a manually retracted breech sleeve. By courtesy of Industrias El Gamo.

In addition to the rifles, El Gamo makes a wide range of pellets, target boxes and accessories, part of which is shown here. By courtesy of ASI.

FEINWERKBAU

Feinwerkbau, Westinger & Altenburger KG, D-7238 Oberndorf/Neckar, Neckarstrasse 43, West Germany. British distributor: ASI, Alliance House, Snape Maltings, Snape, Saxmundham, Suffolk IP17 1SW.

Feinwerkbau is a comparatively youthful airgun maker, entering the local commercial register in April 1949 and making machine-tools and counting equipment until production of recoilless air rifles began in the 1960s. The development to near-perfection of a design credited to Karl Westinger, Ernst Altenburger and Edwin Wöhrstein (the 'WAW Sledge')* has brought out-standing success; beginning with the LG150 in January 1963, Feinwerkbau rifles have held every single world record. The pistols derived from the LP65 still

* German Patent 1140289.

hold most of the records, though increasingly challenged by the Italian pneumatics (Air Match, FAS and Fiocchi-Pardini) and the Walther CP2. The gas-powered Feinwerkbau LP2, based on the same Senfter/Idl patents, appears to have surrendered ground to its Walther rival; conversely, Feinwerkbau's new pneumatic rifle, the LG600, is steadily loosening the grip of the Walther LGR Match Universal. It will be interesting to see what effect the Anschütz Superair 2001, the Steyr gas rifle and the eagerly awaited new Walther will have on the affairs of the LG600, quite apart from the FWB C60!

The Feinwerkbau stand at IWA, Nürnberg, 1987. In addition to the pistols displayed along the front of the stand-counter, a left-hand LG600 is being prominently featured on the wall board. Unlike most pneumatics, the LG600 can even be obtained with a left-hand stock and a right-hand action. By courtesy of *Guns Review*.

Product range: spring-piston sporting and target guns, single-pump pneumatic rifles, and gas-power competition guns.

Discontinued models: these include the earliest representatives of the WAW Sledge System – LG100 (1963-8), LG150 (1963-8), LG200 (1969-72) – and some of the older variants of the LG300 series (q.v.).

Assessment: Feinwerkbau competition guns have no peers, having won medals at every level up to Olympic gold. The sporter is an elegant, effectual design – widely favoured in Britain for its customization potential – but is becoming too expensive and is, as a result, losing ground to the Weihrauch HW80 and HW77.

Buying second-hand. The guns are well made of the finest materials (particularly pre-1975 examples), but the recoilless spring-piston mechanism is complex and somewhat delicate. However, there is no reason why a Feinwerkbau should not continue to serve for many years provided its seals are sound and there is no obvious wear in the sliding components.

SPRING-PISTON GUNS

LP65 series

Introduced in January 1965, this diminutive of the WAW Sledge System has seen outstanding success for more than twenty years. The cocking lever lies on the left side of the receiver (most marksmen, being right handed, cock with the non-grip hand) while

† German Patent 1181590.
‡ German Patent 1703910.

the special micro-adjustable back sight† lies at the extreme rear of the receiver and will accept exchangeable sight-notch plates. The distinctive interchangeable-element front sight is also a patented feature‡, and the trigger may be adjusted down to 500gm (1.1lb). An optional unit with a pull of 3lb (1360gm) simulates cartridge-pistol training – a role in which the recoil-suppressor of the LP65 (though not its successors) can be disconnected for authenticity.

LP65. Often called 'M65 Mark 1' in the USA, this has a small rounded trigger guard, a rounded under-edge to the frame ahead of the trigger aperture, a trigger-lever with a pronounced rearward-projecting web, and a frame ending level with the back sight adjusting-bolt head. The thumb-rest grips may be plastic or walnut, but palm-rest grips are available to special order. A short-barrelled version, apparently arising from Beeman's request for a handier sporting gun, may also be obtained. This is sometimes known as the LP65 Junior (or 'M65 Mark 2' in the USA), but the current Feinwerkbau catalogue simply designates it as a short LP65.

LP80. A refinement of the basic LP65, recently dropped from production in favour of the LP90 (but still available in Britain), this incorporates a greatly improved trigger – adjustable laterally and longitudinally within its squared guard. Unlike the LP65, no web projects back into the frame. In addition, the squared-contour frame extends to the back-sight plate. Three auxiliary weights of 15, 60 or 85gm could be attached below the barrel, replacing the LP65 barrel-sleeve.*

* German Patent 1428621. The three-weight system was abandoned in 1987 and barrel-clamping patterns reappeared; these weigh 70, 75 and 100gm.

LP90. This is simply an LP80 with an effectual electronic trigger powered by a 1.5-volt alkaline battery, which gives a particularly crisp pull of between 480 and 600gm with none of the metal-to-metal friction inherent in conventional systems. The first-stage pull length is also adjustable, though the let-off point and trigger-stop are set by the factory. A red light-emitting diode beneath the pistol-grip must illuminate when pressed, otherwise the battery needs replacing.

The WAW Sledge-type competition pistols include the LP65 (1), the short-barrel LP65 (2), the LP80 (3) and the electronically triggered LP90 (4). By courtesy of Feinwerkbau.

LP65 SERIES

Data: 4.5mm, 15.3in overall, 7.5in rifled barrel, 2.65lb without auxiliary weights.
Features. The safety is similar to that of the LG300 (q.v.); the trigger is fully adjustable for pull-weight and travel (LP65), and also laterally and longitudinally (LP80 and LP90)
Power, LP65: 448fs^{-1} with RWS Diabolo (3.53fp). Easy to cock, the pistols are extraordinarily accurate.

Feinwerkbau

LG120 series

Westinger & Altenburger's only spring-piston sporting rifle was developed in response to requests from distributors in Britain and the USA. The 'FWB Sport' – as it is widely known outside Germany – is a simple break-barrel design, with a one-piece linkage and such clever pivot distribution that it can be cocked with surprising ease. Indeed, cocking even the export-power FWB Sport takes only half the strength required for the comparably powerful Weihrauch HW80 or BSA Airsporter S. Though the gun is well-made, accurate and more than acceptably powerful, its ball detent breech-closing system, crudely adjustable synthetic back sight and unadaptable trigger (which bears no comparison with the Weihrauch Rekord) provide weaknesses. Paradoxically, these shortcomings have inspired many British customizers to refine an otherwise sound action, and FWB Sport rifles modified by Airmasters/Mastersport and others are outnumbered only by Weihrauchs on the British custom airgun market.

LG121. The basic rifle has a plain beechwood stock with a rounded pistol grip and a low Monte Carlo comb, but rather surprisingly lacks a butt-plate. Power is set below 7.5J for the German market, the trigger guard is a stamped strip, and the semi-automatic safety system has been adapted from the pre-war Haenel pattern. The 'Luxusmodell' is essentially similar, but its walnut stock has a chequered pistol grip, with a plastic spacer and pistol-grip cap, and a rubber butt-plate. Sling swivels will be found on the front of the barrel block and on the under-edge of the butt.

LG124. Mechanically identical with the LG121, this simply features greater power. Changes made during its production life have included the substitution of a precision-blanked trigger and a replaceable-insert front sight (usually advertised in Britain as the 'Mark 2') and a field-target version into whose ribbed muzzle-weight a curious conical front sight is screwed ('Mark 3'). Standard and Luxusmodelle are made, their stock characteristics being those of the LG121 (q.v.).

LG125. Made for the American market, this variant has a walnut stock with a US-style cheek piece sweeping into the pistol grip, and a rounded rather than obliquely cut fore-end tip. The pistol-grip chequering also differs, and a slight shoulder may be discerned ahead of the trigger guard.

LG127. This rifle is nothing more than a 5.5mm version of the LG124 (q.v.), originally made for the British market. Most of the guns seen in the United Kingdom are Luxusmodelle, with elegant beech or walnut stocks.

LG120 SERIES
Data: 4.5 and 5.5mm, 43.1in overall, 18.3in rifled barrel, 6.72lb (LG124). Features. A semi-automatic safety catch and an adjustable trigger. Power. ☛ 4.5mm LG124: 857fs^{-1} with RWS Hobby (11.50fp) and 796fs^{-1} with Eley Wasp (10.71fp). ☛ 5.5mm LG127: 608fs^{-1} with RWS Diabolo (11.47fp). Cocking is remarkably easy, consistency and accuracy being outstanding.

Made in several patterns, the Feinwerkbau Sport rifle has enjoyed great popularity in Britain and the USA before being overhauled in recent years by the Weihrauch HW77 and HW80. The the externally identical but very plain LG121 and LG124 (1) have provided the basis for many customizations – such as Airmasters' 'Mastersport FWB Custom' (2).

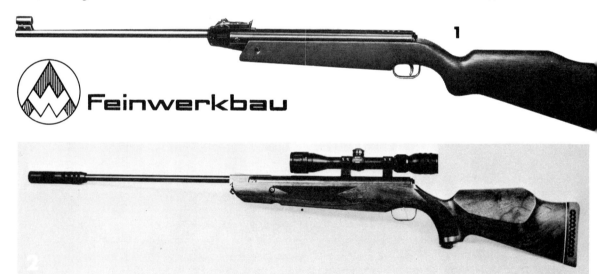

1

Feinwerkbau

LG300 series

Development of the WAW Sledge System, undertaken in 1959-61, led to the first Westinger & Altenburger rifles – the recoilless LG150 and the rarely-encountered recoiling LG100. Production began in January 1963, but the improved LG300 was substituted at the beginning of 1969 and the perfected LG300S appeared in June 1972. The original LG300 (the first examples of which were made with the rounded LG150-style stock) was discontinued in 1973; the last Tirolerschaft or Tyrolean-stocked example left the factory in 1978; and the LG300S Match L was discontinued in 1984. Despite the

By courtesy of Feinwerkbau.

1

2

3

Feinwerkbau®

△
The variants of the renowned LG300 recoilless competition rifle have included the LG300SU (1), the LG300 Junior (2) and the LG300 LS (3).

differences in stock fittings, however, the guns all share an action in which recoil is absorbed by allowing the barrel and receiver to slide back on precision-machined rails set in the stock. Cocking is remarkably easy, and a sleeve-type breech gives direct access to the chamber.

LG300S or LG300S Match. An improved LG300, dating from 1972, this has a stippled pistol grip, a deep squared fore-end with an obliquely cut tip, and a vertically-adjustable rubber butt-plate. The diopter back sight locks into transverse slots on the top of the receiver, varying the sight radius, and the replaceable-element front sight was originally dovetailed onto the muzzle around the removable muzzle weight (newer ones are cast integrally with the weight). The trigger is amongst the best fitted to an airgun, with a lateral adjustment absent from the original LG300.

LG300S Junior. This is identical with the standard full-length gun, apart from an abbreviated fore-end and a shorter barrel lacking the muzzle weight.

LG300S Laufende Scheibe. Destined for moving-target competitions, the original LS variant had a standard stock with a high fixed cheek piece. A second – perhaps later – version has a screw-elevated cheek piece, while a third displays a Lochschaft (thumb-hole stock). All three are intended to be used with optical sights and have broadened fore-ends to improve grip. The wooden butt-plate, muzzle weight and special direct-action trigger† are all distinctive.

LG300S Universal. The perfected derivative of the original '300' appeared in 1978, with a very distinctively-shaped stippled fore-end, revised pistol-grip contours and an angular trigger guard. Its principal distinguishing characteristic was originally the replaceable cheek piece, the NV (niederer Visierlinie) variant offering a low sight line and the HV (hoherer Visierlinie) raising this with a deep cheek-piece insert and blocks under the sights. Finally, a cheek piece adjustable for rake and height appeared at the end of 1983.

† German Patent 2518146.

LG300S

Data: 4.5mm, 43.3in overall (Junior, 40.0in), 19.1in rifled barrel (Junior, 17.1in), 10.74lb with sights (Junior, 8.85lb).

Features. Automatic trigger/piston and sidelever-ratchet safeties, and a comprehensively adjustable trigger.

Power, LG300S: 564fs^{-1} with RWS Meisterkugeln (5.93fp) and 577fs^{-1} with RWS Diabolo (5.85fp). Cocking is extremely easy; accuracy and consistency are outstanding.

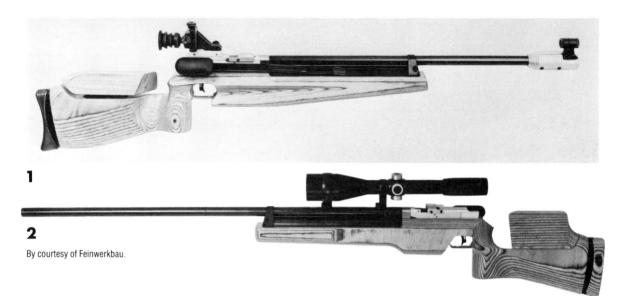

1

2

By courtesy of Feinwerkbau.

PNEUMATIC GUNS

LG600

This gun made an unexpected début at the IWA show in March 1984. It is an interesting single-pump pneumatic clearly intended to compete with the Walther LGR on its own terms. The LG600 has a distinctive laminated stock, claimed to give greater warp resistance, and a short sidelever (pivoted at the front of the receiver) with its handle lying alongside the breech. Left-handed actions are available as well as left-hand stocks. The charging stroke is slightly diagonal, which is claimed to reduce fatigue, and the Feinwerkbau is certainly less taxing to use than the Walther. The loading latch on top of the breech must be raised to expose the chamber, and then closed to prevent it blocking the sight-line. Another interesting feature is the counter-bored muzzle, which minimizes the effects of trigger-snatch or body tremors by freeing the pellet from the barrel as soon as possible. The sensation caused by the rifle on its introduction was equalled by its initial performances. In the 1986 Commonwealth Games, for example, the medal winners in the pairs competition all used LG600 rifles.‡ A moving-target version, the LG600 LS, was announced in 1987; apart from a special trigger and a laminated wood butt-plate, it is distinguished by a lengthened cylindrical barrel. Owing to the position of the breech flap, the LG600 LS requires an extraordinary optical sight mount with a large-diameter clamp ring that holds the *bell* of the telescope rather than the tube. The pneumatic Feinwerkbaus have also provided the basis for the gas-powered C60 and C60 LS.

△ Once it had become clear that the Walther LGR was wrestling some of the superiority away from the spring-piston 300 series, Feinwerkbau countered with the LG600 (1) – a single-stroke pneumatic with an auto-opening loading port and a distinctively laminated stock. The basic rifle has now been adapted to provide a gas-powered version, the C60, and a moving-target pneumatic with an extraordinary-looking stock (2).

‡ One half of the fourth placed team, Scotland, also apparently used an LG600; his partner had a Walther LGR Match Universal.

LG600
Data: 4.5mm, 44.1in overall, 16.7in rifled barrel, 10.65lb with sights.
Features. No safety is required. The trigger is comprehensively adjustable: see LG300S.
Power: 552fs^{-1} with RWS Diabolo (5.35fp). Charging is reasonably easy; consistency and accuracy are outstanding.

HAENEL

VEB Fahrzeug- und Jagdwaffenfabrik 'Ernst Thälmann', DDR-60 Suhl, Meininger Strasse 40, German Democratic Republic. Distributed in Britain by John Rothery (Wholesale) Co. Ltd, Bedford Road, Petersfield, Hampshire GU32 3AX.

Haenel's name has been established in airgun circles for many years, production beginning in 1925 only to cease at the end of the Second World War. The brandname was resurrected in the late 1940s to camouflage that the company had disappeared into the state-run GDR firearms industry.

A selection of Haenels: the barrel-cocking LG300 junior rifle (1), the LG303S junior target rifle (2), the Schmeisser inspired bolt-action LG310 (3, with detached magazine) and the perfected sidelever-cocking LG312 (4). By courtesy of John Rothery (Wholesale) Co. Ltd. ▷

HAENEL

Product range: a small junior spring-piston barrel cocker to a highly sophisticated top-lever recoilless competition rifle. A solitary Sportmodell-type ball-firer is also made.

Discontinued models: the most recent casualty has been the LG311, a bolt-cocking target rifle with a rotary loading tap rather than a box magazine.

Assessment: the Haenels are very sturdily made of good-quality material, and are available in Britain at highly attractive prices. The LG312 target rifle represents the best value for money.

Buying second hand. The earlier variants of the LG303 and its immediate predecessor, the LG302, are most commonly encountered. The simplicity and sturdiness of the basic barrel-cocking design make Haenels easy to repair and maintain provided parts can be obtained.

SPRING-PISTON GUNS

LG300
Data: 4.5mm, 38.6in overall, 15.7in rifled barrel, 4.63lb.
Features. No safety (some have the standard semi-automatic pattern); the trigger is adjustable for travel only.
Power: about 450fs^{-1} with RWS Diabolo (3.56fp). Easy to cock, moderately consistent and acceptably accurate.

LG300

The smallest of the current Haenels has been in production for some years. Its metal-work is well finished, though the hardwood stock benefits from smoothing the uncomfortably angular pistol-grip and fore-end edges. There is neither butt-plate nor cheekpiece, though the distance between the pistol-grip and the trigger is quite acceptable for small hands (cf., Norica Cadet). The sights comprise a hooded blade and a tangent-leaf pattern adjustable for elevation only. Power is low, though the LG300 offers good quality for the price.

LG303 series

The current version of these guns is believed to be the LG303-7, derived from the LG303-5 and 303-6. These had rounded stocks and (in the 303-6 at least) sling swivels on the barrel-block and beneath the butt.

LG303. A lightly-built barrel-cocker derived from the LG300, this offers a longer barrel, a larger air cylinder and a straight-comb butt with a cheek piece; parts of the stocks are uncomfortably angular, the cocking lever is articulated, the open tangent-leaf back sight has a lateral adjustor, and a sight-rail has been welded to the receiver – perhaps as an afterthought, owing to the differences in finish around the rail-edges. A semi-automatic safety catch (the only plastic component in the gun) protrudes from the rear of the air cylinder and the well-crowned barrel is crisply rifled. Unfortunately, the muzzle often droops below the horizontal and fitting an optical sight can be problematical.

LG303 Super. Also known as the 303-8-S, this modified LG303 is destined for basic competition shooting. Consequently, its stock exhibits a deepened fore-end, chequering on the pistol grip, a cheek piece, a low Monte Carlo comb and a black plastic butt-plate accompanied by a narrow white spacer. An additional barrel-locking catch slides longitudinally in a channel on the barrel block, and the much improved multi-lever trigger has a manual safety system. The front sight is a replaceable-element tunnel, while a cheap-but-effectual diopter sight can be attached to the sight-rail above the receiver. This back sight is a curious, clever but technically suspect design in which two threaded bolts push the insert block down and to the left; this actually allows a certain amount of free play, and the block can be pushed diagonally downwards with the thumb. However, despite the shortcomings of the aperture sight, the 303 Super offers particularly good value in its class.

LG310

Apart from the Anschütz LG275, this is the sole remaining example of the pre-war bolt-cocking Sportmodelle. The bolt protrudes from the action midway along the fore-end, from where it can be raised and rocked backwards to cock the action. The return stroke feeds a ball from the box magazine into the chamber and the gun can be fired. Though the limited mechanical advantage obtainable with the short bolt-handle restricts power, the guns are great fun to use…and deadly on empty matchboxes or paper cups up to 30 feet away. The stock is too much like that of the LG303 to be particularly effectual.

LG303 SERIES
Data: 4.5 and 5.5mm (303S, 4.5mm only). *Figures for LG303 and LG303S respectively:* 42.8in or 43.4in overall; 17.6in rifled barel; 6.98lb or 7.85lb.
Features. A semi-automatic safety catch; a trigger adjustable for travel (LG303) or travel and sear engagement (LG303S).
Power: ➡ LG303, 700fs^{-1} with RWS Hobby (7.67fp) and 670fs^{-1} with Eley Wasp (7.59fp). ➡ LG303S: 654fs^{-1} · with Eley Wasp (7.23fp). Cocking effort, consistency and accuracy are all average.

LG310
Data: 4.4mm (ball), 40.6in overall, 12.3in barrel, 6.00lb.
Features. A manual safety catch; a non-adjustable trigger; and a detachable 6-round box magazine.
Power: 387fs^{-1} with H&N lead balls (2.43fp). Though difficult to cock, the action is consistent and accuracy at short range is surprisingly good.

LG312
Data: 4.5mm, 42.3in overall, 16.8in rifled barrel, 10.08lb with sights.
Features. Automatic trigger and sidelever-ratchet safeties, and an adjustable trigger.
Power: 567fs^{-1} with RWS Meisterkugeln (5.99fp) and 643fs^{-1} with Eley Wasp (6.99fp). The gun is reasonably easily cocked, consistent and very accurate.

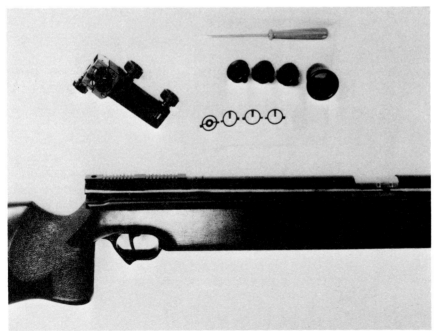

An extraordinary combination of a single-stroke pneumatic and a spring-piston system (though using compressed air to fire the pellet), the Meisterschafts-Luftgewehr 550 represents the finest competition rifle made behind the Iron Curtain. Gun by courtesy of John Rothery (Wholesale) Co. Ltd.

The breech of the LG312, showing the diopter sight, sight inserts, the sight rail and a most distinctive trigger guard. By courtesy of John Rothery (Wholesale) Co. Ltd.

◁

LG312

Haenel's perfected mid-price target rifle is something of a revelation. Though it looks ungainly, its sidelever-cocking action performs surprisingly well. A 'sleeve' breech permits direct access to a curious loading tray, formed by cutting away the top half of the barrel, and automatically seats a pellet when the breech is closed. The metalwork is excellent and the finish of the beechwood stock is also praiseworthy. Among the distinctive features are a cast trigger guard, with integral ribbed thumb-stop, and a vertically adjustable butt-plate. The front sight is identical with that of the 303 Super, but the diopter back sight is a more orthodox pattern adjusted by drums and dovetails. The LG312 is supplied with a selection of front sight elements and back sight apertures, three butt-lengthening spacers and a tool or two. Though production expedients are evident in the back sight, they are not obvious in the solid traditionalism of the gun. Despite its recoil, which is actually very mild, the firing characteristics of the LG312 are essentially pleasant and there is little in its class to beat it for value.

MLG550

The extraordinary Haenel recoilless competition rifle, made in small numbers for Soviet bloc marksmen, departs completely from conventional Western practice. Only occasionally available in Britain, the Meisterschafts-Luftgewehr ('MLG') is basically a single-stroke toplever-charging pneumatic loaded through a turning bolt in the large diecast breechblock on which the diopter sight is carried. The closing stroke of the lever compresses air through what could otherwise be considered a spring-piston system; this must be released to unlock the action before the charging lever can be raised again, the catch protruding above the right side of the fore-end. The gun has an excellent trigger and is very pleasant to use despite its curiously amorphous hardwood stock. It has an extremely long barrel, which promotes excellent accuracy at the expense of velocity, and rather oddly lacks an O-ring seal on the bolt-head.*

LG550

Data: 4.5mm, 42.8in overall, 25.6in rifled barrel, 10.77lb with sights.
Features. The trigger is comprehensively adjustable.
Power: 502fs^{-1} with RWS Hobby (3.92fp), 478fs^{-1} with RWS Meisterkugeln (4.25fp). Reasonably easily cocked, though unusually low powered; the gun shoots only moderately consistently for a pneumatic, but is very accurate.

* This is rather against the current trend (cf., Feinwerkbau LG600, whose muzzle is counter-bored to *reduce* the time the pellet spends in the bore). However, there is no real evidence that a long barrel maximizes the effect of trigger-snatch, as the in-bore time is minimal and the MLG shoots very well.

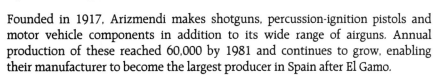

NORICA

Norberto Arizmendi SA, E-20600 Eibar (Guipúzcoa), Avenida Otaola 16 Apartado-68, Spain.

Founded in 1917, Arizmendi makes shotguns, percussion-ignition pistols and motor vehicle components in addition to its wide range of airguns. Annual production of these reached 60,000 by 1981 and continues to grow, enabling their manufacturer to become the largest producer in Spain after El Gamo.

Product range. The selection of barrel-cocking guns, comparatively unsophisticated yet competitively priced, has recently been joined by some new sidelever-cockers (as yet, rarely seen in Britain).

Assessment: Noricas are sturdy, but lack some of the features found on comparable British and German guns. Their metalwork is generally good but, generally on older guns, the woodwork can be a disappointment: inletting is often particularly poorly executed. As the guns are basically quite simple — apart, perhaps, from the Weihrauch-inspired triggers of the Mo.80 series — maintenance is rarely a problem. However, the

British agency has changed several times in the 1980s and spare parts may be difficult to obtain.

Buying second-hand: the low power and scarcity of parts makes the Noricas a poorer buy than, for example, the BSA Meteor or the older M&G Dianas unless obtainable at lower price.

SPRING-PISTON GUNS

Norica Carabina Mo.47

This is a new design, dating from 1986. Its most obvious feature is the straight-butt wood stock, with a separate synthetic pistol grip/trigger guard unit, but closer inspection reveals that it is a particularly neatly designed sidelever-cocker loaded through a rotary port. Apart from the loading tap, which has a lever rather than a drum, the compact style of the back sight and the cocking-lever head are redolent of the Hämmerli 400 series. The Mo.47 and its conventional derivative, the Mo.92 (q.v.), also feature a greatly improved trigger.

Norica Carabina Mo.56, 'Tipo Junior'

This small barrel-cocker made its debut in the Autumn of 1981, probably to compete with the El Gamo Cadet (q.v.). The Mo.56 has a pistol-gripped beech stock, with a shallow Monte Carlo comb, but lacks a separate butt-plate. The back sight was originally a spring-leaf pattern, but this was substituted by a more modern tangent-bar pattern in 1986. Seemingly based on Mayer & Grammelspacher practice, this sight is notable for its unusually clearly marked adjustor drums. The front sight remains a hooded post. Power is on the low side and, for a junior gun, the Mo.56 has an inordinately long distance between the pistol grip and the trigger.

NORICA MO.47

Data: 4.5mm, 41.3in overall, 17.5in rifled barrel, 6.83lb.
Features. A semi-automatic safety catch; and a trigger adjustable for travel and pull-weight (minimum 400gm).
Power: 623fs^{-1} with unspecified pellets (mf). Reasonably easily cocked; consistency and accuracy seem only average.

NORICA MO.56

Data: 4.5mm, 37.6in overall, 16.3in rifled barrel, 5.18lb.
Features. A semi-automatic safety catch; a non-adjustable trigger.
Power: 541fs^{-1} with unspecified pellets (mf). Otherwise as Mo.47.

NORICA MO.61

Data: 4.5 and 5.5mm, 40.6in overall, 17.7in rifled barrel; 5.51lb (Mo.61 and Young), 5.71lb (Mo.61-C) or 6.06lb (Mo.90).
Features. No safety; a non-adjustable (Mo.61, Young), or travel-adjustable trigger (Mo.61-C).
Power, 4.5mm Mo.61-C: 587fs^{-1} with RWS Diabolo (6.05fp) and 607fs^{-1} with RWS Hobby (5.77fp). Cocking stroke, consistency and accuracy all no better than average.

Norica Carabina Mo.61 series

This group consists of several similar barrel-cocking rifles, the principal differences concerning the stock and trigger system.

Mo.61. The basic rifle has been in production for some years, but the post-1986 guns have better handling characteristics than their predecessors and a tangent-bar rather than spring-leaf back sight.

Mo.61, Tipo Feria. This gun now has a stock with a low Monte Carlo comb and a smoothly tapered fore-end which, together with the improved back sight, present an altogether neater appearance than the old square pattern pictured in the previous edition. The simple trigger remains non-adjustable. The very first examples lacked dovetail grooves for a telescope sight, though this was speedily rectified. In addition, the ball detent can be stiff enough to hinder barrel-opening.

Mo.61-C, Tipo Comando. This derivative features an improved stock and a trigger adjustable for travel. Although much the same size as the standard Mo.61, the 61-C can be distinguished by its deep rounded, rather than tapered square-cut fore-end.

Mo.90. This is a Mo.61-C fitted with an optical sight above the barrel block and a ribbed muzzle weight. Its performance duplicates that of the 61-C, though it is about 150gm heavier. A sliding-stock variant appeared in the Spring of 1987.

Modelo 'Young'. Simply a Tipo Feria with a coloured stock, this gun is not unlike the M&G Diana Sport 1000. As the choice of hues is identical (red, blue, yellow, white, black) and the decorative transfers are surprisingly similar, this may not be entirely coincidental.

Modelo 'Survival'. A variant of the Mo.61 was exhibited at IWA 1987 by the German Umarex company, with a strange plastic stock displaying transfer-printed 'essential information' and a map of the world. It is assumed that a compartment for survival aids contains the usual waterproof matches, fishing line/hook, compass and scalpel blades, but no additional information has yet been forthcoming.

![NORICA]

△
A collection of Noricas: Mo.61-F (1), Mo.61-C (2), Mo.73-T (3), Mo.80-C (4) and Mo.80-G (5). These are all pre-1983 models, current guns exhibiting minor differences — the variants of the Mo.61 now have refined stocks and the Mo.80 has a safety catch protruding from cylinder cap. By courtesy of Norberto Arizmendi SA.

NORICA MO.73
Data: 4.5 and 5.5mm, 41.7in overall, 17.7in rifled barrel, 6.39lb.
Features: No safety; the trigger is adjustable for travel only.
Power: 583fs⁻¹ with RWS Diabolo (5.97fp). Otherwise as Mo.61.

NORICA MO.80
Data: 4.5 and 5.5mm, 42.9in overall, 17.9in rifled barrel, 6.84lb (80) or 7.28lb (80-G).
Features. An automatic (1978-86) or semi-automatic safety catch (1986 to date); the trigger is fully adjustable for travel and pull-weight.
Power, Mo.80-G: 573fs⁻¹ with RWS Meisterkugeln (6.12fp) and 618fs⁻¹ with RWS Hobby (5.98fp). The rifle is reasonably easily cocked; consistency is only average, but accuracy is quite good.

Norica Carabina Mo.73

Sometimes known in Britain as the Phantom, the 'Tipo Tiro' is an improved 61-C with an interchangeable-element front sight, a refined trigger and a better stock with a plastic butt plate and pistol-grip cap. The first guns had a spring-leaf back sight and a front sight mounted on short dovetail grooves, but the muzzle-enveloping Mo.80 pattern and the new tangent-bar back sight were fitted from 1986.

Norica Carabina Mo.80 and 80-G

Dating from 1978, the perfected Arizmendi-made barrel-cocker has a sophisticated multi-lever trigger system adapted from the Weihrauch Rekord, a better stock than its predecessors and (on post-1986 guns) a semi-automatic safety. The metalwork is well finished and attractively blued, though the woodwork is sometimes less satisfactory. There is also a great deal of plastic in the construction and an idiosyncratic slider-and-inclined-plane back sight.

Mo.80, Tipo Competición. The basic rifle has a butt with a pistol grip, a cheek piece, a Monte Carlo comb, a crescentic plastic butt-plate and an angular plastic pistol-grip cap. The fore-end is comparatively shallow. Unfortunately, by British standards, the Mo.80 is too light for competition shooting and insufficiently powerful for fieldwork.

Mo.80-G, Tipo Gran Competición. This variant has a deeper, heavier stock than the standard Mo.80 and is usually found with the curious Norica aperture sight on the receiver, although the inclined-plane open back sight can be substituted when required. For effectual target shooting, the Mo.80-G needs more weight and a better back sight to capitalize on its pleasant shooting characteristics.

The current Norica catalogue cover illustrates the Models 92, 'Young' and 80 rifles, and the Mo.83 pistol.

Norica Pistola Mo.83

Arizmendi's first pistol appeared in 1983, bearing a superficial resemblance to the old-style M&G Diana LP5. It has a well blued barrel/receiver assembly, a large synthetic grip/frame unit, an adjustable tangent-bar sight at the extremity of the air cylinder, and a ramp-mounted hooded post sight on the muzzle. Following in the tradition of the El Gamo Center and Falcón, the Mo.83 is a sound and workmanlike product.

Norica Carabina Mo.92

This gun combines the sidelever action of the Mo.47 (q.v.) with a wood stock not unlike that of the Mo.80, complete with plastic butt plate and pistol-grip cap. The peculiarly squared-off trigger guard and the design of the breech gives the Norica a superficial resemblance to the Hämmerli 400 series.

NORICA MO.83

Data: 4.5mm, 14.7in overall, 6.3in rifled barrel, 3.05lb.
Features. A semi-automatic safety catch; an adjustable-travel trigger.
Power: 394fs^{-1} with unspecified pellets (mf). Reasonably strenuous to cock, consistency and accuracy are about average.

NORICA MO.92

Data: 4.5mm, 41.3in overall, 17.7in rifled barrel, 6.72lb.
Features, power. Otherwise as Mo.47.

SAXBY-PALMER

Saxby & Palmer Ltd, 3 Swan Industrial Estate, Avenue Farm, Birmingham Road, Stratford upon Avon, Warwickshire CV37 0HR.

The origins of this business lay in a separately-charged cartridge airgun designed by Michael Saxby in the late 1970s, and in the formation of the Ensign

Arms Company in 1982 to develop the idea. Unfortunately, the partners in Ensign parted company in 1984 and the guns reappeared under the Saxby-Palmer banner. The first rifle, the Elite, was successful enough to fund the first of a series of excellent revolvers. Subsequent exploits have included a military training cartridge; an interesting adaptation of the old British Lee-Enfield rifle; and, latterly, the Herald sporting rifle.

Product range: a series of guns based on the distinctive pre-charged cartridges. Apart from the Sabata, the revolvers all fire one cartridge-pattern; however, the Lee-Enfield and Herald rifles share the 0.223-calibre military training cartridge, while the original Saturn and Galaxy retain the original large-diameter rifle type.

Assessment: though by no means new — the principle dates back to 1871 — the pre-charged cartridge awaited modern technology until it could be satisfactorily exploited. The perfection of the cartridge reservoirs to withstand high pressures without the seals failing, and the development of simple pumps requiring no more than ten strokes to charge each cartridge, has been vital to success. The revolvers have proved particularly effectual for rapid-fire practice, but the long-term mass distribution of the system depends on the airgunning public accepting that the separately-charged cartridge cannot be treated in the same way as a tin of plinking pellets.

Buying second-hand. Caution is necessary when buying an old Ensign, as many changes have been made to minor components. However, obtaining spare parts for the current Saxby-Palmers should present little difficulty. It is wise to test the pressure-retaining capabilities of the cartridges, as the original synthetic body types initially proved the Achilles' heel of the system and some variation in pressure retention is to be expected.

GALAXY SERIES

Data: 0.22in, 40.4in overall, 15.0in rifled barrel, 6.35lb.
Features. A semi-automatic safety catch; an adjustable trigger.
Power. ☞ Saturn, 615fs^{-1} with Eley Wasp (11.85fp). ☞ Magnum, 882fs^{-1} with Eley Wasp (24.38fp). Though very taxing to charge, the cartridges shoot verv consistently if they are carefully selected; the guns are unusually accurate.

The Saxby-Palmer Elite rifle ▷ (formerly the Ensign Elite) is remarkable for its pre-charged pneumatic cartridge.

CARTRIDGE PNEUMATICS

Note: all Saxby-Palmer guns require a separate charging system. Currently, a heavy-duty bench-mounted pump and a 'Slim Jim' hand-held pattern are available. The cartridge nose-cap is uns-crewed, the cartridge body threaded into the pump-socket and then charged with four to ten pump strokes; a pellet is then inserted in the nosecap, which is replaced on the cartridge body and loaded into the gun. The original cartridge design favoured roundnose or cone-point pellets, and would not always perform properly with flatheads. The revolver cartridges, however, will shoot most types of pellet. The Lee-Enfield and the Herald are confined to special 0.223 zinc-alloy bullets.

Galaxy series

The design of these guns dates back to Ensign days. The turning-bolt unit slides in the diecast receiver, chambering a single cartridge that has been placed in the feedway. Once the safety has been re-set and the gun has been fired, retracting the bolt permits the extractor/ejector system to pull the spent cartridge out of the breech and kick it out of the gun. Once teething problems had been overcome, the rifles attained a reputation for power and accuracy provided the cartridges were selected to give optimum velocity. The adjustable trigger is surprisingly good, with a sweet pull, and the guns are com-pletely recoilless. This, in turn, allows them to be short and light. The original synthetic cartridges were later supplemented by alloy-body patterns, as the extractor soon tore through the weak plastic case-rims.

Galaxy. This has an elegant wood stock, with a Monte Carlo comb, a chequered pistol grip, a ventilated rubber butt-plate and a distinctive concave curve to the underside of the schnabel-tipped fore-end.

Magnum. Identical to the Galaxy in all but ammunition and a heavier striker, this fires a high-powered cartridge capable of developing 20 ft lb or more.

Royale: a deluxe version of the Galaxy, with a selected walnut stock and a roll-over comb.

Saturn. This is simply a Galaxy action in a solid synthetic stock. The contours of the butt differ radically from the wood version and the rifle presents an altogether different character.

Herald

This is an extraordinary airgun; externally, it is all but identical with the Parker-Hale Midland 2100 sporting rifle. It has a modified Mauser action with a bolt not unlike that of the US M1903 Springfield rifle, apart from the position of the safety catch, and operates similarly to the firearm – except that it is necessary to charge the cartridges before loading them into the magazine. Unlike the Lee-Enfield (q.v.), the Mauser action has a non-rotating extractor that slips over the cartridge-rim as the latter rises from the magazine. Laying a cartridge on top of the magazine and attempting to chamber it simply by closing the bolt risks damaging the extractor; correctly, even a single cartridge must first be placed in the magazine. The long barrel promotes excellent accuracy and a typical sporting rifle stock – with chequering on the butt and fore-end – gives excellent handling qualities.

HERALD
Data: 0.223in, 44.5in overall, 24.0in rifled barrel, 8.00lb.
Features. A manual safety catch; an adjustable trigger; and a 4-round internal box magazine.
Power: 566fs^{-1} with Saxby-Palmer ammunition (11.67fp). Otherwise as Galaxy (q.v.).

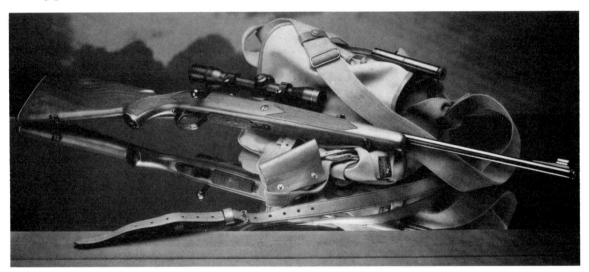

Lee-Enfield

The development of the 0.223 training cartridge allowed Saxby & Palmer to convert service rifles to fire it. Once the idea had been offered to the Ministry of Defence, conversion of a number of venerable Lee-Enfields (Rifles No.4 Mk 1) began in collusion with World-Wide Arms of Birmingham. These guns have the advantage of a sturdy bolt-action and a detachable box-magazine, and it takes little imagination to see why they are so popular. The original rifles were made to infinitely more exacting standards than most airguns and have a fascinating history: no other airgun offers the same combination.

LEE-ENFIELD
Data: 0.223in, 44.4in overall, 25.0in rifled barrel, 9.06lb.
Features. A manual safety catch; a fixed trigger; and a detachable 10-round box magazine. Otherwise generally as Herald.

The revolvers

These share identical operating principles, even though their construction varies appreciably. The Orion Six set the pattern for its companions by modifying a standard Weihrauch Arminius cartridge revolver to fire air-cartridges. Part of the cylinder periphery was cut away, the barrels were bored-out and sleeved for 4.5mm pellets, and the hammer blow was weakened so that it would not fire a standard primer. The Saxby-Palmer revolvers are incapable of firing cartridges and cannot be converted to do so.

![saxby palmer logo]

The Saxby-Palmer Herald is a four-shot bolt-action pre-charged air cartridge rifle, based on the Parker-Hale Midland 2100 (Mauser) sporter. By courtesy of *Air Gunner*.

The German-made Python 63 (1) and Western 66 (2) typify Saxby-Palmer's pre-charged air cartridge revolvers. By courtesy of Saxby-Palmer Ltd.

Models 52 and 54. These German-made double-action personal defence revolvers, based loosely on Smith & Wesson practice, have yoke-mounted five-shot cylinders that swing out of the frame to the left when the thumb-latch on the left rear of the frame is pressed. The guns have rather crude sights, but are surprisingly accurate at short range; they are also quite powerful.

Orion Six. This modified competition revolver features a yoke-mounted cylinder swinging out to the left, but it has thumbrest-type plastic grips, a ventilated over-barrel rib and a fully adjustable back sight. The Orion is capable of attaining groups of 0.3in ctc or better at 10 yards, as well as considerable power. It is ideal for practising rapid-fire, which, as gas-powered guns require firearms certification in Britain, cannot be undertaken realistically with anything but a Saxby-Palmer air-revolver.

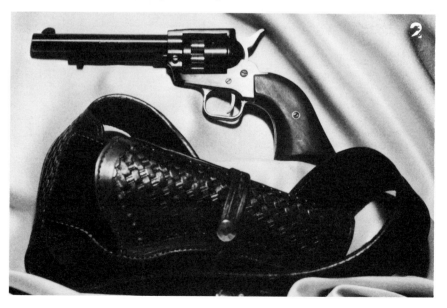

Python 63. Despite its Colt-like name, this is a facsimile of the S&W Magnum revolvers with a side-swinging cylinder and a frame-mounted thumb-latch. The chunky Python has large chequered wood grips and a laterally adjustable back sight.

Sabata Revolver Rifle. This 0.22-calibre carbine is basically the Model 54 fitted with a greatly lengthened barrel, a wood butt and fore-end, fixed open sights and an optical sight rail above the cylinder.

Western 66. Saxby-Palmer's single-action M1873 Colt or Peacemaker-pattern revolver appeared in 1986. Made in Germany, it is a solid and workmanlike gun identifiable by the cutaway cylinder. It retains the classic hinged loading gate on the right side of the frame and an under-barrel ejector rod. The sights comprise a fixed blade and a longitudinal groove in the frame-top, and the standard grips are wood-grained plastic. Like all these guns, the '66' offers very interesting performance and will become a great favourite among quick-draw aficionados and Wild West societies.

REVOLVERS

Data: 0.177in. 6.8in (M52), 8.0in (Python), 8.8in (M54), 10.8in (Western) or 11.4in (Orion) overall; 2in (M52), 3in (Python), 4in (M54) or 6in (Western and Orion) rifled barrels; 1.43lb (M52), 1.50lb (M54), 1.75lb (Python) or 2.20lb (Western and Orion).

Features. A transfer bar safety in most guns; a fixed trigger (adjustable in Orion); and a 6-round cylinder (M52 or M54, 5 rounds).

Power. Maker's claims with Eley Wasp. ☛ M52, 450fs^{-1} (3.42fp). ☛ M54 and Python, 500fs^{-1} (4.23fp). ☛ Orion, 550fs^{-1} (5.11fp).

SHARP

Sharp Rifle Company, No.8, 2-chome, Yotsuya, Shinjuku-ku, Tokyo, Japan. British distributor: Hull Cartridge Company, Bontoft Avenue, National Avenue, Hull, Humberside HU5 4HZ.

This well-known manufacturer of air- and gas-guns was founded in 1952 by Kensuke Chiba, a renowned marksman and inventor. The resulting 'Tokyo Rifle Laboratory' traded until 1955, when it became the Tokyo Rifle Company (the present name being adopted in 1960). Production began with the Victory, Veteran and Tiger multi-pump pneumatics, with a distinctive 'vibrationless/hammerless' valve system. These remained in production for more than a decade, being joined by the first gas-powered gun in 1955, but were never seen in the West. Not until the late 1970s did the Innova make its début in Britain, by which time more than twenty Sharps had been developed. Their chronology and identification remains uncertain, though a summary was attempted in the Third Edition (p.143).

Product range: Sharp currently makes at least five pneumatics, including the highly rated Ace-Target 3P, and gas-powered guns ranging from the U-FP pistol to the pump-action loading GR-75. Only the Innova and Ace are currently seen in Britain.

Discontinued models. Few guns have been declared obsolescent in recent years, and many of the current designs have lengthy pedigrees (e.g., Victory 700 and Pan-Target, introduced in 1969).

Assessment: the Innova and Ace are cleverly designed, well made, offer considerable power and can attain praiseworthy accuracy. Their styling is somewhat inferior to Western European products of comparable price, the deficiencies being most obvious in the stock, the stamped trigger guards, back sights and safety catches.

Buying second-hand. Sharps are sturdy and, provided the valve-seals are still effectual and there is no obvious wear in the pump/piston system, old guns will continue to perform satisfactorily for many years. However, spare parts are difficult to obtain.

Among the multi-stroke Sharp pneumatic rifles are the Ace (1), widely encountered in Britain, the Ace Target (2), the Innova (3) and the Innova Special (4) with a Mini-Micrometer sight. Note that the pump levers of the Ace Target and the Innova Special move diagonally, permitting one-piece stocks. By courtesy of the Sharp Rifle Co.

PNEUMATIC GUNS

Ace series

These rifle were introduced in Japan in 1981, distinguished from the Victory models (q.v.) by changes in the pump system, trigger and breech arrangements.

Ace Sporter. This gun appeared in Britain in 1983, restricted to sub-12fp operation. Its fore-end pump and bolt-loading system are classically American, but the Ace is a true adult-size gun with a long barrel which promotes good accuracy. Aperture sights may be substituted for the crude open sights and an optional adjustable butt-plate transforms

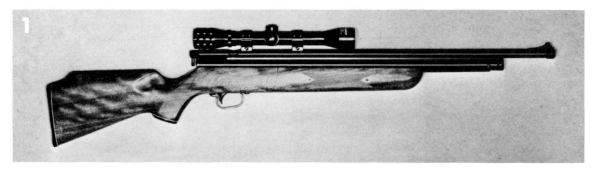

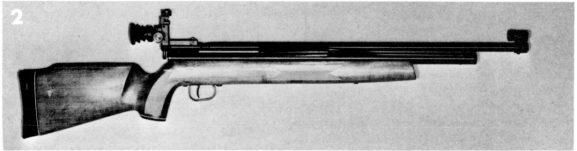

ACE

Data: 4.5 and 5.5mm, 38.4in overall, 23.9in rifled barrel, 6.29lb.

Features. A manual safety catch; a non-adjustable trigger.

Power. ☛ 5.5mm British version, four pumps, 605fs^{-1} with RWS Hobby (9.84fp). ☛ 4.5mm Japanese version, ten pumps, 1,043fs^{-1} with Mount Star Diabolo (mf, 17.23fp). ☛ 5.5mm Japanese version, ten pumps, 892fs^{-1} with Mount Star Diabolo (mf, 23.61fp). ☛ 4.5mm Ace Target, two pumps, 581fs^{-1} with Mount Star Diabolo (mf, 5.35fp). ☛ 5.5mm Ace Target, three pumps, 590fs^{-1} with Mount Star Diabolo (mf, 10.33fp). Taxing to charge, but consistent and accurate.

the rifle for target shooting. The trigger guard, safety catch and bolt-locking plate are light stampings that do nothing for the appearance of what is otherwise an attractive gun. The hardwood stock has a low Monte Carlo comb and a black plastic butt-plate accompanied by a thin white spacer.

Ace-Target Standard and 3P. Though these share the action of the sporting gun, the pump handle lies on the right side of the action to accommodate a one-piece stock and moves diagonally upward at 50°. The Standard Model has a lengthened competition stock, a special heavy barrel, and competition-style diopter back/replaceable-element front sights. It also has an adjustable butt-plate. The stock of the otherwise identical 3P, destined for three-position shooting, deepens immediately ahead of the trigger guard and the pistol grip is chequered to improve grip. The Ace-Target is an effectual and very accurate rifle; it was to be supplemented by the superior single-pump 'World One'

pneumatic, but the latter may not have attained volume production. The Ace target rifles have not been distributed in Britain largely because they are capable of developing far in excess of 12fp, though only two (4.5mm) or three (5.5mm) pumps suffice for competition use.

Innova series

Dating from 1977, the original rifle is a small multi-pump pneumatic with a patented rod-valve system. Once the pump has been used to charge the valve-chamber, the operating button on the right side of the breech is pressed to allow the bolt to spring open. A pellet is placed in the chamber and the bolt pushed back until it locks in place.

Innova Standard. The plain pistol-gripped hardwood butt and slab-sided pump handle of this gun are acceptably finished, though an unsightly gap separates the pump from the vestigial fore-end. Apart from the auto-opening breech, the most distinctive feature is the back sight – a crude spring-steel peep type, used in conjunction with a hooded ramp-mounted blade on the nosecap.

Innova Special. Apparently dating from 1985, this gun displays a diagonal pump-handle adapted from the Ace-Target (q.v.) and a one-piece stock with a pistol grip and a butt-plate. Yet to be seen in Britain, the rifle is usually encountered with the Sharp Mini-micrometer Sight.

Victory Model 700

Small numbers of this comparatively old rifle, originally introduced in 1969, were distributed in Britain in 1982-3 until insuperable power-restricting problems were encountered. The Victory was hailed in the British airgun press as 'an improved Innova', but is the older by eight years and should be considered more as the Innova's proto-type. The Victory has a very distinctive appearance, with the barrel and pump-cylinder of equal length (cf., Ace, which has a protruding muzzle). The trigger, which lies too far from the pistol grip for comfortable shooting, is an adjustable constant-pressure pattern rather than an Ace/Innova system in which pull increases in direct relation to power. The separate charging button on the rear of the Victory's receiver must be pushed to release the semi-automatic bolt, close the exhaust valve and set the trigger. Target-shooting derivatives known as the Pan-Target 700 and Pan Target 3P were also made in small numbers, their most distinctive feature being the laterally-opening pump lever.

INNOVA

Data: 4.5 and 5.5mm, 34.6in overall, 20.0in rifled barrel, 4.55lb.
Features: as Ace.
Power. ☛ 4.5mm Japanese version, ten pumps, 963fs⁻¹ with Mount Star Diabolo (mf, 14.69fp). ☛ 4.5mm British version, four pumps, 798fs⁻¹ with RWS Diabolo (11.19fp). ☛ 5.5mm Japanese version, ten pumps, 774fs⁻¹ with Mount Star Diabolo (mf, 17.78fp). ☛ 5.5mm British version, four pumps, 596fs⁻¹ with H&N Diabolo (11.14fp). Otherwise as Ace.

VICTORY

Data: 4.5 and 5.5mm, 34.1in overall, 19.8in rifled barrel, 5.29lb.
Features, power: as Innova.

The Theoben Sirocco Countryman (1), still available in its original guise, features a plain beech stock, while the Sirocco de Luxe (2, now replaced by the Sirocco Classic) had a chequered walnut stock. Note the stamped-strip trigger guard and obliquely cut cylinder cap on these early guns. By courtesy of Theoben Engineering.

THEOBEN

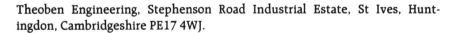

Theoben Engineering, Stephenson Road Industrial Estate, St Ives, Huntingdon, Cambridgeshire PE17 4WJ.

Theoben was formed to make the unique Sirocco gas-piston rifle, designed and patented* by Ben Taylor and David Theobald. Though some time elapsed before the design could be produced in quantity, the Sirocco rapidly attained the reputation that has since provided the basis for many innovative refinements. In addition to tremendous commercial success, the rifles have also been adopted by the RAF for airfield pest-control.

Product range: a series of rifles based on the well-proven gas-piston system, ranging from a basic sporter to a super-power gun offering energies up to 30fp.

Assessment: the Theobens offer several unusual features, not least of which is a very fast action – particularly when fitted with the Zephyr piston-head. The current Sirocco shoots more like a firearm than an airgun. When the guns were first introduced,

The Sirocco Grand Prix, which claims the fastest lock-time of any non-pneumatic airgun, is the company's premier field-target shooting rifle. Note the thumbhole stock and adjustable butt-plate, and the optional safety catch ahead of the diecast trigger guard. By courtesy of Theoben Engineering.

* British Patent 2084704.

however, ignorance of the operating principles caused many airgunners to tamper with the seals and lose the gas-charge, and power was found to fluctuate in relation to ambient temperature. In 1983, the original sulphur hexafluoride ('SF6') charge was replaced initially by an SF6/nitrogen mixture and then by pure nitrogen. As nitrogen is the principal constituent of air, a pump can now be obtained to adjust power when necessary or re-charge the system after maintenance (guns numbered above TB4000 only).

Buying second-hand: owing to their comparative scarcity compared with mass-produced spring-piston rivals, used Theobens are rarely encountered. The principal problems encountered with guns numbered below TB4000 concern the gas-charge, and the seals should be checked before purchase. Most of the 'SF6' guns have long since been re-charged with nitrogen, and few unmodified guns will be encountered.

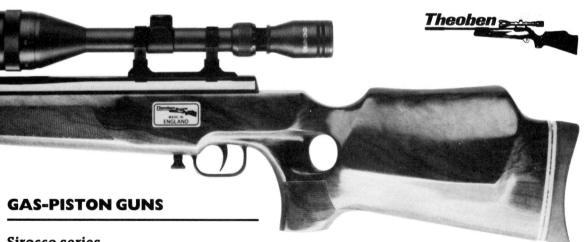

GAS-PISTON GUNS

Sirocco series

Introduced in 1982, this barrel-cocker derives its power from a charge of inert gas in the receiver, where it operates a 'ram' in place of a conventional spring and piston assembly. The gas-unit eliminates spring vibration and reduces the friction that otherwise slows the firing cycle. There is very little mechanical noise in the action, and tests have shown that the shot-to-shot consistency of the gas-piston system equals that of the best spring-piston competition rifles. Unlike the latter, however, the Sirocco can be left cocked for months without power deteriorating. The earliest rifles had fixed optical sight mounts machined as part of the receiver, but a special transverse-dovetail bar and detachable rings are now standard. The barrels were originally supplied by Webley, but post-1983 rifles have Anschütz (4.5 and 5.5mm) or Mayer & Grammelspacher (5.05mm) patterns. Recently, counter-bored barrels have been made to enable the Sirocco to fire Prometheus and Titan Black pellets efficiently.† Most of the rifles made after TB1230 feature the patented Zephyr piston-head, crowned with a combination of an annular channel and radial grooves to maximize air-chamber capacity by reducing dead volume.‡ This piston gave the rifle an even more impressively vibration-free firing cycle than it had previously enjoyed.

Classic. During the summer of 1986, the basic Sirocco action was revised so that a Schräder valve in the back of the action, beneath a protecting screw, could be connected to an air pump to re-charge the action or vary the power. The two-stage trigger system has been refined, a diecast trigger guard replaces the previous stamped-strip, and a semi-automatic safety catch added beneath the fore-end caters for the whims of the American market. When the gun is cocked, the mushroom-head of the safety catch springs *inwards* and must be pulled out before the gun can be fired.* The new Classic stock offers a chequered semi-beavertail fore-end; revised butt contours with sharper pistol-grip radii; a longer, deeper cheekpiece; and an adjustable crescentic rubber butt plate. Production began at gun TB4000 in the Spring of 1987.

† This eliminates the choked muzzle found on some guns and the rather roughly finished internal surfaces of others. It has no effect on the performance of lead pellets, but prevents an accumulation of plastic fouling at the choke.

‡ See 'The Zephyr revealed' by Bluenose, in *Airgun World*, April 1987, pp.23-4. This suggests that the efficiencies of the standard Weihrauch HW77 and HW80 pistons can be improved to raise muzzle energies by 20-25 per cent simply by fitting a Zephyr head.

* Though the catch seems to work in reverse to normal, this was a deliberate feature: otherwise, it could have been accidentally knocked into the firing position much more easily.

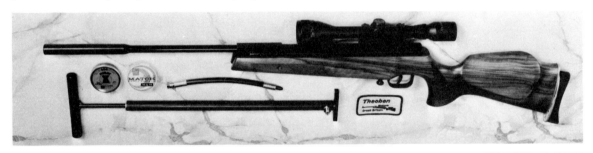

Countryman. The plainest version of the Sirocco has an oil-finished beech stock, with a cheek piece on both sides of the butt and a ventilated rubber butt-plate. Open sights, when fitted, are modified Anschütz patterns.

Deluxe. This refined Countryman — now replaced by the Classic (q.v.) — had a selected European walnut stock with a high Monte Carlo comb, a well-defined cheek piece, and chequering cut into the pistol grip and fore-end. The excellent blueing was a fitting match for the superiority of the gas-piston. Most guns were acquired with the special optical sight mount, though optional open sights could be fitted if required. Muzzle weights and Theoben's one-piece steel silencer were also available on request.

FAC (or Sirocco F). Now replaced by the Eliminator, described below, the original super-power variant of the gas-piston system had its charge adjusted to give near-supersonic velocities with 4.5mm RWS Hobby pellets. Apart from requiring firearms certification in Britain, the rifle is otherwise identical with the Sirocco Deluxe.

Grand Prix. Intended for field-target competitions, this rifle originally combined a heavyweight version of the standard action with a shortened piston stroke, successfully reducing 'action time' to a minimum — but now shares the revised 1987-pattern action

SIROCCO

Data: 4.5, 5.05 and 5.5mm, 43.0in overall, 19.2in rifled barrel, 7.25-7.60lb without sights or weights.
Features. Prior to 1987, no safety was fitted (a manual pattern is now optional); an adjustable trigger.
Power. ☞ 4.5mm Sirocco Deluxe, Anschütz barrel, 855⁻¹ with RWS Hobby (11.45fp) and 773fs⁻¹ with Eley Wasp (10.10fp). ☞ 4.5mm Sirocco Classic, Anschütz barrel, 868fs⁻¹ with RWS Hobby (11.78fp) and 792fs⁻¹ with RWS Superdome (11.78fp). ☞ 4.5mm Sirocco FAC, Anschütz barrel, 1,051fs⁻¹ with RWS Hobby ₁17.20fp) and 972fs⁻¹ with Silver Jet (17.19fp). The guns are comparatively easy to cock, consistent shooters and outstandingly accurate.

with the Classic and claimed to have the fastest action of all high-power non-pneumatic airguns. It also has a special thumbhole stock, with a near vertical pistol-grip for better control, and an adjustable butt-plate.

Eliminator

This is an extraordinarily high-powered version of the basic Sirocco Classic, featuring a new inertia gas-ram brake designed to make the gun controllable at the greatly increased energy levels. The gun has a longer-than-standard action and a Grand Prix-type thumbhole stock. However, 30fp is only achieved at the expense of inaccuracy caused by the weakness of most standard diabolos – some of which simply disintegrate in the bore. Tests have shown that the most appropriate performers are Titan Black – which shoots very accurately indeed – and, to a lesser extent, H&N Barracuda: consequently, Theoben has now begun to cast conventionally-shaped bullets derived from those of the 0.22 Short rimfire cartridge.

ELIMINATOR

Details: generally as standard gun, except that reaching energies up to 30fp would entail velocities of 1,055fs^{-1} with 5.5mm RWS Hobby and 950fs^{-1} with Silver Jet.

The latest Sirocco rifles feature better stocks, considerable internal refinement and a modified gas-spring system in which power can be adjusted by an optional exernal pump, shown here with a Sirocco Classic.

Capable of energies up to 30fp, with neither excessive recoil nor piston bounce (suppressed by an inertia brake and the Zephyr piston head), the Eliminator is the super-power version of the Sirocco. Note the longer action, emphasized by the position of the trigger, and the protruding valve housing. By courtesy of Theoben Engineering.

The Walther factory in Ulm/Donau, pictured in the mid 1970s. By courtesy of Carl Walther GmbH.

WALTHER

Carl Walther GmbH, D-7900 Ulm/Donau, Wilhelmstrasse 28 (Postfach 4325), West Germany. British distributor: Accuracy UK Ltd, 43 Gladys Avenue, North End, Portsmouth, Hampshire PO2 9AZ.

Walther was founded in Zella St Blasii in 1886, making target rifles for the remainder of the nineteenth century. However, a successful automatic pistol was marketed in 1911-12 and many cartridge pistols followed until the US Third Army captured Zella-Mehlis at the end of the Second World War. Walther was subsequently re-established in Ulm, where production of an air rifle commenced in 1951; an air pistol followed in 1952, and airguns – including the highly successful LGR – have been made alongside firearms ever since. Further details of Walther's history will be found in *Guns Review* and many specialized books dealing with the cartridge guns.*

* October-December 1982 and June 1983; or books such as Warren Buxton's *The P.38 Pistol.*

Product range: sophisticated recoilless pneumatic rifles and gas-powered pistols. A new gas-powered rifle is promised for 1988.

Discontinued models: recent casualties include the perfected Walther barrel-cocking spring-piston rifle, the LGV Spezial, together with the LP53 pistol and the LP3 series of single-pump pneumatic pistols. Some details will be found in the Third Edition (pp.153-4).

Assessment: the competition guns rank with the very best in their field, and have helped win gold medals at the highest international level.

Buying second-hand. The Walthers are sturdy and durable, which is as true of the spring-piston guns as it is of the recoilless pneumatics or gas-powered patterns. Assuming seals are effectual and springs still function (which can be tested by chronography), old guns are generally worth considering even though spares are becoming rarer.†

† This does not apply to the LGR series, which is still in production. However, several changes have been made to the basic pneumatic operating system in the last decade and some parts for the earliest models are difficult to find.

SINGLE-PUMP PNEUMATICS

LGR series

The perfected Rückstossfreie-Luftgewehr ('recoilless air rifle') currently vies with the Feinwerkbau LG300 and LG600 for the title of the world's most successful competition air rifle. Though the spring-piston Feinwerkbau has the longer pedigree, winning most of the pre-1977 competitions, the LGR soon made inroads on its rival's supremacy and held the world men's individual (590×600) and team (1753×1800) records until the Feinwerkbau LG600 broke the former with 594×600 at the 1986 European championships and Walther regained the honour with 595×600 in 1987.‡

‡ However, scores of 597×600 have twice been recorded with the LGR, once during the US pre-Olympic trials in 1984, but neither has been accepted as a world record.

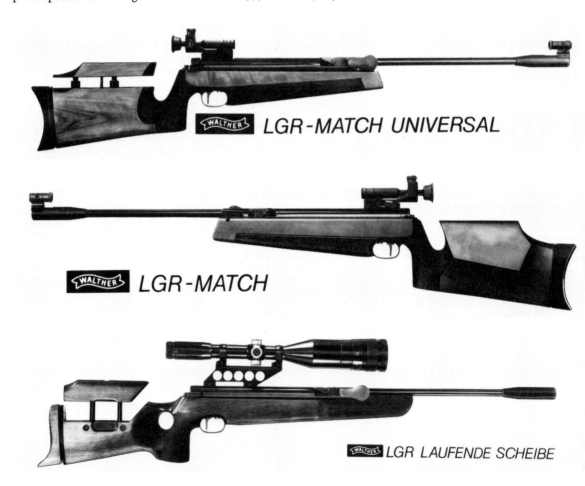

WALTHER *LGR-MATCH UNIVERSAL*

WALTHER *LGR-MATCH*

WALTHER *LGR LAUFENDE SCHEIBE*

LGR SERIES

Data, standard LGR: 4.5mm, 43.9in overall, 19.7in rifled barrel, 10.82lb with sights.

Features. No safety is necessary; the trigger is comprehensively adjustable.

Power, standard LGR: 536fs^{-1} with RWS Meisterkugeln (5.36fp), 551fs^{-1} with H&N Match (5.31fp) and 575fs^{-1} with Eley Wasp (5.59fp). Awkward and taxing to charge (appreciably easier on post-1983 guns), but very consistent and outstandingly accurate.

LGR. After a lengthy gestation, the basic rifle appeared in 1974 with a sophisticated single-pump sidelever-charged pneumatic action derived from patents sought in the early 1960s. Air is compressed into the chamber on the forward or closing stroke of the charging lever, after which a pellet may be inserted once the unique cam-locked double-seal breechblock is raised. Perfecting the sealing system allegedly delayed the introduction of the LGR, but the breechblock mechanism is now regarded as extremely efficient. The LGR is notably more taxing to charge than the Feinwerkbau spring-piston gun and usually generates a little less power, despite notable improvements made to the piston system, lever-linkage and pivot dispositions in 1983. Conversely, the pneumatic action permits a faster lock time than the spring-piston patterns in which the air is compressed in the milliseconds between the release of the piston and the emergence of the pellet at the muzzle: only the trigger levers and the valve-actuating striker move when the LGR fires. The basic rifle has a low-comb competition stock with stippling on the pistol-grip and the fore-end tip, and a vertically-adjustable butt-plate. There are effectual diopter and replaceable-element tunnel-type sights, and the trigger is fully adjustable.

LGR Junior. This diminutive LGR exhibits an abbreviated fore-end stopping short of the charging-lever tip, lacks fore-end stippling, and the distance from the pistol grip to the trigger lever is suitably reduced. The short butt may be lengthened with spacers and the size of the auxiliary barrel weight adjusted as the junior marksman grows.

LGR Laufende Scheibe. Designed for moving-target competitions, this variant has a modified direct-action trigger, a distinctive thumbhole stock with a variable-height comb, a wooden butt-plate and optical sights. The stippled fore-end swells slightly to facilitate grip and the newest guns feature skeletal diecast sight-raising blocks.

The perfected LGR – three differing versions of which are shown here – has a unique cam-locked hinged breechblock with a double-seal. The block is unlocked by pushing the thumblever and rotating it upward to allow a pellet to be pushed directly into the breech. By courtesy of Carl Walther GmbH.

LGR Match. The high-comb cheek piece, greatly refined pistol grip contours and stippling running the length of the fore-end distinguish this LGR variant. Riser blocks are often fitted to allow the standard sights to be used in the popular head-up shooting position.

LGR Match Universal. The original MU had a detachable comb insert, several of which were supplied to vary the height. In 1983, however, Walther perfected a system of risers with which the height and position of the standard comb could be varied to give more than twenty combinations of height and angle.

WEBLEY

Webley & Scott Ltd, Frankley Industrial Park, Tay Road, Rubery, Rednal, Birmingham B45 0PA.

Though Webley can trace its history back directly to 1838, Webley & Scott was not itself created until 1906. An experimental air pistol was patented by William Whiting in 1910, but success waited on the successful introduction of the compact lifting-barrel design patented by Douglas Johnstone and John Fearn. This created a lasting impression on the Empire Exhibition at Wembley in 1923

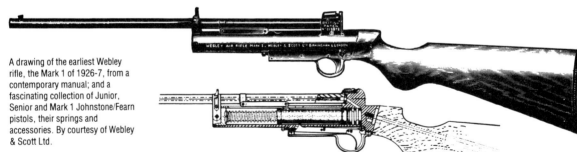

A drawing of the earliest Webley rifle, the Mark 1 of 1926-7, from a contemporary manual; and a fascinating collection of Junior, Senior and Mark 1 Johnstone/Fearn pistols, their springs and accessories. By courtesy of Webley & Scott Ltd.

and led successively through the Mark 1, Junior, Senior and Premier to the modern Hurricane and Tempest. The first rifle appeared in 1926, but only after the end of the Second World War did the company finally shake off its image as a pistolsmithy. The Mark 3 underlever-cocking spring-piston rifle of 1946 – an adaptation of the pre-war BSA Standard Pattern – has led through the Hawk and Osprey (both discontinued) to the Vulcan, the Viscount and the Omega.

Product range: Webley currently offers variations on the well-tried Johnstone/Fearn pistol theme together with barrel- and sidelever-cocking spring-piston rifles. A wide range of accessories is handled, including many emanating from Beeman in the USA,

Made in Germany, and essentially similar to the Diana LG24 apart from the back sight, the trim little Air Wolf is the current Webley junior rifle. By courtesy of Webley & Scott Ltd.

The C1 Carbine is a variant of the Victor (q.v.) with a short barrel and a distinctive straight-wrist butt to control the appreciable recoil. By courtesy of Dr Robert Beeman.

but the 'Webley' pellets are made elsewhere in Britain. Like BSA's, Webley's packaging is much better than Continental rivals and the guns are much less likely to be damaged in transit.

Assessment: the Webley airguns introduced in the mid 1970s replaced with screws and bolts with rolpins – efficient though they are undoubtedly are – and incorporated many stamped components in an attempt to keep costs within reasonable bounds. During the 1980s, Webley has striven to improve the performance of the range up through the Vulcan, Vulcan II and Viscount to the current Omega series, which is as powerful as the British 12fp limit allows, exhibits good-quality construction and offers better accuracy than many of its rivals.

Discontinued models: among the guns to disappear in the 1980s have been the Hawks, three models of which were made in 1973-9, and the standard Osprey (which was substituted by the more powerful Viscount). The Typhoon, discontinued in 1983, was a variant of the Hurricane with a weaker mainspring and a small grip. The Ranger was the Erma ELG10 lever-action rifle (q.v.), a few of which were imported in 1983-5.

Buying second-hand: the post-1980 Webleys are highly recommended for which parts are generally available, are highly recommended. They are strong, have a particularly efficient piston system, are easy to repair and maintain, and spares are generally obtainable. The obsolescent Osprey rarely gives trouble; but the Hawks, particularly the fixed-barrel Marks 2 and 3, are often found with the barrels bent upwards through misuse.

SPRING-PISTON GUNS

Air Wolf

AIR WOLF
Data: 4.5 and 5.5mm.
Features, power: generally as Diana LG24 (q.v.).

Webley's current junior rifle is made in West Germany by Mayer & Grammelspacher (being virtually identical with the Diana LG24) and is marketed in Britain rather at the expense of the appreciably more powerful Victor. The Air Wolf is a trim, efficient little gun, distinguished from its German cousin principally by its standard Webley back sight.

C1 Carbine

C1 CARBINE
Data: 0.177 and 0.22in, 38.5in overall, 14.0in rifled barrel, 6.75lb.
Features. No safety; the trigger is adjustable.
Power, 0.22 version: 605fs^{-1} with 5.5mm RWS Diabolo (11.35fp) and 593fs^{-1} with Eley Wasp (11.02fp). Though arduous to cock, the action is very consistent and shooting is acceptably accurate.

Developed in collusion with Beeman, to whom the straight-line stock has been attributed, this is a powerful diminutive of the Victor (q.v.). The most obvious features are its small size, the absence of the manual safety catch and the lack of a pistol grip. The Carbine is powerful, but difficult to cock. The design of the stock is intended to improve control and the minimal drop at the heel is ideally suited to optical sights. The American inspiration has not proved as popular in Britain as in the USA, despite the C1 Carbine's handiness and attractive combination of size and power.

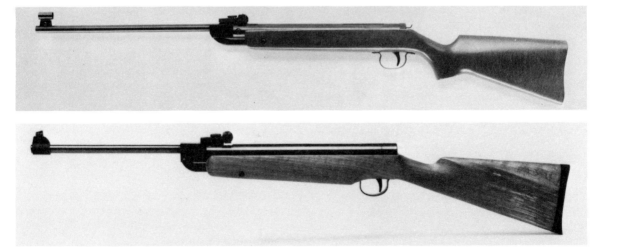

Hurricane

Introduced in the Spring of 1977, this is the current long-barrelled embodiment of the Johnstone/Fearn system, though the special back sight mount and the muzzle protrusion reduce the advantages of the compact design. The Hurricane is cocked by releasing the stirrup-catch on the left side of the air cylinder and raising the barrel. Completing the double-link cocking stroke benefits greatly from practice and no little strength, but power is acceptably high. The standard Webley rifle-pattern back sight is fitted, though an optical sight bracket can be substituted when required. In sum, the Hurricane remains one of the best of all spring-piston pistols but is less handy than the Tempest (q.v.).

Omega and Omega Carbine

Introduced in 1985, the Omega now represents the top of the Webley line. Though retaining the well-proven patented combination PTFE washer/nylon O-ring piston seal developed for the Vulcan, the Omega features an effectual barrel-lock operated by

HURRICANE

Data: 0.177 and 0.22in, 11.1in overall, 8.0in rifled barrel, 2.43lb.
Features. A manual safety catch; an adjustable trigger.
Power. ☛ 0.177, 442fs^{-1} with Eley Wasp (3.30fp). ☛ 0.22, 323fs^{-1} with Eley Wasp (3.27fp). Difficult to cock, but consistent and accurate.

OMEGA

Data: 0.177 and 0.22in. *Figures for carbine and rifle versions respectively:* , 39.2 and 43.5in overall, 15.0 and 19.3in rifled barrel, 7.61 and 7.88lb.
Features. A semi-automatic safety catch; an adjustable trigger; and an active barrel lock.
Power. ☛ 0.177, 779fs^{-1} with RWS Meisterkugeln (11.31fp) and 832fs^{-1} with Eley Wasp (11.70fp). ☛ 0.22, 598fs^{-1} with RWS Diabolo (11.09fp) and 589fs^{-1} with Eley Wasp (11.21fp). Reasonably easily cocked; extremely consistent and very accurate.

Introduced in 1985, the Omega currently represents the top of the Webley range. Among its most interesting features are a distinctively compact back sight, an active barrel lock, a European-type replaceable element front sight tunnel and a semi-automatic safety catch in the end cap. Note the transverse arrestor-block grooves on top of the cylinder, which are particularly obvious in the three-quarter view. By courtesy of Webley & Scott Ltd.

◁

pushing forward on a small T-head bar. An elegant safety-catch is let into the top surface of the receiver-plug where — though applied semi-automatically when the gun is cocked — it can easily be re-set at will. The Omega features a refinement of the Vulcan II stock, with a cheek piece, a Monte Carlo comb, and a rubber butt plate accompanied by a thin ivory-colour spacer. Lateral grooves across the top of the receiver anchor arrestor bars, and there is even a cast trigger-guard. Unusually for a British sporting gun, which usually has a blade-and-notch sight picture, the Omega has a replaceable-element front sight tunnel and a specially-designed compact back sight. The rifle has been steadily improved since its introduction until it is now among the best in its class: powerful, reliable and accurate. Unlike previous Webley-made guns, the bore dimensions have been changed to Continental European rather than British standards, and the Omega tends to shoot better with pellets such as the RWS Diabolo than the larger-diameter Eley Wasps. In 1986, no doubt inspired by the success of the Weihrauch HW77K, Webley lopped several inches from the standard barrel and introduced the Omega Carbine. Apart from overall length, however, the guns are identical.

The Tempest is Webley's smallest and most convenient pistol. A spring-piston design based on the Johnstone/Fearn patents of the 1920s, it may be recognized by its blade-type back sight and minimal rearward protrusion above the grip. Like the Hurricane (q.v.), the piston moves backwards toward the firer during the operating cycle. By courtesy of Webley & Scott Ltd.

TEMPEST

Data: 0.177 and 0.22in, 9.1in overall, 6.9in rifled barrel, 1.98lb.
Features: as Hurricane.
Power. ☛ 0.177, 459fs^{-1} with RWS Hobby (3.30fp) and 414fs^{-1} with Eley Wasp (2.90fp). ☛ 0.22, 327fs^{-1} with RWS Diabolo (3.32fp) and 318fs^{-1} with Eley Wasp (3.17fp). Otherwise generally as Hurricane.

VICTOR

Data: 0.177 and 0.22in, 40.6in overall, 17.1in rifled barrel, 6.76lb.
Features. An adjustable trigger.
Power. ☛ 0.177, 746fs^{-1} with H&N Match (9.73fp) and 760fs^{-1} with Eley Wasp (9.76fp). ☛ 0.22, 525^{-1} with Webley Diabolo (8.22fp, mf). Reasonably easily cocked, the action is consistent and accurate.

Tempest

Introduced in the summer of 1979, this is a compact Hurricane (q.v.) with a blade-type back sight. Shortening the back sight mount, together with limiting the barrel to the length of the air cylinder, provides a powerful but compact pistol. Though somewhat difficult to cock until the peculiar opening stroke has been mastered, the Tempest is a fitting successor to the Premier Mark II.

Victor

The 1981-vintage Victor is a smaller, lighter and cheaper version of the Vulcan I. Though the safety catch has been omitted, the same 'power intensification' PTFE washer/nylon O-ring piston seal offers excellent consistency and no little power from what is basically an intermediate design. Indeed, the export version of the Victor develops the same power as the C1 Carbine. The Italian beech stock has a very distinctive high straight comb, deeply stepped at the wrist, and is accompanied by a simple plastic butt plate. However, the butt is rather short for adult firers and would benefit from additional spacers to lengthen it when necessary. The sights, trigger and breech system are identical with those of the Vulcan II (q.v.).

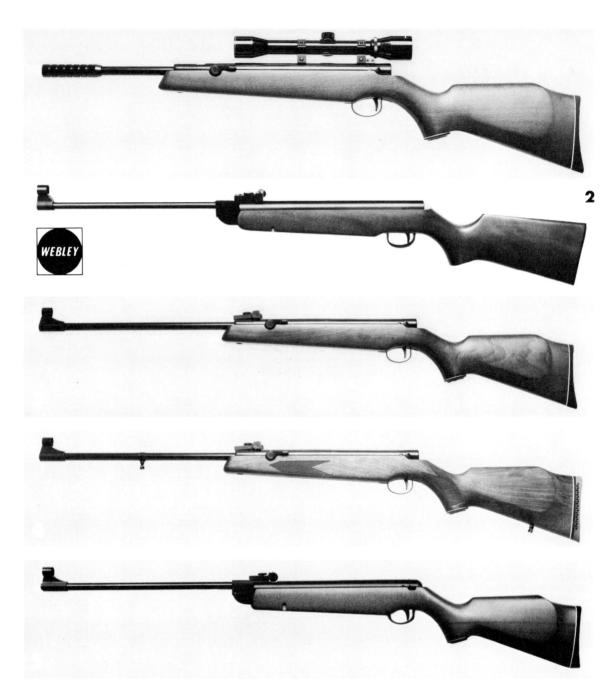

Viscount series

A superbly elegant sidelever-cocking design with the 'power intensification' piston, much favoured in export markets such as Sweden, this replaced the Osprey in August 1982. Apart from the sidelever safety ratchet, the construction of the sidelever, the sights and the rotary loading tap, the Osprey and the Viscount are completely different designs and few of the parts will interchange.

Viscount. The standard rifle has a handsome Italian beech stock, a pistol grip with a black plastic cap, a cheek piece and a Monte Carlo comb. The rubber butt plate is accompanied by a thin ivory-colour spacer and the lasting impression is one of slenderness even though the action is quite broad.

Webley's current rifles include the sidelever-cocking Tracker (1), Viscount (3) and Viscount de Luxe (4), plus the barrel-cocking Victor (2) and Vulcan II (5). By courtesy of Webley & Scott Ltd.

TRACKER

Data: 0.177 and 0.22in, 36.5in overall, 11.4in rifled barrel, 7.00lb without sights.
Features. Automatic sidelever ratchet and manual safeties; an adjustable trigger.
Power. ☛ 0.22, 578fs^{-1} with Flying Scot and 574fs^{-1} with Eley Wasp (both 10.33fp). Otherwise generally as Victor.

VISCOUNT

Data: 0.177 and 0.22in, 43.5in overall, 18.5in rifled barrel, 7.61lb.
Features: as Tracker.
Power. ☛ 0.22, 597fs^{-1} with RWS Diabolo (11.06fp) and 590fs^{-1} with Eley Wasp (10.91fp). Otherwise generally as Tracker

VULCAN II

Data: 0.177 and 0.22in, 43.6in overall, 19.2in rifled barrel, 7.65lb.
Features: A manual safety; an adjustable trigger.
Power. ☛ 0.177, 799fs^{-1} with RWS Diabolo (11.22fp) and 819fs^{-1} with Eley Wasp (11.34fp). ☛ 0.22 post-1982 British version, 602fs^{-1} with RWS Diabolo (11.24fp) and 598fs^{-1} with Eley Wasp (11.21fp). ☛ 0.22 Export, 630fs^{-1} with RWS Superpoint (12.83fp) and 637fs^{-1} with Webley Diabolo (12.11fp). Reasonably easily cocked, very consistent and accurate (post-1983/4 guns preferable).

Viscount de Luxe. To cater for the more discerning, the luxury version features an oil-finished European walnut stock with chequering on the fore-end and pistol grip, a ventilated rubber recoil pad, and sling swivels on the barrel and under-edge of the butt.

Stingray. First exhibited at IWA, Nürnberg, in the Spring of 1987 and due for release in late summer, this is a new all-black version of the Viscount with a bipod and a screw-on silencer. Performance and dimensions are essentially similar to the standard gun.

Tracker. Sold as the Barnett Spitfire in the USA, this is simply a short-barrelled Viscount, usually encountered with a muzzle weight (or the Webley Pro-System silencer on current guns) and a 4×32 optical sight; standard open sights can also be fitted when required. A 'Cammo Tracker', with a camouflage-painted stock, was introduced in 1986 to capitalize on the rifle's popularity for fieldwork.

Vulcan series

This rifle introduced the 'power intensification' piston system in which a PTFE washer combined with a nylon O-ring to provide normal efficiency straight from the box – a claim, incidentally, that most trials appear to confirm.

Vulcan I. Introduced in 1979, small, light yet powerful, the first Vulcan could exceed 800fs^{-1} with lightweight pellets such as the 4.5mm RWS Hobby. The synthetic back sight of the Hawk III was retained, though the hooded front sight was alloy rather than plastic; the breech seal remained on the air cylinder. A single-piece cocking lever was fitted, a trigger with constant sear engagement throughout its entire adjustment range was developed, and the Hawk/Osprey manual safety was retained on the left rear of the receiver.

Vulcan II. Though the original Vulcan was more sophisticated than many of its immediate contemporaries, initially selling very well, an increasingly discerning clientele demanded something more and a new gun appeared in the summer of 1981. The basic operating system was retained, but the Vulcan II was appreciably larger and its better stock eliminated the short butt, uncomfortably square fore-end and badly placed fore-end attachment bolt holes of its predecesssor. Though the trigger remained basic compared with its Weihrauch and BSF rivals, the Vulcan II proved to be powerful and acceptably accurate. Strangely, as production got underway and tooling settled in, power climbed until the standard rifle all but exceeded 12fp; this 'super-power' gun then became an export model, the mainspring was weakened and a new British variant substituted.

Vulcan Custom. Formerly the 'SE' or 'Special Export', this Vulcan I derivative has an oil-rubbed walnut stock, chequering on the fore-end and pistol-grip, a ventilated rubber butt plate and gaudily gold-plated trigger and safety levers.

Vulcan de Luxe. This is simply a Vulcan II with an attractive oil-finished walnut stock, chequering, a ventilated butt plate accompanied by a thin ivory-colour spacer plate, and sling swivels on the barrel and the under-edge of the butt.

WEIHRAUCH

Hermann Weihrauch KG, D-8744 Mellrichstadt/Bayern, Postfach 20, West Germany. British distributor: Hull Cartridge Company, Bontoft Avenue, National Avenue, Hull, Humberside HU5 4HZ (factory appointed). In addition, guns may be obtained from Edgar Brothers, Catherine Street, Macclesfield, Cheshire SK11 6SG, and John Rothery (Wholesale) Co. Ltd, Bedford Road, Petersfield, Hampshire GU32 3AX. The HW77 and HW80 form the basis for many British 'custom conversions', the principal exponents of which are listed in Part Two.

Weihrauch began trading in Zella St Blasii in 1899, making sporting guns and 'Thüringen' brand bicycles until the intrusion of the Second World War. Operations were re-established in Bavaria in 1948, only a few miles from the border with the German Democratic Republic, and output of bicycle components grew rapidly. The Allies then permitted the production of airguns and the first M35 rifle — allegedly designed prior to the war — left the factory in 1951, followed within a year by the first smallbore cartridge rifle. The first 'Arminius' brand revolvers were offered in 1961, and the company now offers a wide range of hunting and sporting guns. Unlike its German rivals, Weihrauch has preferred to concentrate on sporting airguns, the millionth air-rifle (a specially gold-plated HW35) leaving the production line in the autumn of 1983. The company has also benefitted greatly from co-operation with Beeman (see Part Two), whose contributions may be seen in many of the current Weihrauch guns.

Product range: Weihrauch makes spring-piston rifles ranging from the minuscule HW25 junior rifle through a series of intermediate guns to the HW35, probably the world's most famous sporter. Though the modernized HW80 has stolen some of the HW35's glory, the older design is still preferred by many traditionalists even though the HW77 underlever now threatens to dominate the British market as the HW35 did a decade previously. Apart from the HW70, increasingly less common in Britain, the only pistol is the new HW45 — a quirky design representing a giant step away from Weihrauch's previous output.

Assessment: the Weihrauchs, particularly the larger sporters, are universally powerful, accurate, durable and notably well made. They also have in the Rekord system perhaps the best of all mass-produced airgun triggers; some rivals may claim superiority on paper, but the Rekord is that rarity where the performance of the unit is greater than the sum of its individual parts. Though there have been signs that Weihrauch is being increasingly worried by cost effectiveness, the effects are as yet minimal and the company is rightly regarded as one of the last bastions of traditional airgunsmithing.

Discontinued models: though still available, the HW25 junior rifle and most of the HW55 series are increasingly rarely seen. It is also hard to see how the HW35, HW80 and HW85 can co-exist in the long term.

Buying second hand: despite the sophistication of the trigger and the added complexity of the post-1977 safety catch, the Weihrauchs are easily maintained, long-lived, and often command a higher than average re-sale price. Apart from the lack of an adequate cocking lever/safety system interlock on the earliest HW77, which has since been rectified, there are no basic design flaws. Manufacturing quality is usually good, though care should be taken to ensure that the synthetic muzzle-block of the earliest HW77 is not cracked, and that the comparatively thin strip of metal in the 4.5mm HW45 air cylinder between the twin cocking arms has not been buckled by abuse. The Weihrauch barrels are often suited to German-pattern pellets and exhibit minimal breech chamfer. This was especially true of the first batches of HW77 rifles to be distributed in Britain, which, with virtually no chamfer at all, had trouble chambering even German ammunition! Undoubtedly the most serious problem with the HW77 and HW80 (and possibly also with the HW85) is power: many trials have shown that they lie perilously close to the 12fp limit and may even generate illegal velocities with individual shots*. This is particularly true of guns that have been unofficially 'customized' with non-Weihrauch mainsprings. A second-hand gun should be chronographed before purchase.

* It should be remembered that the Dangerous Air Weapons Rules 1969 clearly state that an airgun should be considered as a firearm under the terms of the Firearms Act 1968 if *any single shot* exceeds 12fp.

SPRING-PISTON GUNS

HW30

This is the smallest of the proper juvenile Weihrauchs, though there is also a rarely encountered diminutive known as the HW25. The HW30 is solid and reliable, though a little expensive for a gun of its type.

HW30 M/II. This differs from the original version only in the trigger, the Perfekt system being shared with the HW50 (q.v.). The back sight is an adjustable spring-leaf pattern in which lateral movement is effected by loosening the clamp screws and moving the notch-plate across its mounting block; the standard front sight is a hooded blade

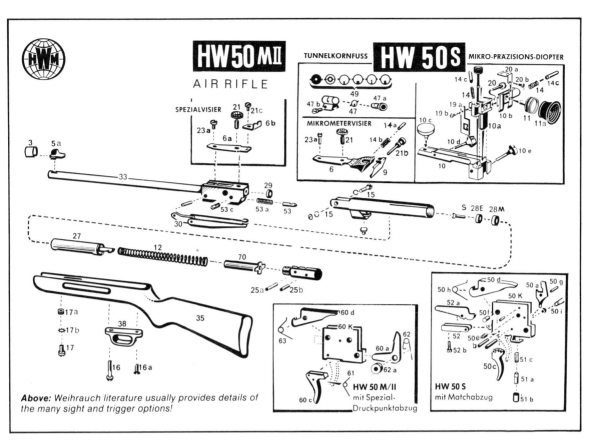

Above: Weihrauch literature usually provides details of the many sight and trigger options!

---

† A stock with a Monte Carlo comb and matching cheek piece is available to special order.

HW30

Data: 4.5 and 5.5mm, 40.2in overall, 16.9in rifled barrel, 5.52lb.

Features. No safety; the trigger may be fixed or adjustable (see text).

Power, 4.5mm: 581fs^{-1} with RWS Diabolo (5.93fp). Easily cocked, consistent and accurate.

HW35

Data: 4.5 and 5.5mm. *Figures for HW35L and HW35E respectively:* 45.3in or 47.6in overall, 19.7 or 22.0in rifled barrels, 8.38lb or 8.64lb.

Features. A semi-automatic safety catch appears on post-1977 guns; the trigger is comprehensively adjustable.

Power. ☛ 4.5mm HW35L, 767fs^{-1} with RWS Hobby (9.21fp). ☛ 5.5mm HW35L, 578fs^{-1} with RWS Diabolo (10.36fp). ☛ 4.5mm HW35E, 766fs^{-1} with RWS Diabolo (10.32fp). ☛ 5.5mm HW35E, 598fs^{-1} with RWS Diabolo (11.09fp). Though arduous to cock, the guns shoot consistently and very accurately.

mounted on a small muzzle ramp. The plain beech stock has a straight comb†, a rudimentary pistol grip and a grasping groove cut in the fore-end, but lacks a butt plate. Guns made before 1983 had leather rather than nylon piston washers.

HW30S. This improvement of the basic design has the Rekord trigger, an asset in a gun of this type but reflected in the price. The stock has a cheek piece, a Monte Carlo comb, and a separate butt-plate.

HW35 series

Introduced in 1951 in a slightly different form (as the 'M35'), this gun remains among the world's most popular sporting air rifles even now that it has been eclipsed by the newer Weihrauch designs. The retention of so much of its reputation arises from its superb trigger, high standards of construction and attractive finish. The standard open sights comprise a replaceable-element tunnel and a fully-adjustable spring leaf with an open notch; the back sight may be a dated design, but it is simple to make and more durable than many newer synthetic-body alternatives. Another feature that continues to attract traditionalists among airgunners is the barrel-lock catch, inlet in the left side of the barrel block, which is claimed (though not proven) to give a more effectual breech seal than the detent system featured on the newer HW80. A poorer feature of some HW35 rifles is noticeable barrel droop which, though making no difference to performance or durability, may hinder fitting an optical sight unless a compensating mount is available.

HW35. The earliest guns had a prototype of the Rekord trigger, which does not seem to have been perfected until the mid-1950s. A manual safety catch was added in 1977 to satisfy the American export market, and the piston washer was changed from leather to nylon in 1983 (with effect from gun 843636). This beneficially affected performance and improved long-term consistency. The standard rifle has a plain stock with a slight hog's back comb, a rounded pistol grip, and a rubber butt-plate accompanied by a black

synthetic spacer. There is no cheek piece, and a grasping groove in the fore-end emphasizes its traditional origins; excepting the BSA Airsporter, the HW35 has the longest unbroken pedigree among current spring-piston rifles.

HW35B. A variant with a beech stock, cheek piece and Monte Carlo comb.

HW35E. The renowned Exportmodell is the most attractive of the series and – perhaps – the best loved of all sporting airguns. The barrel has been lengthened, with more effect on elegance than performance, and the walnut stock displays what may be regarded as the classical German style. The best stocks display superb graining; the butt has a slight hog's back and a very distinctive cheek piece; an elegant rubber butt-plate is set off by an ivory-colour spacer; the pistol grip has a palm-swell (the so-called Wund-hammer grip); chequering is hand-cut; and a black plastic pistol-grip cap is accompanied by a thin ivory-coloured spacer. The HW35E also offers sling swivels on the barrel and the under-edge of the butt. In the opinion of many airgunners, the handling qualities of this sporting airgun are hard to better.

HW35EB. Made for Beeman Precision Arms, this combines the standard short barrel with the Exportmodell stock.

HW35L. The Luxusmodell has a walnut stock, but lacks sling swivels, a pistol-grip cap and (generally) the fore-end groove. The butt features a Monte Carlo comb and a rubber butt plate accompanied by a black spacer.

HW35LS. Made with a distinctive thumb-hole stock (Lochschaft), this truly unorthodox variant cannot be mistaken for others in the series. The oval hole immediately behind the pistol grip and the characteristic drop to the butt plate look clumsy, but the gun handles well and is a pleasure to use. The plain fore-end, uniquely among the HW35 series, displays an oblique-cut tip; and unlike most thumbhole stocks (cf., Air Arms Khamsin), the Weihrauch pattern is ambidextrous.

HW35 Safari. This is simply a variant of the standard HW35, dating from 1985-6, with a curiously green-tinged stock designed to impress field shooters. It has not proved popular in Britain.

HW45
Data: 4.5 and 5.5mm, 10.9in overall, 6.9in rifled barrel, 2.76lb.
Features. A manual safety catch and an adjustable trigger.
Power. 4.5mm, low setting: 443fs⁻¹ with Marksman (3.60fp). 4.5mm, high setting: 552fs⁻¹ with Marksman (5.58fp). 5.5mm, 426fs⁻¹ with RWS Diabolo (5.63fp). The action is reasonably easily cocked for low power, but is otherwise quite strenuous; shooting is consistent and very accurate.

The new HW45 pistol is an interesting toplever-cocking design with two-stage power, in the case of the 4.5mm version. The ghosted view shows how the upper part of the gun is raised to the intermediate cocking position or forward for full power. Like the Webleys, the piston moves towards the firer. By courtesy of Hermann Weihrauch KG.

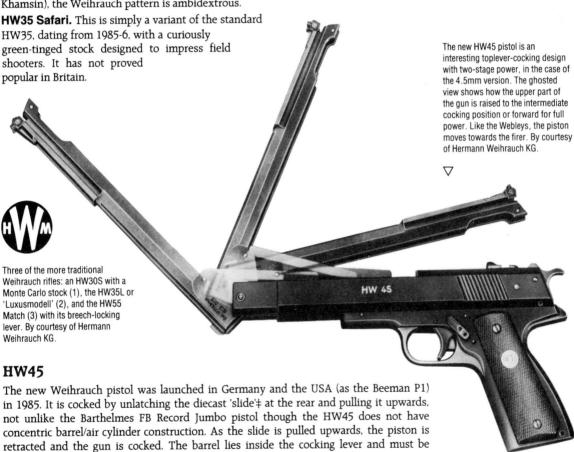

Three of the more traditional Weihrauch rifles: an HW30S with a Monte Carlo stock (1), the HW35L or 'Luxusmodell' (2), and the HW55 Match (3) with its breech-locking lever. By courtesy of Hermann Weihrauch KG.

HW45

The new Weihrauch pistol was launched in Germany and the USA (as the Beeman P1) in 1985. It is cocked by unlatching the diecast 'slide'‡ at the rear and pulling it upwards, not unlike the Barthelmes FB Record Jumbo pistol though the HW45 does not have concentric barrel/air cylinder construction. As the slide is pulled upwards, the piston is retracted and the gun is cocked. The barrel lies inside the cocking lever and must be loaded before returning the mechanism to its locked position in much the same way as the FAS AP604 match pistol. The power of the 4.5mm guns can be selected by raising the cocking piece until it is vertical (low power), or well forward of the pivot (high power) in the manner of the Webleys. An optional shoulder stock transforms the HW45 into a short carbine to capitalize on excellent accuracy and, unlike most handguns, an optical sight will be accepted with ease. The open back sight is adjustable, the fixed front-sight blade being cast integrally with the cocking arm, the trigger is very pleasant to use, and there are chequered walnut grips. The HW45 is interesting to use, but expensive and too new to assess its long-term impact on the airgun scene.

‡ The pistol is modelled as closely as possible on the Colt .45 M1911 'Government' automatic pistol.

HW50 series

Apart from size, the basic gun is identical to the perfected HW30 M/II. The HW50 will generate about 85 per cent of the power of the HW35, but is appreciably lighter and has an easier cocking stroke. Optical or aperture sights can be fitted to the dovetail grooves on the receiver.

HW50 M/II. This has a plain beechwood stock, with a rounded pistol grip, a slight hog's back comb and a grasping groove in the fore-end. It has the simple Perfekt trigger, but no safety catch. A minor variant may be obtained with a better stock with a Monte Carlo comb, a cheek piece, a squarer pistol grip and a butt plate accompanied by a black spacer.

HW50S. The Super version offers the Monte Carlo-comb stock as standard, together with the sophisticated Rekord trigger. The replaceable-element front sight is standard on this gun, post-1977 examples of which also feature the crossbolt safety catch.

HW50SE. This is simply the HW50S with the original hooded blade-type front sight mounted on a muzzle ramp.

HW55 series

The HW55 is basically an HW50S (q.v.) modified by the addition of a radial lever on the left side of the barrel block. This must be pushed forward, releasing a locking wedge, before the breech can be opened. The guns are intended for target shooting and will usually be encountered with aperture sights, even though the standard spring-leaf sporting sight can be attached to the barrel block when required. The back sight locates in any one of three shallow holes drilled into the top of the air cylinder to allow the eye relief to be varied. The guns have attained an enviable reputation for accuracy, but care must be taken to push the pellets fully into the shallowly chamfered breech; otherwise, the projecting skirt is shaved as the breech closes and accuracy suffers. All of the HW55 rifles incorporate the Rekord trigger and rely on their weight to minimize recoil/spring surge effects.

HW55M or 'Match'. This has a fashionably squared beechwood stock which, though it does not handle as well as the Tirolerschaft variant (see HW55T), is destined for shooting

HW50
Data: 4.5 and 5.5mm, 43.3in overall, 18.5in rifled barrel, 6.77lb.
Features. The HW35-type safety is now fitted; the trigger may be fixed or adjustable (see text).
Power, 4.5mm, 547fs^{-1} (9.28fp) with RWS Diabolo. The cocking effort and consistency are about average, accuracy is very good.

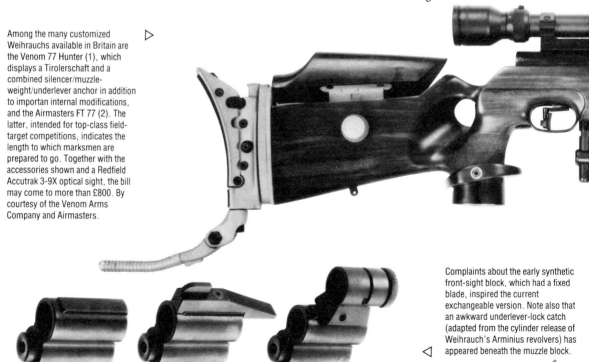

▷ Among the many customized Weihrauchs available in Britain are the Venom 77 Hunter (1), which displays a Tirolerschaft and a combined silencer/muzzle-weight/underlever anchor in addition to importan internal modifications, and the Airmasters FT 77 (2). The latter, intended for top-class field-target competitions, indicates the length to which marksmen are prepared to go. Together with the accessories shown and a Redfield Accutrak 3-9X optical sight, the bill may come to more than £800. By courtesy of the Venom Arms Company and Airmasters.

Complaints about the early synthetic front-sight block, which had a fixed blade, inspired the current exchangeable version. Note also that an awkward underlever-lock catch (adapted from the cylinder release of Weihrauch's Arminius revolvers) has ◁ appeared beneath the muzzle block.

By courtesy of Hermann Weihrauch.

under UIT rules. Stippling graces the pistol grip and the rubber butt plate can be slid vertically in its channel-block. Though the HW55 Match is quite heavy for a gun of its class, it is still appreciably lighter than the massive recoilless rifles; consequently, Weihrauch can supply supplementary barrel-sleeves and an additional weight to be fitted in the fore-end.

HW55MF: a version of the HW55MM, described below, fitted with a detent-locked HW50S action.

HW55MM. This variation has a Bayernschaft (Bavarian-pattern stock), with a distinctive cheek piece whose lower edge runs parallel with the slightly raised comb. The rubber butt plate is crescentic, the exaggerated pistol grip has a Wundhammer Swell, and extensive hand-cut chequering appears on the deep fore-end.

HW55SM. Dating from 1956, the original '55' is perpetuated in this version, with a plain walnut stock, a crescentic rubber butt-plate, hand-cut chequering on the pistol grip and a grasping groove along the side of the generous fore-end.

HW55T. The most remarkable gun of the series has a Tirolerschaft (Tyrolean-style stock), with an extraordinarily high comb and a concave cheek piece that holds the eye unerringly behind the sights; indeed, the back sight can be removed and the gun *still* fired surprisingly accurately. The subtleties of the true Tirolerschaft cheek piece are not always appreciated by British custom stockmakers, whose facsimiles rarely support the cheek as well as Weihrauch's.

HW55

Data: 4.5mm, 43.3in overall, 18.4in rifled barrel, 9.70lb (HW55M wihout auxiliary weights).
Features. Generally as pre-1977 HW35, with an additional active breech-lock on all but the HW55MF.
Power, 4.5mm HW55T: 547fs^{-1} with RWS Diabolo (5.26fp) and 532fs^{-1} with Eley Wasp (4.78fp). The action is easily cocked; though consistency may only be average, accuracy is very good.

1

2

HW70

The first Weihrauch pistol, popular with novice target-shooters, is a barrel-cocker offering low power but minimal recoil/spring-surge effects. The gun has a two-stage trigger and an automatic safety. Unlike the Weihrauch rifles, the HW70 shows evidence of being designed down to a price — with a rifled barrel inside a cast-alloy liner and a synthetic grip/frame unit with a rather slippery feel. Pistols made after April 1976 feature a revised cylinder end-cap, with a clamp screw designed to prevent the receiver cap flying off the gun unbidden.

HW70

Data: 4.5mm, 12.7in overall, 6.3in rifled barrel, 2.35lb.
Features. An automatic trigger safety and an adjustable trigger.
Power. 292fs^{-1} with RWS Diabolo (1.50fp). The cocking stroke is reasonably easy. Accuracy is good, though consistency is usually only average.

HW77 series

Despite its designation, which could be taken to suggest otherwise, this powerful underlever-cocking rifle made its début in 1983. The basic concept owes much to Robert Beeman, but the engineering is pure Weihrauch — based, as far as possible, on the HW80. The HW77 is large and heavy, with the cocking lever beneath the barrel, the lever-tip being anchored in the fixed monoblock front-sight ramp/muzzle block by a ball detent. The sleeve-pattern breech, inspired by the leading competition rifles, permits pellets to be loaded directly into the barrel rather than through an intermediate rotary tap. The underlever is simply pulled downwards, the breech sleeve opens, a pellet is pushed into the bore and the cocking lever closed: simple, efficient, though somewhat clumsily accentuated by the length of the cocking lever. The semi-automatic safety is then reset and the gun can be fired at will. The rifle is no more strenuous to cock than the HW50, which is a tribute to the efficient disposition of the pivots; it also includes the Rekord trigger system, and shoots very well. The standard spring-leaf back sight is mounted on a block that can be moved along the dovetail grooves to alter the sight radius. The original front sight blade was moulded integrally into the muzzle-block, but post-1986 guns feature a detachable open blade or optional replaceable-element tunnel. The beechwood stock design is based on that of the Beeman R1, with an elegant chequered pistol grip, a shallow Monte Carlo comb, a cheek piece and a rubber butt-plate accompanied – like the plastic pistol-grip cap – by a thin ivory-coloured spacer.

HW77K. The full-length rifle is too clumsy to be used effectively in copses or brush, for which the shorter 1984-vintage HW77K (Karabiner, 'carbine') is preferable. The HW77K has a somewhat sharper muzzle blast, but neither accuracy nor power has been affected.

Modified guns. The HW77 was an instantaneous success in Britain, despite the questionable efficacy of the muzzle block/sight ramp (which had a tendency to fracture), the poor chamfering of the breech of the earliest guns, an inadequate cocking lever/safety catch interlock and the weak cocking-lever ball detent. Late in 1985, therefore, the safety system was revised to prevent the cocking lever slamming shut should the safety catch be reset accidentally and the trigger pressed with the breech open, and a sliding longitudinal catch was added to the barrel block to retain the cocking lever.

HW80 series

This rifle is a modernized HW35 with a larger-diameter air cylinder and a nylon 'parachute' piston washer. The opportunity was taken to simplify production in an attempt to keep costs down, and the wedge-pattern breechlock of the HW35 was replaced by a simpler detent. A new one-piece cocking lever was substituted for the older articulated pattern, somewhat weakening the fore-end, but the Rekord trigger and crossbolt safety catch were retained. The elegant rounded stock of the original US version of the rifle – the Beeman R1 – was developed by Gary Goudy, one of America's foremost designers. The original European HW80, however, eschewed this pattern (wrongly, in many enthusiasts' view) in favour of angularity and an oblique-cut fore-end tip. In 1986, the doubters' opinions were vindicated when a new rounded HW80 stock appeared. The HW80 is a very powerful and effectual gun, with a tendency to approach the British limit too closely unless carefully regulated; the export version, indeed, is quite capable of reaching 1,000fs⁻¹ with lightweight ammunition.* The cocking stroke is slightly easier than that of the HW35, owing to revised pivot positions and greater mechanical advantage, but accuracy is unimpaired. This combination of attractive characteristics has led to many HW80 rifles being rebuilt by British customizers with a variety of improvements in the action and stock. Though some of these revisions are more illusory than real, the best of them offers crisper performance and more effectual stock design.

The standard HW80 originally had a stock with a typically German pistol grip and an obliquely cut fore-end tip. Recently, however, the new rounded pattern shown here has been substituted. By courtesy of Hermann Weihrauch KG.

HW77

Data: 4.5 and 5.5mm. *Figures for HW77K and HW77 respectively*: 40.2in or 44.1in overall, 14.6 or 18.5in rifled barrel, 8.68 or 8.95lb.
Features. Semi-automatic and automatic (post-1985 guns only) safeties; the trigger is comprehensively adjustable. Power. ☛ 5.5mm British version, 618fs⁻¹ with RWS Diabolo (11.85fp) and 607fs⁻¹ with Eley Wasp (11.55fp). ☛ 5.5mm export version, 669fs⁻¹ with RWS Diabolo (13.51fp). Comparatively easily cocked, the action is very consistent and outstandingly accurate.

The lightweight HW85 was derived from the HW50 (q.v.), apparently at Beeman's request. Note that the standard stock (1) lacks a cheek piece, and that its fore-end stops at the main barrel pivot. That of the Luxusmodell (2), conversely, has a chequered pistol-grip, a cheek piece and a pistol-grip cap, and extends to the front of the barrel-block. By courtesy of Hermann Weihrauch KG.

HW80

Data: 4.5, 5.05 and 5.5mm. *Figures for HW80K and HW80 respectively*: 41.7in or 45.3in overall, 16.1 or 19.7in rifled barrel, 8.09lb or 8.54lb.
Features. Comparable with the current HW35, but with a simple bolt-type detent. Power. ☛ 4.5mm British version, 819fs⁻¹ with H&N Match (11.72fp). ☛ 4.5mm export version, 963fs⁻¹ with H&N Match (16.21fp). ☛ 5.5mm British version, 612fs⁻¹ with RWS Diabolo (11.61fp) and 595fs⁻¹ with Eley Wasp (11.09fp). Reasonably arduous to cock, but very consistent and extremely accurate.

* At the time of going to press, it was announced that the British importers had requested Weihrauch to test each gun individually before shipping them. However, the company has averred that the guns *are* tested before despatch, and it is concluded that the problems arise largely from lubricant seeping past the piston washer during transit

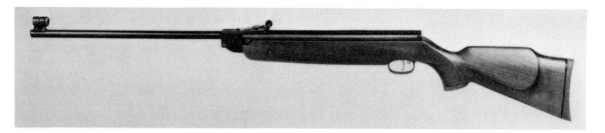

HW85

Data: 4.5 and 5.5mm, 43.5in overall,
18.1in rifled barrel, 7.63lb.
Features: as HW80.
Power, 4.5mm export version: 1,000-
1,017fs^{-1} with unspecified pellets (mf,
RWS Hobby?). Otherwise generally
similar to the HW80, but easier to cock.

This customized HW80 displays a
new walnut stock, Venom's greatly
modified action and scroll engraving
on the air cylinder, sight mount,
barrel block and silencer — typical of
the treatment the best of these guns
attract in Britain. By courtesy of the
Venom Arms Company.

HW80K. In 1985, a carbine appeared to compete with ultra-handy field guns such as the Air Arms Bora or Webley/Beeman C1. It is, however, still a large gun.

HW85 series

This, the latest of the Weihrauch-made sporters to be seen in Britain, was launched in the USA as the Beeman R10. Based on the HW50S, the action has been subtly redesigned to increase power markedly without changing the pleasant cocking stroke. The Rekord trigger and crossbolt safety catch have been retained, but a new M&G-type sight rail appears on top of the air cylinder. Results include excellent accuracy, light weight and velocity of 1,000fs^{-1} or more with pellets such as the Beeman Laser or RWS Hobby. The HW85 and HW85K feature a plain American-inspired stock not unlike that of the HW77, with an elegantly shaped butt and a rounded fore-end tip. The optional deluxe stock has a long fore-end, hand-cut chequering on the pistol grip, a shapely cheek piece and an improved rubber butt-plate.

Directory Two
Airgun Centre to Ye-wha

LESSER MANUFACTURERS

The three previous editions of *The Airgun Book* dwelt at some length on companies whose products are rarely encountered in Britain. As Milbro and BSF guns – though once common – are now only seen on the second-hand market, the status of their manufacturers has been reduced and cross-referral made to the relevant portions of the previous edition. Other inclusions in this section are companies which make only one airgun; several which declined to supply details of their products; the specialist customizers; and others that have apparently failed to achieve true series production.

THE **AirGun** CENTRE

AIRGUN CENTRE

John Stevens' company, The Airgun Centre (107 London Road, Rayleigh, Essex SS6 9AY), converts HW77 rifles for use with the Theoben-designed Zephyr piston system (q.v.). The new self-lubricating polyurethane piston-crown has a scraper ring to prevent the ingress of lubricant into the air-chamber, eliminating dieseling, but the most important feature is the radial grooving on the face of the crown. This communicates directly opposite the transfer port and virtually eliminates piston bounce. However, the essence of the Zephyr 77 is more than just simple piston-crown; the entire piston unit is substituted by a lightened component bearing only at the edges and coated with PTFE to reduce friction; the mainspring is a Teflon-coated Titan; a Theoben silencer is added; and the stock replaced by a special custom pattern. The resulting Zephyr 77 is one of the smoothest-shooting of all customized rifles.

AIRGUNAID

Formerly trading in Chelmsford, Essex, this business was destroyed by fire in 1981 and has not resumed trading. Owned by the airgun writer Eddie Barber, Airgunaid built sporting and target rifles (the SP5 and TR2) on the basis of Milbro Diana G80 rifles. Production was very small, however, and the guns are now rare. TAB3, p.65.

AIR LOGIC

Air Logic Ltd (3 Medway Buildings, Lower Road, Forest Row, East Sussex RH18 5HE) is best known for its excellent silencers, marketed under the Whisperer and Sound Soaker brands. The company introduced a powerful single-pump 0.22-calibre pneumatic rifle

The Airgun Centre's Zephyr 77 rifle, built on the ubiquitous Weihrauch action, incorporates the unique Theoben piston-crown – with which it has attained a reputation for smoothness all but unmatched by its rivals. By courtesy of *Airgun World*.

Airmasters customizes Feinwerkbau and Weihrauch rifles. Shown here are the FT ('Field Target') stocked HW80 (1) and FWB Sport (2). Note the set-back brass trigger on the former – among other features – and the Anschütz match-rifle buttplate assembly on the latter. By courtesy of Airmasters.

GENESIS

Data: 5.5mm (others to follow in 1988), 45.9in overall, 17.7in rifled barrel, 9.50lb with integral silencer/muzzle weight but no sights.
Features. No safety; comprehensively adjustable trigger; offset 'Mosquito' sight mount.
Power: about 600fs^{-1} with RWS Superdome (11.65fp).

Air Logic's Genesis is the first full-power single-stroke pneumatic hunting rifle to reach series production. Capable of attaining 12fp with one easy stroke, it also features a sliding barrel and an offset optical sight mount. By courtesy of Air Logic.

of its own design in mid-1987. Credited to Richard Spencer, called the Genesis, and capable of delivering power consistently up to the British 12fp limit with a charging stroke no more arduous than that of the Walther LGR, the rifle features a forward sliding barrel (controlled by a bolt), an integral silencer, a uniquely shaped stock with a cutaway underbelly on the butt, and a special 'Mosquito' sight rail. Only prototypes had been released at the time of writing, but series production was due to begin in the summer of 1987.

AIRMASTERS

Airmasters (alias 'Mastersport'), based at 2 Hibbert Street, Luton, Bedfordshire LU1 3UU, customizes the ubiquitous Weihrauch HW77/80 and Feinwerkbau Sport rifles. Unlike many of the smaller specialist tuners, who are content to tinker with a few parts and add a custom stock, the Welham brothers make extensive modifications:

'We replace the mainspring, modify or replace the piston, replace the trigger assembly on the FWB Sport, shorten barrels, rework the transfer port and, if required, fit a barrel locking system to- ...break-barrel air rifles.'*

* David Welham, personal correspondence, May 1985.

The guns are powerful and efficient, the actions are smoother and faster, and the new double-pull Feinwerkbau Sport trigger is a vast improvement on the original. Among the current products are the Mastersport FWB and FWB Tyrolean, an HW80 carbine sporter and an HW77 Tyrolean at prices between £175 and £500 or more, the price usually depending upon the sophistication of the optical sights. The top field-target guns include the 77 or 85 Dominator, the FT77 and the FTS77, all of which are built on Weihrauch actions. The carbine-style FTS has a thumb-hole competition stock with an adjustable comb and butt-plate, and can be obtained with a Redfield Accutrak telescope sight with which it costs more than £800! In addition to the guns, Airmasters also handles Knok-Down targets (made by its parent company, Knok-Down Targets Ltd) and manufactures Phantom silencers for Oliver J. Gower Ltd of Leighton Buzzard.

AIR MATCH

Air Match SRL (I-20081 Abbiategesso/Milano, Via Cassolnuovo 9, Italy) makes a single-stroke pneumatic pistol designed in 1978 by Giacomo Cagnoni. The CU400, CU600 and CU650 Olimpic pistols all share the same basic action, though there are differences in the grips and trigger systems. The unique action features a floating barrel that moves away from the breech as the sidelever is opened. Compression occurs during the closing stroke, which requires considerable strength and a practised art. The Air Match pistol offers some very advanced features, including a detachable trigger unit and a low bore-line in relation to the handgrip. It is powerful and very accurate: so good a performer, indeed, that international championships have been won with it. Once distributed in Britain by Phoenix Arms Company of Eastbourne, the Air Match has failed to dislodge the Feinwerkbau on the British market and is now rarely seen. It remains in full-scale production, however, and may yet reappear in earnest. TAB 3, p.66.

ARCOS

José Artes de Arcos (8-Hortaleza, Madrid-4, and Barcelona, Spain) made the multi-stroke pneumatic Setra AS 1000 rifle, a powerful Sheridan-inspired design capable of exceeding the British 12fp limit by a considerable margin; power was extremely erratic — guns tested by the Home Office Forensic Science Laboratory in the mid-1970s proved capable of generating anything between 6 and 20fp. Restricted-power AS 1000 guns enjoyed a short-lived vogue in Britain in the early 1980s, thanks to the efforts of Sussex Armoury and Scalemead Arms Company. Less than a hundred sold in Britain. TAB3, p.66.

BEEMAN

Having accorded Beeman full manufacturer status in the earlier editions, it may seem churlish to reduce the company's coverage once again. Founded by Robert and Toshiko Beeman in 1972 — originally as a hobby — Beeman Precision Arms, Inc. (3440

The Air Match CU600 pistol offers excellent accuracy and an unusually consistent single-stroke pneumatic action. By courtesy of Giacomo Cagnoni.

CU600

Data: 4.5mm, 13.2in overall, 8.8in rifled barrel, 2.06lb without auxiliary weights. Features. No safety; comprehensively adjustable trigger; and optional extension sights.
Power: $416fs^{-1}$ with H&N High-Speed Match (2.81fp). Despite an awkward charging stroke, the gun is an exceptionally consistent and very accurate performer.

Airway Drive, Santa Rosa, California 95401, USA) remains America's premier airgun distributor. The company has grown enormously from its humble beginnings, handling Weihrauch, Feinwerkbau and Webley airguns with great success until a spirited expansion into firearms was made in 1983. BPA has also been responsible for many spring-piston airguns that have since become renowned in Europe under different names. The Weihrauch HW45, HW77 and HW80, for example, all reflect Beeman's commitment to airgunning:

"Our first 'complete' airgun was the Beeman R1. That began... with a meeting between Mr and Mrs Weihrauch and myself and Mrs Beeman... in the gun room of our former home in San Anselmo, California. We presented the full results of a long computer simulation program which we had been working on and which we had verified by means of some experimental gun modifications. The key point of that study was to determine why the HW35 was not producing the kind of power that its internal measurements should produce. Our result was the development of a new power plant that

This selection of Beeman's extensive product range includes some of the company's own-brand lubricants and the Webley Tempest pistol case, together with (top to bottom) the Falcon 1, R1 and R8 rifles. By courtesy of Dr Robert Beeman.

could be used as a basis for the most powerful spring piston gun on the market. We asked that 'our' new safety, 'our' nylon parachute piston seal, a new barrel detent mechanism (more convenient than the HW35 mechanism) and a stock completely of our design...be incorporated in the new gun. They [Weihrauch] expertly put this together with their Rekord trigger, the classic HW sights and some other minor Weihrauch parts. We then specified the development of the Beeman R7 and R8 as takeoffs of the R1 stock design on modifications of the HW30 and HW50 mechanisms..."†

† Dr Robert Beeman, personal correspondence, 20th November 1986.

Beeman is also well-known for the Blue Ribbon telescope sights; a vast range of accessories including the Pell-Seat and Pell-Size; and a series of pellets incorporating the company's designs, though made by Haendler & Natermann and Hasuike Seisakusho. Most of the Beeman guns were covered in detail in the previous edition (pp.76-8), but are rarely seen in Britain owing to their power and the fact that duty raises their price above competing designs (the HW80, for example!) imported directly from the European Economic Community. The Falcon 1 and Falcon 2 are based on the Arizmendi-made Norica Mo.80-C and 73-T, though with better US-inspired stocks and other detail changes; the Beeman R1 and R10 were the inspiration for the Weihrauch HW80 and HW85 respectively; the R7 and R8 are modifications of the HW30S and HW50S with US-style stocks; the R5, which was produced only in small numbers, was based on the Feinwerkbau Sport; the HW77 is considered in the Weihrauch section; and the Beeman P1 is sold in Europe as the HW45. Details of the Beeman/Webley C1 carbine, built on the Webley Victor action, will be found in the Webley section.

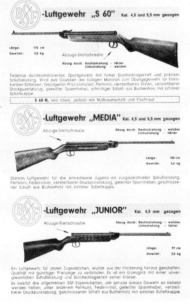

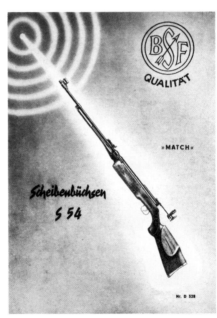

The products of the late lamented BSF organization included the S60, Media, Junior and S 54 rifles, shown here on advertising leaflets dating from the 1960s. Shortly before the company's liquidation, the distinctively stocked S 54 Sport (1) and S 80 (2) appeared — too late to affect its fate.

BOWKETT

In the early 1980s, John Bowkett (3 Welford Road, Shirley, Solihull, West Midlands B90 3HX) developed an excellent sidelever-charging single-stroke pneumatic rifle for competition and sporting use, in the latter guise effortlessly attaining 12fp. These guns are distinguished by a bolt-loading system and a lever hinged at the front of the action, and have since been made in small numbers on a limited basis. However, the inventor is now concentrating on gas-powered guns with a unique constant-pressure valve system.

BREMA

In 1981 the Brema company – since acquired by Fabbrica Armi Giuseppe Tanfoglio of Magno-Gardone Val Trompia, Italy – began to copy obsolescent M&G Dianas. Small numbers of Brema Modello 23, 25, 27 and 35 rifles were distributed in Britain by Precision Arms Ltd of Paddock Wood, Kent, in 1983-4. The agency then ceased owing to comparatively poor quality and intermittent availability. The Bremas are virtually identical with the old-style Dianas of the same numerical designation: TAB3, pp.127-30.

BSF

Once an important spring-airgun maker, Bayerische Sportwaffenfabrik of Erlangen, founded in 1935, was liquidated in July 1985. The sudden collapse five years earlier of Norman May & Co., the principal British importer of 'Bavaria' brand guns, caused such a crisis that many of BSF's workforce of about 130 was laid-off and the future looked bleak. Though Herbert Gayer purchased BSF from the Schütt family in 1982, even radical surgery failed to save the company. The extensive range of spring-piston guns has not been encountered in Britain since the early 1980s. The junior Bavaria 35, intermediate Bavaria 45/55 and full-power Bavaria 55/S60/S70/S80 barrel-cockers (together with the S54 series of underlever-cockers) were covered in pp.88-90 of the Third Edition. BSF's demise is a shame; together with Weihrauch, the company represented last of the traditionalists in the German airgun industry.

Em-Ei 45

Lion P-45-3

CHINESE STATE FACTORIES

When the Third Edition was being prepared, the P-45-3 Lion underlever-cocker and the EM-45 Emei sidelever-cocker were still encountered in small numbers, together with the Arrow (a barrel cocking junior rifle) and the Industry Brand Type 6235 pistol. Currently, however, most of these guns have disappeared again. A newer sidelever-cocker, sometimes known as the P-45-4 and once offered by Phoenix Arms Company as the Tiger, has also disappeared. This leaves only the barrel-cocking Models 61 (small) and 62 (large), otherwise known as the Pioneer/Hunter or Super Hunter. An improved underlever-cocking Lion designated B3-1 Magnum has been distributed in the USA, but is yet to be seen in Britain. The Chinese products are usually crudely if reasonably sturdily made, and offer lower power and inferior accuracy than most of their Western European rivals.

COBRA INTERNATIONAL

The trading style of a subsidiary of L.J. Cammell (Merseyside) Ltd – of 53 Borrowdale Road, Moreton, Wirral – Cobra International Arms Ltd currently distributes Champion pellets and several types of airgun. These have included the popular French Manuarm pistol, plus the Cobra Hunter, Cobra Junior, Cobra Strike Magnum and Mustang. The Cobra Hunter and Junior are the Norica Mo.80-G and Mo.56, covered in detail in the relevant section; the Strike Magnum, however, is a modified 0.25 calibre BSA Mercury IV (q.v.) with a matt black beech stock and a multi-coloured cobra transfer on the butt-side. The Mustang appears to be a Schmidt HS9A pistol.

DAYSTATE

Newcastle Street, Stone, Staffordshire ST15 8JU. Founded to promote tranquiliser equipment in 1979, Daystate also makes a number of airguns to order. These have included an American-style multi-stroke pneumatic rifle known as the Sportsman (no longer being made) and the Competa pistol, with a large-diameter under-barrel air reservoir. Three variations of the well-established Huntsman reservoir pneumatic are currently being offered – the standard rifle, with a comparatively plain Monte Carlo comb beech stock; the Huntsman Midas, with a custom walnut stock, a shortened lock-time and variable power (100 shots at 12fp or 250 at 5fp from the standard British version); and the unique Huntsman QC or 'Quick Charge', which combines the variable power system with exchangeable air cylinders. Though the air capacity of the QC is less than half that of the fixed-cylinder Midas, this is largely irrelevant if extra pre-charged cylinders are available. Daystate products are well engineered, offering good performance, but are expensive and rarely encountered outside field-target competitions or pest-control operations.

HUNTSMAN QC

Data: 0.22, 37.5in overall, 19.0in rifled barrel, 7.7lb including gas cylinder.
Features. No safety; a free-floating barrel and exchangeable gas cylinder; variable power; and a rotating bolt-type cocking/loading system.
Power: approximately 5 or 12fp (variable). Super-power versions are also obtainable.

Daystate's Huntsman QC is the only pre-charged pneumatic rifle to feature exchangeable reservoir cylinders. It also incorporates a floating barrel and a power regulator. By courtesy of Daystate Ltd.

EM-GE

Em-Ge Sportgeräte GmbH & Co. KG, Gerstenberger & Eberwein (D-7921 Gerstetten-Gussenstadt, Postfach 26), makes three spring-piston barrel-cocking pistols. The best known is the LP3A, which was popular in Britain in the 1970s, but small numbers of the LP100 and LP101 have been imported by Frank Dyke & Co. Ltd. Despite the quality of these guns – which are well made and shoot accurately – the strength of the Deutsch-mark makes them expensive compared with the cheap Spanish and Italian imports. The LP3A is the most traditionally made, with sturdy metal air-cylinder/frame construction and small plastic grips; the LP100 is a modernized version with a one-piece synthetic grip/frame; and the LP101, which dates from 1983, is basically an LP100 with a stippled wooden target-type grip that lowers the bore-line in relation to the hand.

ENSIGN

Formerly trading in Newbury, Berkshire, the Ensign Arms Company was a partnership between Saxby & Palmer and Tasco, formed to market the former's bolt-action pre-charged cartridge air rifle. The Elite, Magnum and Royale rifles were launched in a blaze of publicity in 1982 but – within two years – the partnership had been dissolved by mutual consent and business transferred to Saxby-Palmer Ltd (Part One, q.v.).

ERMA

Erma-Werke GmbH (D-8060 München-Dachau, Postfach 1269, West Germany) has

Erma's ELG 10 is the best of the lever-action pseudo-Winchester airguns; though expensive, it is highly sophisticated and very accurate. By courtesy of Erma-Werke GmbH. △

ELG 10

Data: 4.5mm, 38.2in overall, 17.7in rifled barrel, 6.39lb.

Features. Automatic and manual safeties; a cleaning rod in the the 'magazine tube' beneath the barrel; and a travel-adjustable trigger.

Power: $519fs^{-1}$ with RWS Hobby (4.19fp). Though strenuous to cock, the action is consistent and the gun shoots extremely accurately.

AP 604

Data: 4.5mm, 11.4in overall without sight extension, 7.5in rifled barrel, 2.18lb without auxiliary weights.

Features. A comprehensively adjustable trigger.

Power: $386fs^{-1}$ with H&N High-Speed Match (2.42fp). Reasonably taxing to charge, but a consistent and very accurate shooter.

the excellent, if expensive ELG 10 lever-action air rifle. Small numbers of this Winchester M1894 lookalike, designed by Josef Eder in 1980, have been sold in Britain as the Webley Ranger. The gun is distinguished by a sophisticated breech-sleeve action, made of high quality material with no concessions to alloy or synthetic parts, and is surprisingly accurate. Velocity is on the low side but the gun is great fun to use. TAB3, pp.108-9.

FAS

Fabbrica Armi Sportive SRL (I-20091 Settimo Milanese [Milano], Via E. Fermi 8, Italy) makes the excellent AP604 toplever-charging single-stroke pneumatic match pistol. Air is compressed into the valve chamber on the closing stroke, which is more arduous than the cocking stroke of the FAS's Feinwerkbau spring-piston rivals – though the action is very consistent and contributes greatly to excellent accuracy. The competitively priced FAS originally lacked adjustable grips; several fixed sizes (three right-hand, two left-hand) were offered instead. These have now been joined by a fully adjustable palm-rest pattern. The pistol soon proved itself capable of winning championships at the highest level, but has now been overshadowed by the Air Match and the Fiocchi-Pardini. Small quantities of the AP604 have been sold in Britain by Oliver J. Gower Ltd of Leighton Buzzard; Gower also handles the FAS cartridge guns, for which the air pistol was initially conceived as a trainer. See TAB 3, p.100. A prototype of the highly interesting top-lever action AP606 pneumatic pistol was exhibited in 1987; it is assumed that production will begin in 1988.

In addition to the LP100 barrel-cocking pistol, Em-Ge also markets a variety of pellet-catchers. By courtesy of Karl Schäfer. ▷

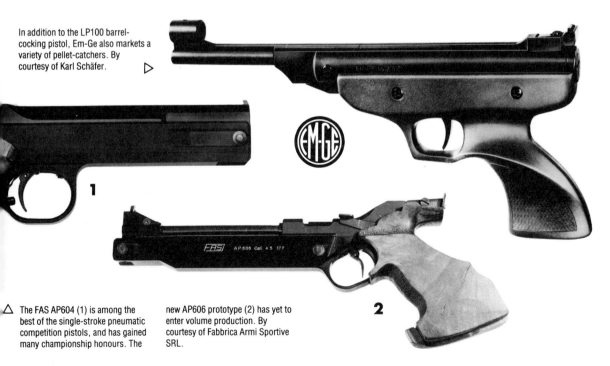

△ The FAS AP604 (1) is among the best of the single-stroke pneumatic competition pistols, and has gained many championship honours. The new AP606 prototype (2) has yet to enter volume production. By courtesy of Fabbrica Armi Sportive SRL.

The FB Record LP77 (1) and Jumbo (2). By courtesy of Fritz Barthelmes KG.

◁▷

FB RECORD

The products of Fritz Barthelmes KG Sportwaffenfabrik (D-7920 Heidenheim-Oggenhausen, Watzmannstrasse 17, West Germany) were featured extensively in pp.72-4 of the Third Edition. However, no changes have been made to the range in the intervening period and the efficient, low-cost pistols have not attained the distribution levels that had been expected. This is largely due to the strength of the Deutschmark since 1984, which has removed much of the guns' competitiveness despite the efforts of John Rothery (Wholesale) Co. Ltd. The FB Record LP1, LP2 and LP3 are barrel-cockers, with a very distinctive bifurcated breech and an articulated cocking-lever system. Made largely of alloy, with baked-on black paint finish, they are distinguished from each other by their sights and grip: the LP1 has fixed sights, the otherwise identical LP2 has a fully adjustable back sight on the end-cap, and the LP3 is an LP2 with an enlarged synthetic grip. The FB Record LP68 is a large barrel cocker made from sturdy stampings. It shoots well on account of its low power/weight ratio and is appreciably better value than some of its cheap Italian rivals. The LP77 is an extraordinary design with a ventilated over-barrel rib and a curious synthetic frame unit with a hand-slot down the front of the grip beneath the trigger. However, the back sight is fully adjustable and the pistol shoots amazingly well for such a cheap design. The newest of the FB Record pistols is the 'Jumbo', an unusually compact concentric barrel/cylinder design cocked by raising the bifurcated cocking arm once the receiver-end catch has been released. The Jumbo is

LP1

Data: 4.5mm, 10.9in overall, 5.1in smoothbore barrel, 1.60lb.
Features. No safety; a non-adjustable trigger.
Power: 259fs^{-1} with RWS Hobby (1.04fp). Comparatively easily cocked and reasonably consistent, the LP1 is accurate only at short range.

LP68

Data: 4.5mm, 14.6in overall, 7.0in rifled barrel, 3.09lb.
Features. No safety; the trigger is adjustable.
Power: 335fs^{-1} with RWS Hobby (1.75fp) and 276fs^{-1} with Eley Wasp (1.29fp). Comparatively easily cocked, the action is consistent and accurate.

LP77

Data: 4.5mm, 12.4in overall, 5.9in rifled barrel, 2.07lb.
Features. An automatic safety and an adjustable trigger.
Power: 389fs^{-1} with RWS Hobby (2.36fp) and 341fs^{-1} with Eley Wasp (1.97fp). Otherwise as LP68.

JUMBO

Data: 4.5mm, 7.3in overall, 6.1in rifled barrel, 1.94lb.
Features. A manual safety catch, a non-adjustable trigger and a pellet magazine in the butt.
Power, British version: 302fs^{-1} with RWS Hobby (1.42fp) and 256fs^{-1} with Eley Wasp (1.11fp). Reasonably strenuous to cock, the Jumbo shoots consistently and is quite accurate.

P10

Data: 4.5mm, 14.1in overall, 7.7in rifled barrel, 2.32lb.
Features. No safety; the trigger is comprehensively adjustable; and the loading port opens automatically.
Power: 399fs^{-1} with H&N High-Speed Match (2.58fp). Reasonably easily charged, the P10 shoots unusually consistently and is very accurate.

neither particularly easy to cock nor especially powerful, but its compactness is advantageous. The guns initially had fixed sights set for 10 metres, but the latest Jumbo Target (dating from 1983) has a fully adjustable back sight on a fluted top-rib.

FIOCCHI

Fiocchi Munizioni SPA (I-22053 Lecco, Via Santa Barbara 4, Italy) is perhaps best known for its ammunition. However, the company also markets a series of pistols — including Free, standard and rapid-fire designs and an airgun designed by Gian Piero Pardini. The Fiocchi-Pardini P10 is the third of a trio of effectual Italian-designed single-stroke pneumatics which has challenged the domination of the Feinwerkbau spring-piston pistols in European competition shooting. The P10 is an underlever-charger, using a trigger-guard lever to force air into the valve chamber on the closing stroke. It has a vibrationless striker-operated valve system and is easier to charge than either the Air Match CU650 or the FAS AP604, as the length of the underlever gives better mechanical advantage. Consistency is high, accuracy is excellent and the trigger is superb; the result is an interesting, elegant design that took the gold medal at the 1983 European championships in Budapest. Importer: Hull Cartridge Company (for address, see 'Weihrauch').

GALWAY

Perhaps best known for its excellent silencers and sound moderators, the Galway Arms Company (5A Springbank, Medbourne, nr Market Harborough, Leicestershire) also makes small quantities of the good-quality Fieldmaster rifle, perfected by Jack & John Fletcher and placed on the market in 1983. The Fieldmaster Mark 2 is a reservoir-type pneumatic, replenished from an air cylinder, and can fire up to 50-60 shots per charge. Power can be set to exceed 12fp by a wide margin, and one important aspect of the design is the ease with which the barrels can be changed. Generally supplied in 4.5 or 5.5mm, 5.05mm can also be obtained to special order. The quality of the metalwork and the high-comb walnut custom stock of the rifles is extremely good, as befits a bespoke product.

▷

An early prototype of the Galway Fieldmaster, this displays the elegant lines that have made the rifle popular among field shooters. The Fieldmaster II exhibits numerous detail differences, and is usually encountered with one of the company's excellent silencers. By courtesy of the Galway Arms Co.

FIELDMASTER II

Data: 4.5 and 5.5mm, 39.0in overall, 20.0in barrel, 7.04lb without sights.
Features. No safety; an adjustable trigger; and a rotating-bolt cocking/loading system.
Power: 658fs^{-1} with RWS Hobby (11.52fp). Super-power FAC versions are also available. Reasonably easily cocked, the rifle is a consistent and accurate performer.

GECADO

This brandname, owned by G.C. Dornheim of Suhl prior to 1940, is now associated with M&G Diana guns made for certain regional German and export markets.

GECO

A brandname used by Gustav Genschow & Co. AG of Berlin: founded in 1887, purchased by Dynamit Nobel in 1959 and merged with the parent company in 1962. Geco brand rifles were made by Mayer & Grammelspacher and handled by Dynamit Nobel. The RWS brand is now favoured instead.

GUNSPORT

This company (125-127 Wellgate, Rotherham, South Yorkshire S60 2NN) makes Ox mainsprings, the Quikrest bipod, and the 'Stealth' and 'Super Stealth' combination sight/silencer systems. The Maximiser kit for the HW77 (q.v.) comprises a special mainspring, two compression limiters, a stainless steel spring-sleeve, specialist lubricants and suitable instructions to smooth the action of the standard Weihrauch rifle. Though considerable improvement can be made, with a reduction in vibration and an appreciable improvement in consistency, care should be taken to ensure that the resulting super-efficient rifle does not exceed 12fp (which even the ex-factory HW77 may nudge uncomfortably).

Gun Toys makes a series of spring-piston airguns sharing a similarly unsophisticated action.

GUN TOYS

Gun Toys SRL (Milano, Italy) makes low-cost barrel-cocking pistols and pistol-carbines from a collection of alloy and synthetic parts. Though quality is well below that of some of the similar German guns (cf., FB-Record, Em-Ge), the Italian products have been marketed aggressively in Britain and are surprisingly common. The RO71 is the most basic design, with a diecast frame/air cylinder unit and separate plastic thumbrest-style grips. However, the gun also features a replaceable-element tunnel front sight and an adjustable back sight based on M&G Diana practice; though performance is only adequate, and the guns are virtually incapable of repair when they break, value for money is truly outstanding. Currently marketed as the Scalemead Hotshot Standard‡, the RO71 has inspired many novice airgunners to better things. The one-piece synthetic grip/frame of the RO72 (Scalemead Hotshot de Luxe*) improves balance and handling qualities, and the action offers slightly greater power. The RO76 carbine has an oddly shaped hardwood stock with a separate pistol grip, while the RO77 pistol-carbine's most distinctive features are the lengthened barrel and rod-type shoulder stock screwed directly into the receiver end-cap. The RO80 is a minor variation of the RO72, with a plain receiver end-cap and other detail differences, and is usually encountered with a grey rather than black butt.

RO72
Data: 4.5mm, 14.2in overall, 7.2in rifled barrel, 2.34lb.
Features. An automatic safety and a trigger adjustable for travel only.
Power: 352fs⁻¹ with Eley Wasp (2.09fp). Note: power can fluctuate appreciably from gun to gun. The cocking stroke is reasonably easy, but consistency and accuracy are rarely impressive.

‡ Also known as the Bullseye, Sussex Armoury Panther, Classic and IGI202.
* Also known as the Super Bullseye, Sussex Armoury Panther de Luxe, Classic de Luxe and IGI203.

2

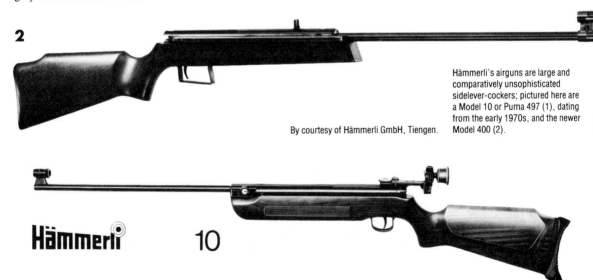

By courtesy of Hämmerli GmbH, Tiengen.

Hämmerli's airguns are large and comparatively unsophisticated sidelever-cockers; pictured here are a Model 10 or Puma 497 (1), dating from the early 1970s, and the newer Model 400 (2).

Hämmerli 10

HÄMMERLI

Hämmerli Jagd- und Sportwaffenfabrik und Apparätebau GmbH, D-7890 Waldshut-Tiengen, Postfach 1147, West Germany. The reduction of Hämmerli-made airguns to this section, after enjoying full manufacturer status in earlier editions (see TAB2, pp.73-5, and TAB3, pp 120-1), arises from the infrequency with which they are now seen in Britain. Though the 400-series spring-piston guns are still available in Germany, the production line of the well-known gas-powered pistols was destroyed by fire in 1977 and work has never resumed. The sidelever-cocking rifles of the 490 series (introduced in 1971), lacking any form of sidelever safety, were replaced by the improved Model 400 in 1978. The Model 400 is the standard version; the Model 401 has a fully adjustable back sight; the Model 402 is suitable for optical sights only; and the Model 403 is a target-shooting version with a Weihrauch-type aperture sight, a sliding butt-plate and an optional barrel sleeve. (Beware: some guns advertised in Britain as 'Model 403' are actually the 402-pattern fitted with aperture sights and are identifiable by the fixed plastic butt-plate.) Discontinued in the early 1980s, the Model 420 had an olive-green military-style ABS stock with an integral pistol grip. The Hämmerlis are large guns, with very plain stocks and — surprisingly — no sidelever-locking catch. They are only available in 4.5mm and are comparatively low powered.

HARPER CLASSIC GUNS

Northridge, Preston Road, Gawcott, Buckinghamshire MK18 4HS. This company converts Weihrauch, Sharp and other rifles to 0.25 calibre, generally by boring out the existing rifling and inserting a specially micro-rifled brass liner. A reduction in the rifling pitch, to one turn in eight inches, increases the spin (and, therefore, the stability) of the comparatively slow-moving pellets. Guns incorporating this rifling are advertised as 'Super Spin', e.g., Weihrauch SS80K. Air canes and the '3D' cartridge-type guns are also being made.

HARRINGTON

T.J. Harrington & Son Ltd. of Magda Works, Walton-on-Thames, Surrey, has made the popular telescoping-barrel Gat pistol since the early 1950s. The Gat is a low-cost cast alloy design, available in black or nickel finish and usually sold in a pack containing pellets, darts and corks — which it will fire with equal facility. A safety catch was added in 1984 to satisfy the American market. Though the gun suffers all the problems associated with this class of pistol, the most notable of which is the change of gravity and jerk as the barrel runs out on firing, it has certainly provided the foundation on which the subsequent enthusiasm of many a British airgunner has been based. Harrington apparently intends to introduce a junior rifle built on the same principles towards the end of 1987, but, at the time of writing, no further details are available.

GAT
Data: 0.177, 9.0in overall with barrel extended, 6.0in smoothbore barrel, 1.12lb.
Features. A manual safety catch on the latest guns; removable breech-plug; a fixed trigger.
Power: not known.

HEALTHWAYS

Beginning in 1955-6, Healthways — latterly in Compton, California — made gas-powered BB pistols to the patents of Richard Kline and Kenneth Pitcher, as well as a spring-piston gun known as the Topscore 9100. The Healthways Plainsman and Plainsmaster pistols were made in two calibres, 0.175 (BB) and 0.22, with magazines containing 100 and 40 balls respectively. The guns are still occasionally seen, but production and distribution has apparently ceased.

HY-SCORE

The numerical designations of the Mayer & Grammelspacher, BSF, Hämmerli and other European spring-piston guns distributed in the USA by this now defunct company — formerly trading in Brooklyn, New York — were listed in the previous edition (p.122). In addition, Hy-Score manufactured surprisingly effectual spring-piston pistols designed in 1938-46 by Andrew Lawrence and Stephen Laszlo. Trials have shown that surviving

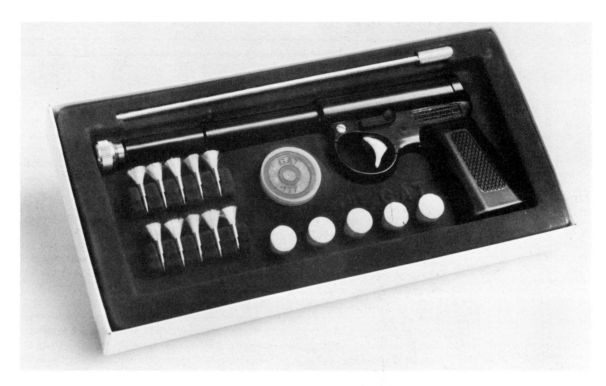

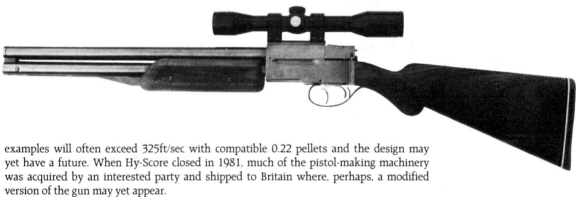

examples will often exceed 325ft/sec with compatible 0.22 pellets and the design may yet have a future. When Hy-Score closed in 1981, much of the pistol-making machinery was acquired by an interested party and shipped to Britain where, perhaps, a modified version of the gun may yet appear.

IMPERIAL AIR RIFLE COMPANY

The first product of this company (which can be reached through The Airgun Centre, q.v.) was announced in March 1987. Designed by Michael Childs, best known for the Skan chronoscopes, the 'Double Express' is a unique multi-stroke pneumatic rifle with twin bores in a single barrel housing – 0.177, 0.22, 0.25 or any combination of two – and a shotgun style twin-trigger system that allows either barrel to be fired first. The Double Express offers the 'fastest two shots in the airgun world without recharging or reloading', as a maximum of ten pump strokes charges both reservoirs at once. The gun is loaded by pressing a lever atop the breech and swinging the breechblock aside. Two pellets are inserted, one in each bore, and the block is closed. Pushing the large brass catch protruding from the back of the action then automatically seats the pellets in the rifling and sets the triggers. The Double Express has a very shotgun-like appearance, arising from the separate pistol-gripped butt and the twin triggers. Quality is excellent, the guns being built on a semi-custom basis at the rate of fifty a year; though they are expensive, they will undoubtedly become one of the most desirable airgun status symbols.

DOUBLE EXPRESS

Data: 4.5, 5.05, 5.5 or 6.35mm (or any combination of two), 37.6in overall, 17.7in rifled barrels, 7.55lb without sights.
Features. No safety; adjustable double triggers; bolt-type cocking/loading system.
Power: up to 12fp with multiple pump-strokes, though super-power FAC versions can be obtained. Pumping is quite arduous, but the guns are accurate and consistent shooters.

ITALGUNS (IGI)

Italguns was essentially a wholesaler, a constituent of Ravizza Caccia Pesca Sport SpA. Its airguns, a list of which was given on p.122 of the Third Edition, were bought from Gun Toys, Molgora, Air Match or FAS and are considered separately.

IZHEVSK MACHINE FACTORY

The Soviet plant in Izhevsk, apart from making smallarms, also makes considerable quantities of the barrel-cocking IZh-38 spring-piston rifle — exported to the West by V/O Raznoexport of Moscow as the Baikal or Vostok. This 4.5mm rifle is obviously intended for juveniles, as it has a small action and a very short butt. Befitting the ultra-low price, quality is comparatively poor: the IZh-38 is a typical Russian product, crude but sturdy, and is accompanied by a kit of spare parts. Accuracy is uninspiring, while power is low and erratic: rifles selected at random gave average muzzle velocities of 410-498fs^{-1} with Marksman pellets (3.08-4.55fp). Claims are sometimes made that the Vostok is 'powerful' with velocities 'up to 700fs^{-1}', but these are wildly optimistic; none of the test guns was as powerful as the BSA Scorpion pistol. The most distinctive feature of the IZh-38 is the stock shape, though the radial breech-locking lever inlet in the left side of the barrel block is also noteworthy.

IZh-38
Data: 4.5mm, 40.7in overall, 17.9in rifled barrel, 5.29lb.
Features. Automatic safety; a radial breech-lock on the barrel-block; a travel-adjustable trigger.
Power: see text. Easily cocked, the action is, however, inconsistent and accuracy is usually only fair.

◁ The Harrington Gat is usually sold in a kit containing corks, darts, pellets and an ejector rod.

◁ Distinguished by twin bores in a single barrel tube above the pump-housing, the unique shotgun-like Imperial Double Express is the premier British representative of the multi-stroke pneumatic genre. By courtesy of *Airgun World*.

JUARISTI

The barrel-cocking spring-piston guns made by Armas Juaristi of Eibar in Spain, under the brandnames Ideal-Extra and Super-Especial, have never been distributed in Britain during the currency of *The Airgun Book*. Quality is believed to parallel Bascaran's.

MANCHESTER AIR GUNS (MAG)

Like many other British airgun distributors, this company (trading from 470 Oldham Road, Failsworth, Manchester M35 0FH) has promoted its 'own' guns. Obtainable in the early 1980s, the MAG Mercury Magnum was an otherwise standard BSA Mercury III modified to 0.20 or 0.25 calibre.

MANUARM

These French spring-piston airguns, believed to be made by Manufrance SA (31-57 Cours Fauriel, F-42033 St Etienne), have been distributed in Britain by L.J. Cammell (Merseyside) Ltd — makers of Champion-brand pellets — and its affiliate, Cobra International Arms Ltd. The inexpensive barrel-cocking pistol features a large number of alloy parts, but the barrels are well rifled, the sights are surprisingly effectual and the two-stage ball-sear trigger gives a crisp (but rather stiff) action. The black plastic grips display amazingly fine-quality chequering, while velocity is higher than may be anticipated at the price. A carbine sharing an essentially similar action is encountered but rarely.

PISTOLET MANUARM
Data: 4.5 and 5.5mm, 14.3in overall, 7.3in rifled barrel, 2.71lb.
Features. No safety, though the trigger is adjustable.
Power: 5.5mm: 369fs^{-1} with Champion Standard (4.32fp). Reasonably arduous to cock, the Manuarm shoots reasonably consistently and is acceptably accurate.

MARKSMAN

Marksman Products, Inc. (then of Torrance, California), made gas-operated pistols to the Harris patents until production ceased about 1980. Two inexpensive barrel-cocking spring-piston rifles — the Models 740 and 742 — have also been made and, briefly, the Milbro Diana G80 was sold as the Model 746. Now a Division of S/R Industries, Inc., Marksman Products currently handles Saxby-Palmer airguns and 'Mauser' (i.e., H&N) pellets from a base at 5622 Engineer Drive, Huntingdon Beach, California 92649, USA.

MARSHALL

Peter Marshall designed the Whaley-Crosman (q.v.), thereafter converting Crosman 761XL, 766 and 1377 multi-stroke pneumatics so that the well-proven Crosman valve could serve as an air reservoir. Several constant-velocity shots could then be fired at the expense of some undesirable valve-heating. The guns were only ever made on a limited basis and are no longer available.

MAUSER

Though the well-known Mauser name and banner trademark will be encountered on Mayer & Grammelspacher-made Diana LG30 ball-firing rifles, the connexion is tenuous: the legitimacy of the marking arises from a licence negotiated between Mauser and Umarex GmbH under which the latter may apply the banner mark to blank-firers, airguns, pellets and similar items. Mauser is not involved in production in any way; the 'Mauser' pellets, indeed, are actually made by Haendler & Natermann and the blank-firers usually come from the once-independently owned Reck-Division of Umarex. However, some advertising is sufficiently ill-judged to persuade prospective purchasers that the rifles are Mauser-made. In addition, their 'hunting power' is really no more than a couple of foot-pounds!

The bolt-cocking Diana LG30, widely encountered with 'Mauser' marks, is a low-powered 4.4mm ball-firer often mischievously advertised as developing hunting power. By courtesy of Dianawerk.

▽

MAY

Norman May & Company, formerly trading in Bridlington before liquidation was concluded in 1981, distributed BSF, Hämmerli and Weihrauch rifles in Britain alongside Bimoco pellets. The 'Normay Vixen' was a Weihrauch HW35, 35L or 35E with a special mainspring and detail improvements.

MEYER & SCHAEPPI

This newcomer to the ranks of the airgun makers (CH-5000 Aarau, Kirchgasse 13, Switzerland) announced a sidelever charging single-stroke pneumatic competition rifle at the beginning of 1987. Built with Swiss precision by Carl Schaeppi Sportwaffen of CH-5105 Auenstein, the gun has an unusually deep lever – 'cocking plate' describes it more accurately – pivoted at the front of the hand-made oil-finished walnut stock, and a free-floating barrel whose breech is unencumbered by the breech-sleeve associated

SCHAEPPI TARGET
Data: 4.5mm, 41.3in overall, 21.7in rifled barrel, 10.41lb.
Features. A comprehensively adjustable trigger and Anschütz match sights.
Power: 551fs^{-1} with H&N Match (5.31fp). Reasonably easily charged, the action is impressively consistent and capable of excellent accuracy.

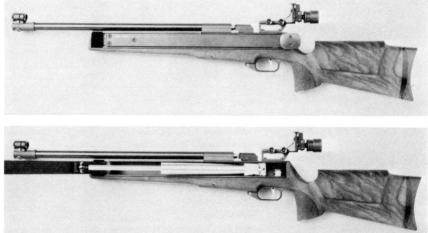

with the spring-piston competition rifles. The breechblock is linked to the cocking lever and moves radially to give access to the chamber. The final movement of the lever cams the breechblock forward to effect an excellent seal. The first series of 25 of these highly desirable guns was completed in the Spring of 1987, with the promise of more to follow. The Meyer & Schaeppi rifle is expensive, at a little under £1,000, but delivers excellent performance.

Typical of Milbro's final innovative, but ill-starred products were the G5 Cougar pistol (1), the Black Major (2), the G85 Bob Cat (3) and the G80 sporting rifle (4).

Sole representative of the Swiss airgun industry, the Schaeppi target rifle is an excellent hand-built single stroke pneumatic. These illustrations emphasize the unusual design of the sidelever (interestingly, on the left of the gun) and the radially pivoting breechblock. By courtesy of Carl Schaeppi.

MILBRO

The collapse of Milbro Ltd (formerly Millard Brothers Ltd), then Britain's third largest airgun maker, is an indictment of the British airgunners' readiness to purchase foreign-made guns. Extensive coverage was given to the products in the previous book (pp.134-7) but, five years after Milbro's liquidation, very few of the guns are still to be seen. Some are regarded as collector's pieces while the later ones, owing to the manufacturer's demise, are in no great demand on the second-hand market. It is ironic that the perfected barrel-cocking spring-piston G5 Cougar pistol and the G80 rifle should have had so much more to offer than many of the cheap Spanish and Italian imports. The short-lived Black Major, a cleverly packaged adaptation of the Cougar with a skeletal shoulder stock and a reflector sight system, came too late to repair Milbro's declining fortunes; and the G85/1 Bobcat junior rifle also promised more than it was allowed to deliver. Unfortunately, the guns were all comparatively low powered at a time when BSA and Webley designs were approaching the legal power limits; this alone may have allowed Sussex Armoury, itself a short-lived operation, to make considerable inroads in a market fit for only three major indigenous producers.

MOLGORA

Modesto Molgora (I-20127 Milano, Via del Valtorta 38, Italy) makes an extensive range of toy guns, blank firers and a few cheap airguns under the MMM-Mondial brandname. The barrel-cocking spring-air Oklahoma, Oklahoma N.T. and Zip pistols are made alongside the gas-powered Roger and a selection of cheap rifles. The Zip was seen in small numbers during the mid-1970s, distributed here by Yaffle and others, while the Oklahoma has been sold by Phoenix Arms Company in more recent times. Like the York barrel-cocking rifle (once handled by David Nickerson), the pistols offer comparatively crude cast-alloy construction at very competitive prices. Though virtually incapable of repair, being more-or-less throwaways, Molgora pistols have started many an enthusiast on the airgunning trail.

Typical of the Polish airguns distributed in Britain in the 1970s was this barrel cocking Predom Lucznik Kl.188.

NATIONAL

The products of India's premier airgun maker, National Rifles Ltd (Village-Vinzol, Pin 382445, Ahmedabad), have yet to be extensively distributed in Europe. Labour costs are low in their country of origin, and they could probably be imported very competitively. Products include the Hämmerli-like gas-powered Cadet, made on machinery imported from West Germany; the National-25 and National-35 barrel-cocking spring-piston rifles inspired by Mayer & Grammelspacher practice; and a comparatively new National-35L sidelever-cocker.

NSP

These guns represented an intermediate stage between the Sussex Armoury Jackal rifles and the current Air Arms range, NSP Development & Manufacturing Engineers being the latter's parent company. A few 'NSP Jackals' and 'NSP Sporters' were sold in the period immediately after the collapse of Sussex Armoury.

Molgora makes a series of simple guns under the MMM-Mondial banner, some of which are pictured in these extracts from the company's 1983 catalogues. By courtesy of Modesto Molgora.

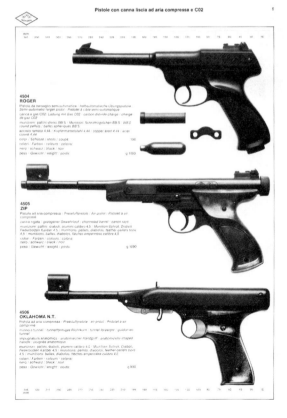

3

2

Rossi airguns are rarely seen in Britain, though small quantities of the Dione (1) were imported in the late 1970s. The interesting military trainer, the EB-79 (2), and its Mo.82 civilian counterpart (3) have never been seen here.

1

By courtesy of Amadeo Rossi SA.

PHOENIX

The Phoenix Arms Company (Phoenix House, Churchdale Road, Eastbourne, East Sussex BN22 8PX) is best known for distributing Italian- and Chinese-made airguns, together with blank-firers, knives and accessories. During 1987, it is believed, the company will enter the manufacturing scene with products of its own; though no details have yet to be released, they are believed to include a junior spring-piston pistol comparable to the obsolescent Milbro Diana SP50.

PREDOM

Small quantities of these Polish airguns, made by Zaklady Metalowe im Gen. Waltera of Radom under the brandname 'Predom Lucznik', were distributed in the late 1970s by Viking Arms Ltd. Their performance was not especially impressive and, even though they were sturdy and reliable, production had ceased in favour of sewing machines by 1980. The barrel-cocking spring-piston Kl.187 rifle was once reasonably common, together with the essentially similar Kl.188 (which had a Slavia-type locking catch beneath the barrel) and the Kl.170 butt-cylinder pistol copied from the Walther LP.53.

EB-79

Data: 4.5mm, 43.3in overall, 17.0in rifled barrel (excluding smoothbore muzzle extension), 9.92lb.

Features. A carrying handle, a dummy magazine and a simulated flash-hider; no safety; and a fixed trigger.

Power: probably about 570fs^{-1} with standard-weight pellets. Easily cocked.

ROSSI

The products of Amadeo Rossi SA, Metalúrgica e Munições, of P.O.Box 28, 93000 São Leopoldo RS, Brazil, are rarely encountered in Britain. They include three barrel-cocking spring-piston guns: the simple woodstocked Mo.17, or 'Dione'; the Mo. EB-79, which is modelled closely on the Brazilian FN FAL service rifle, complete the with magazine, carrying handle and 'flash hider'; and the Mo.82, a short-barrelled sporting version of the EB-79 lacking the dummy magazine.

RWS

RWS and RWS Diana airguns — made by Mayer & Grammelspacher for Dynamit Nobel and Dynamit Nobel of America, Inc. — are sold in Britain by Leslie Hewett Ltd., distributor of RWS-brand pellets. There are a few minor disparities, the RWS 45 and 50 displaying stocks that differ from their M&G Diana prototypes though the ranges are otherwise generally comparable. The RWS 45 is sold in the USA as the Crosman Challenger 6800, with a stock derived from the now discontinued Diana LG35S. Additional details will be found in the Diana section.

Though the Slavia Tex Model 3 (or vz.086, 1) has been sold in small numbers in Britain by Edgar Brothers, the ball-firing Schmidt HS71 (2) is practically unknown.

Smith & Wesson's Model 80 BB Gun, now out of production, is another of the many guns rarely encountered in Britain.

SCHMIDT

Waffenfabrik Schmidt GmbH (D-8745 Ostheim/Rhön, Nordheimer Strasse 11, West Germany) is much better known for its excellent Western-style cartridge and blank-firing revolvers than its two simple airguns — the HS9A, a cheap telescoping-barrel cocking pattern firmly in the Quackenbush (or Gat) tradition, and a sidelever-cocking ball-firer designated HS71. The HS9A will be encountered in Britain as the Cobra Mustang.

HS9

Data: 4.5mm, 8.3in overall, 5.0in smoothbore barrel, 0.77lb.
Features. No safety; a fixed trigger; and a removable breech-plug.
Power: very low — probably similar to the Gat (q.v.).

SHERIDAN

The bulk of the Sheridan shareholding was acquired by Benjamin (q.v.) in 1976; eventually, as a result of rationalization, the two companies were merged under one roof in the Sheridan factory in Racine.

SLAVIA

Exported by Merkuria of Prague, these guns are made in Uherský Brod in Czechoslovakia. Small numbers of Slavia rifles are occasionally imported into Britain by Edgar Brothers of Macclesfield, but none has been seen for some years. Only the Slavia Tex 086 (or Model 3) barrel-cocking spring-piston pistol has been encountered in the 1980s. This efficient low-cost trainer, based on the ZVP of 1960-72, is solidly machined from good quality forgings and is distinguished by an absence of synthetic parts.

SMITH & WESSON

Though this renowned revolver and automatic pistol maker was once involved with non-powder guns, the production line for the Models 78G and 79G was sold to Daisy (q.v.) in 1980 and the Models 77A (multi-stroke pneumatic) and 80G (gas-power BB Gun) are no longer in production.

SOFT-AIR

Also known as 'Air Soft', this designation covers a selection of Japanese air- and spring-guns. Most of the former feature self-contained air cartridge, not dissimilar in appearance to the Saxby-Palmers but actually a spring-piston system in miniature. These are forced over a special 'cocking block', loaded with a plastic projectile (generally a small ball or a soft synthetic pellet), placed in the gun and fired by pressing the trigger. The revolvers may be fired just as quickly as the trigger is pulled and some of the 'automatics' will auto-load. Accuracy is fair only at short range; power is low. However, the guns are great fun to use and rather more than mere toys — the pellets sting and could do considerable damage to an eye.

The guns range from facsimiles of Lugers, S&W revolvers, Uzi submachine-guns and even a full-size Heckler & Koch G3 to a series of free-form designs that bear a greater resemblance to ray guns. Made by Masudaya, Marubeni, Marusan and others, they are marketed by Battle Orders, Daisy (through SSM) and Scalemead in Britain.

Made by several different Japanese manufacturers, Soft-Air guns come in a great variety; they range from plausible facsimiles of the Heckler & Koch MP5K (1), the Smith & Wesson Model 57 (2), the Ruger Mini-14 (3) and the Remington 870 Wingmaster shotgun (4) to freestyle designs such as the Urchin! By courtesy of Daisy.

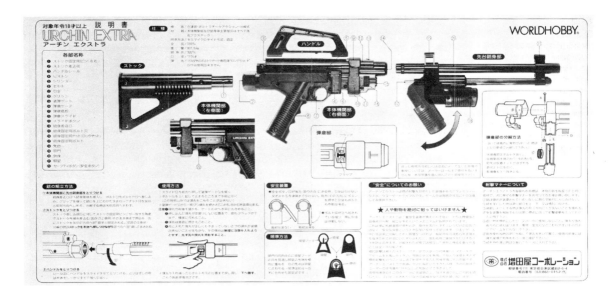

SPORTSMATCH

Best known for its excellent optical sight mounts, this company entered the airgun-making ranks in 1987 with the announcement of the GC-2 reservoir pneumatic, designed by Gerald Cardew and John Ford. Though the design is not as revolutionary as some of its rivals (cf., Theoben Sirocco and Air Logic Genesis), the first guns have been beautifully made of first class materials. The trigger is comprehensively adjustable and complements the muzzle brake, intended to minimize 'muzzle flip', while the superbly made thumbhole-pattern walnut stock gives superb handling characteristics. The butt plate is also adjustable. Though expensive at £850, which includes the air

Coming immediately after the cheap and largely synthetic Soft-Air guns, it is ironic that the Sportsmatch GC-2 reservoir pneumatic should be one of the most sophisticated and expensive of all the British-made air guns. Note the distinctive thumbhole stock and the slotted muzzle compensator. By courtesy of J. & J. Ford Ltd.

GC2

Data: 4.5, 5.05, 5.5, 6.35 and 7.62mm (most to become available in 1988), 43.0in overall, 20.0in rifled barrel, 7.85lb without sights.
Features. Bolt-type cocking/loading system; a comprehensively adjustable trigger; and an integral muzzle compensator.
Power: normally set to deliver about 11.9fp, though super-power variants offer up to 40fp.

The Masudaya Urchin ranks among the oddest-looking Soft Air guns. By courtesy of Battle Orders.

The Sterling, now being made by Benjamin (q.v.), has a most distinctive bolt-action loading system. This British-made HR81 has its back sight on the action block rather than, as in the newer American guns, atop the air cylinder above the bolt.

Sussex Armoury's Jackal Pack included (top to bottom) an early AR7 with a Singlepoint sight, the wood-stocked version of the Jackal Parabellum, the highly controversial ABS-stocked pseudo-military gun, and an experimental target-shooting derivative of the Parabellum with Anschütz competition sights.

bottle, the prototype GC-2 has already taken important field-target shooting honours and looks set to battle with the somewhat similar Air Arms Shamal (q.v.) for overall supremacy.

STERLING

The unwieldy Sterling HR81 (standard) and HR83 (deluxe) underlever cocking spring-piston rifles, loaded through a bolt system, were originally made by the Sterling Armament Company of Sterling Works, Dagenham, Essex. Production ceased in the summer of 1984, the production rights being sold to Benjamin; the current 'Sterling' rifles, made in the USA, are described in the Benjamin section. The original British HR81 had a different underlever design, with nothing more than a ball-type detent, while the back sight lay on the breechblock ahead of the loading port. The HR83 offered an improved longitudinally sliding underlever catch and a better walnut stock, which has been perpetuated by Benjamin with minor modifications. British-made Sterling rifles were made in comparatively small quantities and enjoyed only a brief period in vogue. Benjamin parts, even assuming they can be obtained, will not necessarily interchange with British ones; the trigger system underwent several changes even during the brief period of British production!

SUSSEX ARMOURY

Founded in 1968 by David Pickering and Richard Marriott-Smith, Sussex Armoury rose to fame through the militaria and replica boom before graduating to blank-firers and own-brand airguns. Though the company collapsed in 1982, to be replaced by (among others) Scalemead and Phoenix Arms Company, the Jackal sidelever-cocking spring-piston rifles have had an important effect on the contemporary British airgun scene. Starting with the Jackal Parabellum of 1977, progressing through the Jackal AR7 to the Jackal Firepower, Hi-Power, Woodsman and Woodstock, the guns subsequently laid the basis for the current Air Arms range. The Sussex Armoury products were assessed in the Third Edition (pp.148-9); the guns were strong, powerful, acceptably accurate and moderately reliable – though this was less true of the original Jackal Parabellums, which suffered an assortment of teething troubles. Jackals are still seen in profusion on the second-hand market; unfortunately, the appreciable changes made to the basic design under the Air Arms banner ensures that few of the modern parts will interchange.

TELLY

Made by FÉG, exported by Artex (POB 1390, H-1390 Budapest), and distributed in Britain by Relum Ltd, under whose brandname they are best known, these Hungarian spring-piston airguns are more common in Britain than the Czech Slavias or even the East German Haenels. Though very competitively priced, Telly rifles are crude by Western European standards and offer very little competition for the BSA Meteor or the El Gamo range. A list of obsolescent models appeared in the Third Edition (p.110), but only four are currently being distributed. The barrel-cocking Zephyr and Rapide are identical apart from calibre (4.5 and 5.5mm respectively), while the Taurus differs from the Rapide principally in a lengthened butt. The Hungarian designations are LP22 4.5mm, LP22 5.5mm and LP27 respectively; or, alternatively, Telly 422, Telly 522 and Telly 527. The Super Tornado or LG15V is a clumsy underlever-cocker offering a double concentric mainspring but, surprisingly, no great power. However, it is quite sturdy, features a rotary loading tap, and has a unique saddle-pattern back sight.

LG15V

Data: 5.5mm, 42.9in overall, 18.9in rifled barrel, 7.78lb.

Features. No safety; a trigger adjustable for sear-engagement and pull-weight; and a double concentric mainspring.

Power: 494fs^{-1} with RWS Diabolo (7.57fp). The gun is usually quite difficult to cock, and is only rarely consistent or particularly accurate.

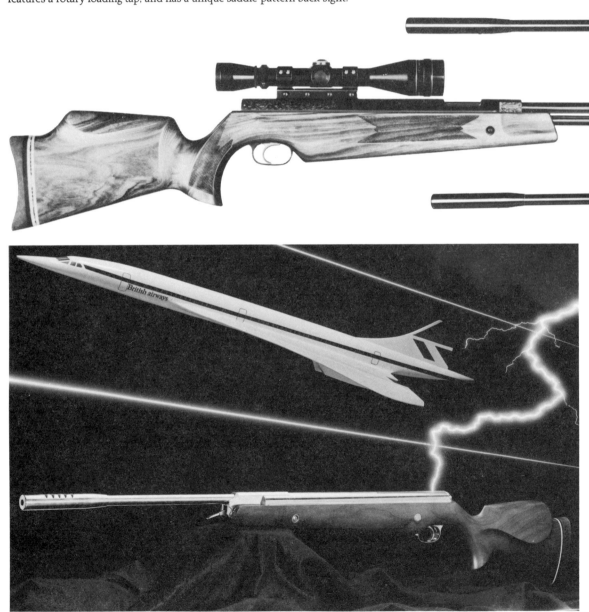

VENOM

Weihrauchs customized by the Venom Arms Company (Unit 1, Gun Barrel Industrial Centre, Hayseech, Cradley Heath, Warley, West Midlands B64 7JZ) include:

'...a modified transfer port; the piston re-machined and fitted with a specially designed high-performance head; a new spring guide tube machined and fitted; the cylinder sized and checked for symmetry; a Venom Swedish steel high performance mainspring fitted; all internal parts correctly lubricated; and the removal of any sharp or rough edges from areas such as the cocking slot, slipper and detent housing.'*

* David Pope, personal correspondence, February 1984.

The work carries a twelve month guarantee, and the mainsprings are unconditionally guaranteed for six months. The results more than justify the outlay, as anyone who has fired a Venom Weihrauch will testify. Though the Weihrauch HW77 is ordinarily easy to

1

2

3

Venom's customized Weihrauchs have attained great popularity since the third edition of *The Airgun Book* appeared in 1984. Shown here are an HW80 Varminter (1), an HW77 Vantage (2) and the latest HW85 Sporter (3). By courtesy of the Venom Arms Co.

In addition to customization work, David Pope and Ivan Hancock of Venom have also developed the Mach One rifle, an expensive but extremely sophisticated barrel-cocker here imaginatively paired with British Airways' Concorde for advertising purposes. By courtesy of the Venom Arms Co.

cock and fire, it is mass-produced and subject to all the problems that this entails: variable tolerances, roughness in some components and poor lubrication, resulting in vibration and spring-noise. The Venom derivations have a notably faster action, and an almost total absence of vibration or noise traceable to the spring/piston train. The current products include the Hunter 80 (or 85) and Vantage 77, with standard stocks, and a selection of more expensive guns including the Custom HW85 and the Venom Trophy. The Trophy is built on a much-modified HW77 action, with a shortened underlever and a knurled cocking grip. A barrel weight and silencer are standard fittings, together with a special walnut stock that deepens appreciably ahead of the trigger-guard to permit the competition-style stance in which the gun is rested on the knuckles or the finger-tips; stippling graces the lengthened fore-end and the pistol grip, the butt-plate is adjustable, and finish is immaculate. Though the Venom Trophy is expensive, it is a veritable king among customized Weihrauchs.

Venom has also converted the new Diana LG52 to 'Trophy' standards, and has refined the full-power version to give the Lazer 52 — distinguished by its elegant sporting-style stock and a muzzle-brake. Not content with this, small quantities of the Mach One barrel-cocking spring-piston rifle are also being made to order; priced at £875, this amazing combination of the finest walnut and stainless steel offers velocities in excess of the speed of sound (hence its name) allied with superb handling characteristics. A barrel-cocker owing something to the HW80, it features a clutch-lever barrel lock inspired by that of the Anschütz LG335 and a special trigger unit with a pull even better than the vaunted Weihrauch Rekord. The Mach One trigger can even be fitted to 'Trophy' Weihrauch conversions on request.

WARD

Ward & Co. (1 Military Road, Colchester CO1 2AA), formerly known as Schaefle, customizes an assortment of spring-piston rifles – Weihrauch HW77, 80 and 85, and the Webley Omega – together with the Sharp Innova multi-stroke pneumatic, all of which are then sold under the Skorpio banner. A particularly useful part of the service is the adaptation of the cocking-lever catch of the HW77 to one-hand operation.

WHALEY

Prior to its demise in 1984, Whaley's of North London distributed appreciable numbers of 'Whaley-Crosman' rifles, based on the Crosman 761XL adapted by Peter Marshall (q.v.). These could be obtained with a number of different stock/finish options – including nickelling, with oak or walnut butts – but the improvements were insufficient to satisfy more than a short-lived multi-stroke pneumatic boom in the early 1980s.

WHISCOMBE

John Whiscombe – another of the highly innovative British experimenters – builds small numbers of a unique double-piston spring-type gun, the prototypes of which were based on BSA Mercury actions. Unlike the Mayer & Grammelspacher Giss patent, whose second piston opposes the movement of the first and contributes nothing to power, the pistons move towards each other in the Whiscombe system and contribute their total swept volume to pellet-propulsion. The mechanism can easily generate 30fp, but its enormous potential has never been exploited on anything other than a limited basis.

YE-WHA

These guns have been made by Tong-Il Industrial Company of Seoul, South Korea, but are rare in Europe. The 3-B Dynamite is a multi-stroke pneumatic of faintly archaic design, still using a longitudinally-sliding foot anchored pump of the type pioneered by Benjamin in the 1920s. However, it can generate velocities of $1,000fs^{-1}$ or more with a 0.25-calibre projectile and a hundred pump-strokes. A mere thirty suffices to 'top-up' for the next shot. The Target 200 was an unlicensed copy of the Feinwerkbau LG150, externally all but indistinguishable from its German prototype but internally crude enough to discourage otherwise-discerning prospective purchasers attracted by its low price. Only a few dozen guns were sold in Britain.

OTHERS

Great difficulty is sometimes encountered tracing custom guns. Recent marques have included the Marauders, conversions of Anschütz 335, Diana LG45 and other spring-piston guns by Worcestershire Black Powder Supplies of Bewdley; the Predator, a 'bullpup' conversion of the Weihrauch HW80 by Kestock Conversions of Rotherham; the Sierra and Sierra Gold range, mostly Weihrauch-based, from the Northern Arms Company of Doncaster; the Piranha and Vixen, variants of the Diana LG38 and LG52 respectively offered by Cindy's Shooting Shop of Heanor, Derbyshire; conversions of the Sharp Ace, among others, by Streatham Armoury of London; and the Hunter, based around the major components of the HW77 by Colchester Airweapon Workshops.

In addition to the custom guns, little information was available at the time of going to press about the 'Duo', an Italian-made top-lever charging pneumatic imported by May & Co.; and the 'Podium' – a Spanish copy of the Crosman 760, occasionally available through Battle Orders but currently out of stock.

Sights

The rapid change in the status of the airgun in the last fifteen years – from child's toy to a serious sporting gun – has been accompanied by a tremendous boom in the sales of optical sights.

The modern telescope sight* consists of a drawn seamless aluminium tube containing a series of lenses and a reticle†, together with, in most systems at least, provision for adjusting the focus and the position of the reticle in relation to the lens system.

The lens – more accurately, a composite of several elements – farthest from the shooter's eye is called the *objective*, which forms the 'primary image'. Were it not for the *erector* lens, this would be perceived upside-down; however, the erector inverts the primary image and presents it to the *eyepiece* from which it enters the eye-pupil. Sights normally incorporate some element of magnification; those that embody variable magnification are called *zoom*, and are almost always heavier and more delicate than fixed-power patterns.

Optical sights suffer several inherent weaknesses, most of which are due to the lenses. As it is all but impossible to grind a single-element lens to avoid all forms of aberration – and even though multi-element lenses can be corrected to minimize their effects – chromatic and spherical aberrations, distortion, field-curvature, astigmatism and a special phemonenon known as 'coma' may all be encountered.

Chromatic aberration arises when a lens cannot focus differing light rays at a single point. Ordinary 'white' light is, in fact, composed of a rainbow, each component having a differing wavelength; each of these will have a different focal length and, if the lens is not corrected, a blurred image with a coloured corona may result. Sandwiches of thin glass are used to unify focus, each layer bending a portion of the light at a different angle.

Spherical aberration results when the many parts of the image cannot be focused at one point; light rays from the margins of the lens are commonly focused ahead of those from the middle, preventing a sharp image, unless corrected by accurate grinding. This must be done without upsetting the essential colour corrections.

Image distortion occurs when the lens or lens-system has been ground in such a way that overall surface magnification is inconsistent, whereupon parts of the image may be twisted or bent.

Field-curvature arises when the erector lens-system (particularly) produces a final image whose margins are out-of-focus when the centre is sharp – or, conversely, whose centre may be poor while the margins are precisely defined.

Astigmatism, common in human eyes, is a condition in which the lens is unable to focus lines that cross each other at widely diverging angles.

Coma occurs when a lens cannot focus light passing through it obliquely, smearing the image outward towards the lens-margins.

Even modern budget-price optical sights, the vast proportion of which emanates from the same three factories in Japan, make some concession to these problems. Generally, the standards of production are high; the performance,

* This designation is preferred to the more common 'telescopic sight'; the body of the sight is fixed rather than telescoping.

† Often wrongly rendered as 'reticule' – which the *Oxford English Dictionary* describes as a small purse or bag. A reticle is strictly a series of intersecting parallel lines, which makes its application to a circle-and-dot questionable! 'Graticule', another widely misunderstood substitute for 'reticle', refers to a grid on a plan or map intended to facilitate use.

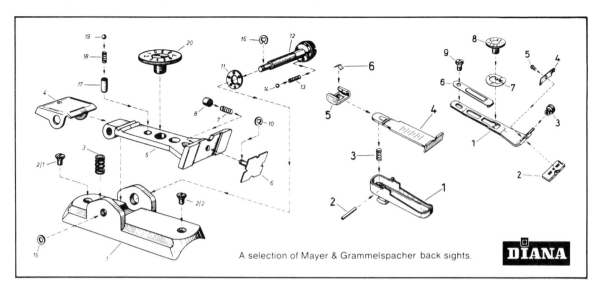

A selection of Mayer & Grammelspacher back sights.

DIANA

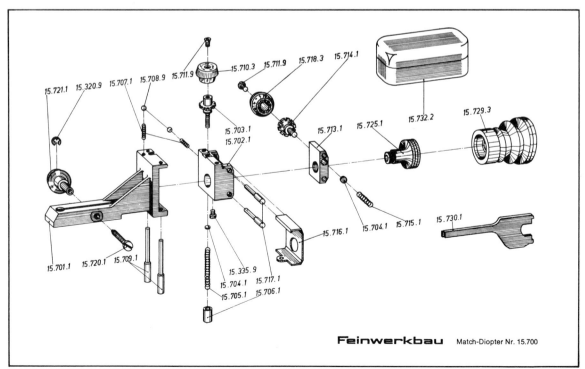

Feinwerkbau Match-Diopter Nr. 15.700

almost always adequate. Naturally, the time and care lavished on the most expensive sights – particularly those made in Germany by Zeiss and Schmidt & Bender, or by any of the leading US manufacturers – is reflected in their price, though there is little doubt that their performance justifies the cost. However, sights are comparatively delicate and it is wise to check a sight carefully before accepting it... particularly should it be second-hand.

Apart from fractured reticles and visible deterioration of the coatings on (or adhesive between) the lens-elements, which will show as fogging or spotting, the following tests are suggested:

i) Check that the image is in focus and that there are no obvious coloured halo or corona effects, particularly around small objects. If these are absent, the lens system has been corrected satisfactorily for chromatic aberration.

ii) Check that the image focuses properly in one plane, and that different parts of it do not focus when adjustments are made. This should indicate that the lenses have been adequately corrected for spherical aberration.

iii) Focus on a brick wall or similar grid-like pattern in the middle distance. Check that the horizontal and vertical lines are straight, and that they are all in sharp focus with no variation across the entire field of view. If the sight passes this examination, the chances are that it has been corrected for image distortion, field-curvature and coma.

iv) Repeat iii, if possible, on a chicken-wire or similar diagonal-link fence. If the strands running from left to right are seen as clearly as those running right to left, then there is no astigmatism in the lens system.

Among the most imporant descriptive terms are 'achromatic', 'aplanatic', 'orthoscopic' and 'anastigmatic' – showing that the systems have been corrected for chromatic aberration; spherical aberration and/or coma; distortion; and astigmatism respectively.

Many marksmen with corrected eyesight may experience additional difficulty with optical sights. This is not so true of contact-lens wearers, who will usually look through the same part of the lens, but spectacle-wearers may look through a different part of their lenses when canting their heads behind the sight. The spectacle lens then interferes with the lens-system in the sight and performance suffers. Some shooters may be unable to focus on the target and the reticle at the same time, though this can usually be overcome by concentrating hard on the target before looking through the sight. Others' eyes may unwittingly cancel out the anastigmatic correction already applied to the lens!

Ideally, it is better to adjust the sight to compensate for deficiencies in eyesight – assuming this is possible – and then discard the spectacles. Unfortunately, this is difficult for those who need the latter permanently; unlike target shooters, who may have prescription lenses inserted in aperture sights, the field shooter has no easy way of achieving optimal performance.

These exploded-view drawings show typical simple Dianawerk back sights, the more sophisticated version being shown in the photograph (1) together with a competing Anschütz pattern (2). Competition rifles feature a diopter sight, a Feinwerkbau drawing of which is also shown.

SIGHT FEATURES

Telescope sights come in hundreds of varieties, offering a wide range of magnification. Advertising literature often sets great store on terms such as 'true magnification', 'enhanced resolution', 'maximum objective lens diameter', 'superior image brightness', 'TV-style field of view' or 'parallax corrected', and it is important to establish whether these have any practical value.

The *magnification* is simply the ratio of the object-size viewed through the sight to that viewed with the naked eye. This can be assessed directly by keeping the second eye open, focusing on the object and comparing the two images. Alternatively, a piece of thin paper can be placed over the eyepiece of a sight pointed at a bright light. Without moving the sight, the paper can be taken backwards; as it moves, the circle of light diminishes until, once a certain point has been passed, it grows again. This establishes the 'eye-point', the optimum distance at which the eye should be placed, and measuring the diameter of the circle of light at its smallest point gives the 'sight aperture'. The magnification of the sight is often expressed by dividing the sight aperture into the diameter of the objective lens.‡

The *resolution* of a lens in a small-diameter telescope is limited by the performance of the human eye. The average eye is capable of resolving detail as fine as a minute of arc (i.e., one sixtieth of one degree), though there is some latitude; some people, for example, can read a notice at considerably greater distances than others with equally 'perfect' vision. To find the potential acuity of the eye when presented with a magnified image, it is simply necessary to divide the minute of arc by the true magnification; thus, a 6× sight would improve the resolution to one-sixth of a minute of arc (10 seconds of arc). Provided the objective lens diameter is sufficient to satisfy this eye-performance – say 12mm – the sights will all perform adequately. Larger objectives make no difference at all to resolving power.

The principal advantage of great *objective lens diameter* is to improve the relative brightness of the lens system and give the firer's eye the maximum possible vertical and lateral movement. It has no effect on magnification. To determine the relative brightness of a particular sight, it is necessary to square the result of dividing the effective objective lens diameter (see cautionary note above!) by the sight aperture. Thus, if we assume that our hypothetical 6× telescope sight has an objective lens diameter of 40mm ('6×40') and a sight aperture of 5mm, then its relative brightness is 64. A 4×20 sight with a comparable sight aperture would return a figure of 16. The transmission of light from the sight, however, is limited by the iris in the human eye, which adjusts to the strength of ambient light. In ordinary daylight, the iris diameter rarely exceeds 3mm and, therefore, any relative brightness greater than 9 is wasted; at dusk, the iris can expand to a little over 5mm for an optimal relative brightness of 25-30. Some of the larger sights will provide relative brightnesses as great as 100; their value lies in an innate ability to allow the eye to resolve detail in conditions where ambient light is insufficient for the fully-opened iris in the eye to see clearly unaided.

A superior *image brightness* is obtained in telescope sights with coated lenses, identifiable by their purple-blue or strawed colour. As much as a third of the incidental light is lost travelling through the lenses of an ordinary sight, partly in the glass itself but mostly by reflection at the air/glass interfaces. Despite matt-black internal finish, this reflected light bounces around the sight-tube and may emerge from the eyepiece to give washed-out colour, ghosting, light-scatter or a generally inferior image.

The widespread application of reflection-reducing lens coatings has undoubtedly improved the transmission of light through the systems and, by inference, the image quality. Instead of losing up to a third of light during the passage, the primary image of a modern coated-lens telescope may lose less than a sixth.

The *field of view* depends not on the size of the objective lens, but on the effective diameter of the eyepiece lens, the magnification and the eye relief. Thus, fitting an enormous objective lens means very little unless the eyepiece lens is commensurately enlarged. The field of view results solely from dividing the angle of view by the magnification. Too restricted a view makes target acquisition difficult; though this has little bearing on field-target shooting,

‡ However, the internal design of some scopes – including those with internal diaphragms or deeply recessed objective lenses – reduces the effective entrance pupil well below the nominal objective lens diameter, with the result that the sight magnification is quoted too optimistically.

where the targets are immobile, the same cannot be said of hunting. The British Army has always accepted that 4× sights offer the best compromise of magnification and field-of-view; the Austrian Bundesheer, conversely, has recently accepted 1.5×, for which its experts claim maximal field of view, reduced body-tremor effects ('shake') and suitability for firing with both eyes open.* Fields of view can be enlarged by increasing the diameter of the eyepiece lens or shortening the eye relief. Moving the eye nearer the eyepiece is less hazardous with airguns than with firearms, on which the sight may be easily driven back into the face if eye-relief is insufficient. A 'TV' or wide-screen image is provided by a rectangular rather than circular objective lens; however, unless this is associated with an enlarged eyepiece (rectangular or circular) or reduced eye-relief, it is a sham. A 'wide screen' sight generally performs no differently to a sight with the same eyepiece diameter and a smaller circular objective lens.

Optical sights come in weird and wonderful variety. Shown here, to no common scale, are a selection of fixed-power examples: (1) a 1.5×15 Dianawerk pistol sight, which requires a lengthy eye relief; (2) a German-made synthetic Uniscope with its integral mount; and (3) a typically low-price 4×20 sight with a one piece folded-sheet mount of a pattern popular among novice airgunners.

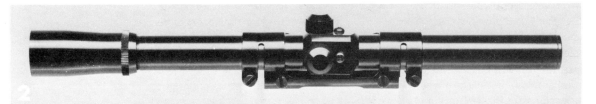

Parallax-free sights do confer some advantages, but these are often overstated. The phenomenon is most noticeable when, with the crosshairs of the reticle on target, the head is moved up and down or from side to side. Parallax occurs if the crosshairs seem to wander over the target as the head moves. Most ordinary telescope sights are parallax-corrected for particular distances — usually 30 yards for airguns. When aim is taken at an object at this precise range, the crosshairs stay motionless on the target independently of head movement. This occurs because the objective lens of the sight is designed to superimpose the primary image on the plane of the reticle and relative movement is impossible. At longer ranges, however, the primary image focuses ahead of the reticle; at short distances, it lies behind.

Adjustable-parallax sights work efficiently provided the firer can gauge range accurately — though their value is reduced appreciably by setting the corrector drum for 25yd when the target is actually 40yd distant. The extent of parallax hysteria may be gauged by realizing that there can be no such effect when the

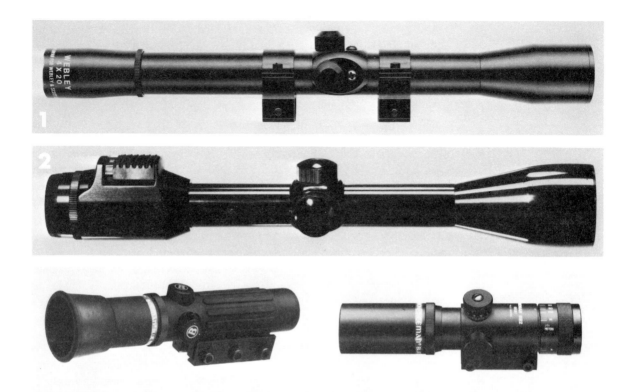

eye, the centre of the reticle and the target-image all lie on the longitudinal axis of the sight: a rifle sight corrected for 300yd would then be as suitable as a 'special' airgun pattern.

Many *reticle designs* are available, some of which incorporate a 'range-finding' facility; this feature is useful in a military sight, all soldiers being much the same size†, but has lesser application to rabbits and is only rarely adjustable to the diameter of the kill-zone on a field target. The most popular reticle is the so-called duplex crosshair – a combination of thick and thin hairs – though standing-post, tapered post and cross-on-circle are among the popular alternatives.

Some sights incorporate a *BDC* ('Bullet Drop Computer') or *PDC* ('Pellet Drop Computer') system on the elevation adjusting-drum cap.‡ A locking screw permits the cap to be rotated to a zero-point without moving the drum itself; the screw is then tightened and the new 'zero' locked in place. Changes in elevation can then be made with reference to a known point, though many airgunners still prefer to estimate the holdover rather than adjust their sights.

† The most popular size (cf., used in the Russian PSO-1 sight) is 5ft 7in. About 75 per cent of men are within an inch of this average, which makes the range-finder useful provided a man is standing up. Most of the 'airgun' range-finding sights developed for firearms were originally designed to accommodate full-grown deer!
‡ Some sights also have the BDC ('Bullet Drift Computer') system on the azimuth adjustor.

TYPES OF SIGHT

Novice airgunners almost always begin by purchasing cheap 4×15 or 4×20 sights. The best of these perform acceptably and – though not perhaps the acme of sophistication – will be sturdy enough to give many years of service. Even 4×15 sights generally offer elevation and azimuth adjustments through click-emitting screws on the top and right side of the reticle housing. These adjustors are protected by screw-on caps or (in at least one case) pivoting plastic sliders. However, the integral mounts are rarely suitable for powerful sporting air rifles unless a supplementary arrestor block is fitted.*

* An arrestor block is a small clamp placed behind the mounts and, where possible, locked into a hole or groove cut into the metal of the receiver. The Weihrauch block has a locking stud, but most alternatives use allen-head bolts.

4×32 and 4×40 are amongst the most popular of the larger 4× sights, the latter being favoured owing to its superior performance in poor light. Fixed-power sights of this group are usually sturdy, effectual and offer good optical performance. Some of the most expensive even offer illuminated reticles, useful when firing against a dark background or in conditions when the reticle is difficult to see.

Optical sights of 4×28 and above are often supplied with detachable lens-caps, the translucent patterns doubling as filters for use on particularly bright days. Others will be encountered with range-finding graticles and projectile-drop computers; some even offer rubberised 'armour', which is useful for field use.

Only the 6×40, 6×42 and 6×45 fixed-power sights are notably popular among the larger magnifications, though 8×56, 8×58, 9×56 and others up to 12× or more may be obtained. There is no denying the virtues of these items, though they magnify body tremors appreciably and are often expensive; consequently, many shooters opt for variable-power systems instead. There has also been something of a move towards compact scopes, such as the excellent Beeman 2.5×16 SS1 and 3×21 SS2 Blue Ribbon patterns or the Bushnell Scopechief series. Shooters all too rarely appreciate that these small sights perform just as well as some of the 'magnum' versions with a consider-able economy of weight.

Among the most popular of the 'zoom sights' is 3-9×, which offers a good range, though 1.5-6×, 1.75-5×, 3-6×, 3-7× and 3-12× are also encountered. Whether large magnification is of any real use to the airgunner is moot, particularly as the effective range of an airgun is only a fraction of that of 0.22in rimfire firearms. However, the 'killing area' on a rat or a pigeon is so small that large magnification may prove a boon in awkward conditions.

Pistol shooters are less lucky, but then the need for such an optical sight is less pressing – particularly in Britain, where hunting with an air pistol is, in

More fixed-power optical sights: (1) a 4×20 Webley sight with two-piece tip-off mounts; (2) a 4×40 Bushnell Banner 'Lite-Site' with self-contained reticle illumination; (3) a compact Beeman SS-1 2.5×16 pattern; and (4) the slightly larger 3×21 Beeman SS-2 sight, with BDC and parallax correction, which offers good performance while economizing on size and weight.

Variable-power or 'zoom' optical sights also come in considerable variety: (1) a 3-7×20 Dianawerk example, with a monoblock mount sliding on a dovetail under the sight body (popular on some older 'own-brand' BSA sights); (2) a 1.5-6× German Schmidt & Bender sight, expensive but offering excellent optical quality; and (3) the renowned Zeiss Diavari-C 3-9×36, which costs more than many complete airguns.

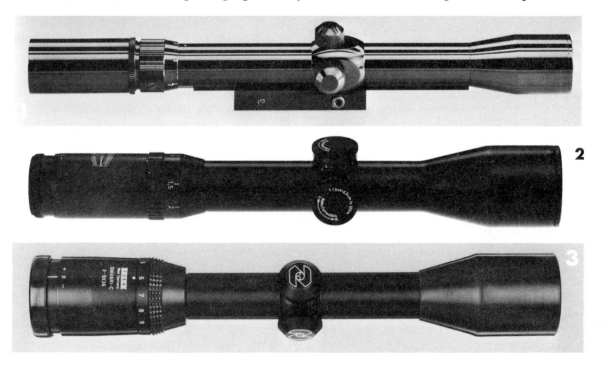

◁

A 3-9×40 rubber armoured sight, popular for fieldwork.

This El Gamo Magnum rifle, with a 3-9×56 ASI sight, shows some of the problems inherent in such large objective lens diameters. Apart from the cumbersome bulk of the sight, which adds appreciable weight to the combination, special high mounts are obligatory. And, if the scope was much longer it would foul the barrel block! By courtesy of ASI. ▽

essence, cruel even if it develops power up to the 6fp. The standard pistol sight is 1.5×15, offering a long eye relief and, as a result, a very restricted field of view. Attempts have been made to mount these sights on the barrel-blocks of barrel-cocking rifles (cf., the Webley Teleskan system or the current El Gamo Hunter), but these have rarely been other than short-lived.

Most of the leading airgun manufacturers offer 'own brand' telescope sights through the courtesies of the principal Japanese contractors, and the differences among the various 4×32 sights – for example – amount largely to markings and external finish. Apart from 'Made in Japan', the sights rarely give a direct clue to their manufacturer. Brandnames include Kassnar and Tasco (distributed in Britain by Gunmark and Webley respectively), Bushmaster, Bisley (distributed by John Rothery [Wholesale] Co. Ltd), Optima (imported by Optima Leisure Products), Shrike (available through Air Arms), Bentley and Nikko Stirling (from Parker-Hale Ltd). In Europe, however, several companies make sights of their own. These include Zeiss and Schmidt & Bender in Germany, or Swarovski-Optik in Austria. Most offer impeccable quality at a high price, and are rarely seen outside competition shooting. Bushnell, Bausch & Lomb and Weaver still make their own lenses in the USA; but, regrettably, there are now no British manufacturers.

Though many of the cheap 4×15 and 4×20 telescope sights are supplied with integral mounts, these are not universally suitable for airguns. Unfortunately, airgun makers still use a variety of dovetail-groove widths and a selection of proprietary mounting rails that demand compatible mounts. This should be investigated *before* buying a telescope sight, even though most patterns larger than 4×28 invariably require separate mounts. The most popular form of mount is a double ring, which can be spaced as far apart as necessary along the dovetail groove to suit the length of the sight and the positioning of the reticle adjusting block. These mounts are simple, cheap and can be obtained in several patterns with base-widths suiting particular makes of gun. The upper part of the split-ring is generally retained by two or four slotted-head bolts, though cap-head bolts are sometimes substituted. Among the best mounts are the German Ernst Apel brand, but they are phenomenally expensive: more expensive, indeed, than some complete air rifles. The tendency is, therefore, towards the cheaper anodised aluminium patterns emanating from Japan. Though these are usually strong enough for their purposes, the finish is not especially durable and care should be taken that the edges of the clamp-rings (which are sometimes surprisingly sharp) do not bite into the telescope-sight body. A ring of tape generally suffices as protection.

▷

A selection of mounts suitable for airguns. Note that the Beeman patterns (1) have a series of adjustor bars suitable for a range of dovetail widths, while some of the Sportsmatch patterns (4) are specifically designed for rifles such as the BSA Airsporter/Mercury series — with a rearward extension — or the Sharp Innova, which requires a cutaway for the loading port. By courtesy of Dr Robert Beeman, Karl Schäfer and J. & J. Ford Ltd.

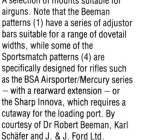

Recently, the excellent range of British-made Sportsmatch sight mounts has found increasing favour. These include some excellent two-piece mounts and some special monoblock patterns whose length usually renders an arrestor block superfluous. Among the best of competing mounts is the massive monoblock originally made for Sterling by H.R. Engineering and now marketed as the 'Supamount'.* Clamped to the rail by four cap-head bolts, two allen-head bolts then tighten the grip by effectively tipping the jaws inwards.

An Austrian Waldläufer Superior 4-12×56 zoom sight, typical of the modern high-power patterns with a large objective lens.

† The 'Supamount' is now marketed by Spot-On Products Ltd of Tottenham, North London.

PROBLEMS

Provided the maker's instructions are followed, mounting telescope sights should be straightforward. However, the barrels of many Weihrauch HW35 rifles angle downwards in relation to the air cylinder on which the optical sight is mounted; similarly, the barrels of many second-hand Webley Hawk rifles may have been bent upwards as a result of heavy use. On these, it is sometimes impossible to align the reticle with the point of impact even at the limit of the sight adjustment. All that can be done is to pack insulating/drafting tape or thin card under the front (Webley) or back mount (Weihrauch) to counteract the barrel angle. The Weihrauchs are rarely so bad that this will not cure the fault, but be warned: old Webleys may be!

Once the sight has been fixed to the gun so that is approximately parallel with the barrel, which can be checked visually, a shot or two should be fired at a suitable large target from a short distance – say five yards – to locate the point of impact. An arrow on the azimuth adjusting screw, marked 'L' or 'R', shows the direction in which the screw must be turned; if the gun is shooting to the left, the desired movement is towards the right and the screw should be turned *towards* 'R' or *away from* 'L'.

Repeating the process to determine vertical displacement (the control drum for which will be marked 'Up' or 'Down' with an arrow) should allow the range should be increased to 10 yards, whereupon ten shots can be fired to establish an approximate group-centre. Adjustments should be made until this coincides with the aim-point, and another ten-shot group fired to confirm that the centre of the new group lies in much the same place as the crosshairs of the reticle. Individual shots may vary, of course, which is why a group should be fired (particularly with a new or freshly re-sprung gun). The process can be repeated at 20 or 30 yards until the desired optimal range-setting is achieved, preferably using a makeshift rest. Shooting at short and intermediate distances establishes the point of impact as early as possible; otherwise, it is quite easy to set up at 30 yards, fire ten shots and miss the target without so much as an idea of the strike-point.

Though optical sights are reasonably durable, they are nonetheless delicate internally. Many sights are filled with nitrogen and attempting to remove the lenses, breaking the seals, not only courts disaster but also understandably invalidates the manufacturers' guarantees. Mistreating the reticle by attempting to force the adjustor screws past their stop point is also quite common, and the flimsier sights may not take kindly to overtightened clamp-rings. Neat rings of tape around the sight-body in the clamps prevents damage to the comparatively delicate anodised finish, while, if necessary, a small sliver of tape in the dovetail groove will minimize 'creep' — a phenomenon associated with the more powerful spring-air guns, whose spring-surge/recoil may cause the sight and mounts to move imperceptibly with each shot. This is more common with two-piece mounts than monoblocks, but is generally cured by adding an arrestor block.‡ On Weihrauchs, for instance, this block locates in a hole drilled into the top of the receiver and acts most positively.

‡ An additional arrestor block may be necessary in front of the mount to counter spring-surge, or because the spring operates towards the firer (e.g., Weihrauch HW45).

Though it may seem all too obvious, it is essential that an optical sight will fit on the gun for which it is intended. Sights with objective-lens diameters exceeding 40mm may require special high mounts, and the bell of super-power sights may foul the back sight or — worse still — prevent the opening of the breech. Care should also be taken that the underside of the mounts allows sufficient rise to accommodate the curve of the airgun cylinder, and that the angle of the jaws is compatible with the design of the dovetail groove.

Alternatives to optical sights include the Daisy Point-Sight 800 (1), a simple reflector unit reliant on ambient light, while the battery powered Tasco-Rama R1 (2) appears to project a red aiming dot when the firer looks through the sight tunnel. The Swedish Aimpoint Electronic Mark 3 (3) is similar to the R-1 but very expensive; however, performance with the optional 3× magnifier tube (4) raises the Aimpoint above most comparable rivals. By courtesy of Daisy and Karl ▽ Schäfer.

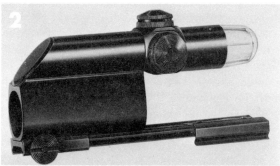

Ammunition

The previous edition of *The Airgun Book* devoted considerable space to a summary of the historical development of the diabolo pellet.* This time, however, a reversion has been made to the detailed register of the first two books.

The diabolo remains supreme even though – in Britain at least – the Prometheus maintains a strong foothold in the market. However, a change in the laws restricting the use of lead will be needed before the comparatively expensive synthetic projectiles gain the ascendancy. The reduction in British formal airgun target shooting in favour of field-target competitions has precipitated a renaissance of 0.22 calibre (5.5 or 5.6mm), though this is confined largely to Britain. Owing to worldwide distribution and the amount of money invested in their development for ISU target-shooting purposes, 0.177 (4.5mm) pellets still offer the best quality.

As had been expected, 0.25 (6.35mm) is still proving unsatisfactory thanks to a poor choice of ammunition and the low velocity attainable within the British legal limit.† No large-volume manufacturer is currently making guns in this calibre, though Cobra International offers a variant of the BSA Mercury IV (as the Cobra Strike Magnum) and Harper Classic Guns converts a selection of guns – usually Weihrauchs – to micro-rifled SS ('Super Spin') standards. Lincoln Jeffries and Milbro still make ammunition in this calibre, as does Haendler & Natermann. The smaller 0.20 pellets (5.0 or 5.05mm), believed by many to offer an attractive weight/power compromise, have still to gain widespread acceptance in Britain. Cammell, Hasuike Seisakusho and Haendler & Natermann all make suitable pellets, while Mayer & Grammelspacher and Weihrauch make guns; despite this, distribution is still greatly restricted.

The 0.22 pellets, which often weigh twice as much as the 0.177 patterns, have a lower initial velocity but usually retain speed better (owing to better sectional density), are less affected by crosswinds and air resistance, and retain greater momentum at long range. Perhaps surprisingly, diabolo pellets – whether 0.177, 0.20 or 0.22 – achieve similar maximum ranges.‡

Velocity can vary greatly, even though pellets may be of similar nominal size; energy can fluctuate even more owing to the additional effects of pellet weight. Pellet selection is very important in the search for optimal performance, particularly in the 0.22 (5.5mm) calibre group: the skirt and head diameters of German-made 5.5mm pellets are often slightly smaller than the true English style 0.22 type.* The latter usually generates lower velocity in German-size bores, owing to increased friction, though the converse is not necessarily true: a small-diameter pellet may begin to move up a large-diameter bore before full working pressure has been generated.

* TAB 3, pp.166-71.

† Generally a maximum of 525-540fs^{-1}, but dependent on pellet weight (cf., 610fs^{-1} and 830fs^{-1} for 0.22 and 0.177 respectively).

‡ The maximum range of British '12fp' sporting airguns is generally reckoned to be about 1,100-1,250ft, but is affected greatly by pellet head-shape and headwinds.

* However, British manufacturers often buy barrels from Anschütz, Hämmerli, Mayer & Grammelspacher and Lothar Walther. Together with the introduction of guns such as the Webley Omega, with a British-made German-dimension barrel, and the production of small-diameter pellets by Cammell and others, the distinction is being slowly (but surely) blurred.

The bores of small-calibre British and German rifles usually measure 0.1770in (4.496mm), with little detectable difference between manufacturers – apart from some older Weihrauch examples, which have been as small as 0.1735in (4.407in). The British 0.22 barrels average 0.2175in (5.525in) compared with 0.2130in (5.410mm) for their German equivalents and, though this disparity may seem small, appreciable performance differences can be expected. Pellets with undersize heads will often tip slightly when they are inserted in the breech and rarely shoot accurately. Undersize, however, is a relative term; and poor behaviour in a large British 0.22 barrel may mean optimal performance in a German 5.5mm.

As manufacturers accept a certain amount of tolerance on their barrel dimensions, variation between guns of the same model is unavoidable. Though bore diameter is held reasonably tightly – five 0.22 BSA Mercury rifles gave a mean dimension of 0.2150 ± 0.0005in – the groove diameter may be somewhat looser (0.2235 ± 0.0010in in these same guns) and the widths of the grooves may also fluctuate. Consequently, the tightest bore will ally minimum bore/groove diameter with the smallest acceptable groove width, while a loose one, at the other extreme, has the largest bore and the widest grooves. While they are nominally the same calibre, the amount of friction generated with constant-size pellets will clearly vary and it is unreasonable to expect velocity to be identical. Accuracy, however, may be unchanged.

Coverage: the material below lists the salient characteristics of the most common pellets. However, the periodic absences of foreign ammunition from the British market hinders assessment of quality changes, and a tendency for airgun makers to market 'own brand' ammunition made elsewhere can be confusing. Synonyms are listed where appropriate. The abbreviation MLV – maximum legal velocity – notes the highest figure attainable within the British 12fp limit. As it is based on the average pellet weight, individual shots may still exceed the limit; similarly, as pellet weights vary (in some cases surprisingly greatly), a suspiciously high-velocity shot may actually be *below* 12fp.

Discontinued lines. Like airguns, pellets come and go. Some are acclaimed as innovative, but encounter little success and soon disappear; a few alter character when their distributorships change; others have vanished after the collapse of their manufacturer. The most notable casualty in the 1980s has been Bildstein, Mommer & Co., maker of Bimoco pellets, which disappeared after the liquidation of its principal British distributor (cf., the affairs of BSF). Lanes has undergone a fundamental change of management in recent years and now concentrates only on a single pellet type rather than a dozen or more. Apart from the reconstituted rump of the former Milbro organization, Milbro Caledonian Pellets Ltd, no new manufacturers have made much of an impact on the airgun scene since the Third Edition. Gunpell Ltd 'clones' pellets – selecting and sizing them for competition use – but is not truly a manufacturer.

ARIZMENDI

Norberto Arizmendi SA of Eibar, Spain, promotes a selection of conventional 4.5 and 5.5mm German-style flathead diabolos under the Norica and Commando brandnames.

BARBERBLADEFABRIK

Available through the Abbey Supply Company, Reading, Berkshire.

PALLET

The roundnose Pallets, made by a unique process, are attractively priced and perform competently – though rather too short in the body to achieve outstanding accuracy. Synonyms: Black Box, Abbey Diabolo. 4.5 and 5.5mm; packed in boxes of 500. Weight: 8.21 and 14.13gn (MLV 811 and 618fs^{-1}). Length: 0.203 and 0.244in.

BASCARAN

C. y T. Bascaran SRC of Eibar, Spain, makes a semi-roundhead ribbed-body 4.5mm 'Cometa' diabolo pellet. This is believed to be similar to Lanes' old Beatall. Synonym: Nickerson or Lincoln Diabolo.

BENJAMIN

Benjamin Rifle Company, Racine, Wisconsin, USA.

HI-COMPRESSION

These pellets are generally regarded as inferior to the Eley Wasp, though the higher-than-normal sectional density of the 0.177 type partly offsets its head shape. The head diameters are much smaller than usual (0.174 and 0.213in) and H-C pellets do not always perform well in guns with 'English' 5.6mm bores. Manufacturing quality is good, however, and the pellets are very popular in the USA. 0.177 and 0.22in; packed in tins of 250 and 500. Weight: 9.40 and 14.26gn (MLV 758 and 615fs^{-1}). Length: 0.210 and 0.250in.

SHERIDAN DIABOLO

This ribbed flathead diabolo was developed for the Sheridans, but also suits any of the 5.05mm European rifles. 0.20in; packed in flip-top plastic boxes of 500. Weight: 13.10gn (MLV 642fs^{-1}).

SHERIDAN SLUG

A parallel-side pointed hollow-base slug with a raised basal 'driving band', used almost exclusively in the powerful Sheridan Model C, this has a good ballistic coefficient and retains velocity well. Synonym:

Bantam. 0.20in; packed in flip-top plastic boxes of 500. Weight: 15.14gn (MLV 597fs^{-1}). Length: 0.270in.

CAMMELL

L.J. Cammell (Merseyside) Ltd, 53 Borrowdale Road, Moreton, Wirral, Merseyside, England, markets 'Champion'-brand pellets through Cobra International (Directory Two, q.v.). Many of those tested for the earlier editions exhibited fluctuating tolerances that belied their excellent-looking manufacturing quality, and the meagre head diameters caused considerable problems in the British-style 5.6mm rifles. In addition to its own-brand pellets, Cammell makes ammunition for companies such as Webley (Flying Scot) and BSA (Fieldsman and possibly also the new Huntsman), as well as for export.

ALOUETTE

Intended for field target competitions, this roundhead has a comparatively long body and a short, flattened nose; accuracy is above average, owing to the distance between the bearing surfaces. 0.177 and 0.22in; packed in tins of 250 and 500.

BALLISTIC

This interesting pellet contains a hard steel ball within a lead outer shell. There is a short flared skirt, no fewer than four sealing rings and a hemispherical head. Sectional density is better than rival designs, excepting the H&N Barracuda. 0.22in; packed in tins of 200. Weight: 17.87gn (MLV 549fs^{-1}).

FLYING SCOT

Made specially for Webley, this semi-flathead features a multi-ring seal and a short ribbed skirt. Some samples have exhibited small head diameters, and seem to perform better in the Omega than older Webley rifles. 0.177 and 0.22in; packed in tins of 500. Weight: 7.30 and 13.92gn (MLV 859 and 622fs^{-1}). Length: 0.202 and 0.248in.

HUNTER

Now not unlike H&N Pointed, this replaced an earlier pellet with a peculiarly flattened semi-point. (The short-lived 'Hunter II' had a very broad head band on which lay a thin peripheral sealing ring.) Head diameters as small as 0.170in have been encountered in the 0.177 version. Packaged in tins of 450 (0.22) or 500 (0.177). Weight: 7.45 and 13.48gn (MLV 851 and 633fs^{-1}). Length: 0.258 and 0.270in.

△ The Abbey Diabolo pellets, made in Denmark, have appeared in many types of packaging – most recently, in these transparent-top plastic 'tins'.

POLARIS

This copy of the 5.5mm Silver Jet, well made with a triple-ring head, has a rather longer ribbed skirt than its Japanese prototype. Packed in tins of 250.

SPECIAL 25

A heavyweight 0.25 variation of the Hunter (q.v.), this has a poorer ballistic coefficient than the 0.22 pattern owing to its lower sectional density. Packed in tins of 350.

STANDARD

This classically English roundhead has been made for some years. Performance is unspectacular, but the price is keen and the Champion Standard represents good value for money. It has also been made in 0.20-calibre (10.54gn, 0.256in long), but some batches had particularly small head (0.190in) or skirt (0.195in) diameters and did not always seal properly in the bore. Additionally, the head diameter of pre-1985 0.177in pellets could be as small as 0.171in. Synonym: Nickerson Roundhead. 0.177 and 0.22in; packed in tins of 250 and 500. Weight: 7.41 and 14.30gn (MLV 853 and 614fs^{-1}). Length: 0.212 and 0.267in.

TIGER

A twin-ring roundhead pellet with a ribbed skirt, the Tiger is comparatively new and, as yet, little seen. 0.177 and 0.22in; packed in tins of 250 and 500.

CROSMAN

Crosman Air Guns, East Bloomfield, New York State, USA. Distributed in Britain through Crosman (UK) Ltd.

CHALLENGER

This plain-skirt match pellet has yet to be seen in Britain, though it is said to offer world-class performance. Weight: 7.96gn. Length: about 0.210in.

COPPERHEAD

These pellets feature a ribbed sub-diameter medial ring and a semi-conical/roundhead nose-shape. Performance seems to be no better than average, despite the distinctive design, but manufacturing quality is good. Packaging: flip-top plastic boxes of 175 (0.22) and 250 (0.177).

DAISY

Daisy Manufacturing Company, Rogers, Arkansas, USA; distributed in Britain by SSM International Trading.

DAISY DIABOLO

A conventional ribbed-skirt flathead, now known as the 'Quicksilver', this is made in several differing grades up to International Match. Daisy also makes 0.177 roundhead and 0.22 cone-point pellets, introduced in 1986 but as yet rarely seen in Britain. Packed in flip-top boxes of 250 (0.177 and 0.22) or 500 (0.177 only). Weight: 7.47 and 14.47gn (MLV 850 and 611fs^{-1}). Length: 0.206 and 0.256in.

DYNAMIT NOBEL

Troisdorf/Oberlar, West Germany. UK distributor: Leslie Hewett Ltd,

Upton Cross, Liskeard, Cornwall. Dynamit Nobel makes uniformly excellent quality pellets under the RWS brand.

RWS DIABOLO
An excellent long-body ribbed-body flathead diabolo with a distinctive reinforced base, chosen as an 'industry standard' for *The Airgun Book,* this is ideal for general-purpose, practice or low-grade competition use. 4.5 and 5.5mm; packed in tins of 500. Weight: 7.91 and 13.96gn (MLV 826 and 622fs^{-1}). Length: 0.209 and 0.254in.

RWS HOBBY
A lighter, cheaper version of the RWS Diabolo offering similar construction but rather poorer quality, this paradoxically finds greater favour among field-target shooters owing to its higher velocity. 4.5 and 5.5mm; packed in tins of 500. Weight: 7.02 and 11.98gn (MLV 876 and 671fs^{-1}). Length: 0.205 and 0.255in.

RWS MEISTERKUGEL
These are conventional plain-body flathead competition pellets, made in several differing grades but all offering outstanding quality. At the

Los Angeles Olympic Games, for example, 80 per cent of marksmen used RWS Meisterkugeln — including the winner of the men's rifle event, whose 594 × 600 then constituted a new world record. A 5.5mm Meisterkugel (13.59gn, 0.257in overall) was made briefly, but is rarely encountered in Britain. 4.5mm; packed in tins of 250 and 500, or selected 100-pellet trays. Weight: 8.39gn (MLV 802fs^{-1}), pistol type 7.80gn (MLV 832fs^{-1}). Length: 0.217in.

RWS SUPERDOME
Dynamit Nobel's first English-style pellet offers a German-style long body, good accuracy and above-average retention of velocity. 4.5 and 5.5mm; packed in tins of 500. Weight: 8.35 and 14.57gn (MLV 804 and 608fs^{-1}). Length: 0.225 and 0.291in.

RWS SUPER-H-POINT
Claimed to be ideal for pest control, this comparatively new hollow-nose 'truncated Superpoint' is intended ensure adequate penetration and maximum shock transmission. Its inspiration is clearly the H&N Semi-Wadcutter (q.v.)! 4.5 and 5.5mm;

packed in tins of 500. Weight: 7.30 and 13.63gn (MLV 860 and 629fs^{-1}). Length: 0.224 and 0.286in.

RWS SUPERPOINT
One of the best of the pointed pellets, this is distinguished by its unusually thin-walled skirt and accurately made spire tip. As the pellets dent easily during transit, care should be taken when using them. The heads may be too small (0.213in) for British-bore guns. 4.5 and 5.5mm; packed in tins of 500. Weight: 7.90 and 14.57gn (MLV 826 and 608fs^{-1}). Length: 0.272 and 0.337in.

RWS KUGELN
Dynamit Nobel still makes a selection of polished- and coppered-lead balls for repeating air-rifles such as the Anschütz LG275. Only sizes 7 and 9-12 are made, their diameters being officially listed as 4.30 (0.169in) and 4.40 to 4.55mm (0.173-0.179in) in 0.15mm increments; weights are 7.10gn (no.7, MLV 872fs^{-1}, plain finish only), 7.87gn (no.9, MLV 829fs^{-1}), 8.04gn (no.10, MLV 819fs^{-1}), 8.22gn (no.11, MLV 810fs^{-1}) and 8.49gn (no.12, MLV 797fs^{-1}).

ELEY
Eley Ltd, Box 705, Witton, Birmingham, England, makes the popular Wasp, perhaps the best known of the true English-style roundheads. In addition, Eley has made the Webley GP roundhead (nominal weight 7.3 and 14.3gn in 0.177 and 0.22 respectively), as well as experimenting with a 'Field Special' 0.177 pellet weighing 9.25gn. The 'Eley Match' pellet, however, is made by H&N.

WASP
The timeless Wasp ribbed-body roundhead has lost none of its appeal — partly owing to its attractive price, but also to its excellent velocity-retaining qualities, consistency of manufacture and exemplary accuracy. Synonym: BSA Pylarm (the Scalemead Mosquito is similar, but heavier at 14.41gn). 0.177 and 0.22in; packed in tins of 250 and 500. Weight: 7.34 and

A selection of the popular Dynamit Nobel-made RWS pellets. Note the individually packed match pellets in the left foreground. By courtesy of Leslie Hewett Ltd.

14.27gn (MLV 857 and 615fs⁻¹), though older 0.177 batches were often heavier: 7.61gn (MLV 842fs⁻¹). Length: 0.204 and 0.248in.

EL GAMO

Industrias El Gamo SA, Sant Boi de Llobregat, Barcelona, Spain (British distributor: ASI), makes a selection of diabolo pellets; weight fluctuations are usually minimal, but the pellets often display small head diameters (e.g., Magnum sample, 0.174in) and the tins contain excessive loose casting flash.

BOLAS METALICAS
El Gamo's standard polished lead ball ammunition weighs 8.08gn (MLV 817fs⁻¹) and has an average diameter of 0.177in.

TIPO INGLÉS
El Gamo's English-style roundhead, possibly no longer in production, has a long ribbed skirt more akin to German prototypes. 4.5mm; packed in tins of 250 and 500. Weight: 8.39gn (MLV 802fs⁻¹). Length: 0.228in.

TIPO MAGNUM
Samples of this multi-ring-seal cone-point pellet displayed very variable overall length and small head/skirt diameter. Performance proved to be inferior to Silver Jet, on which the Magnum is clearly based. 4.5 and 5.5mm; packed in flip-top plastic boxes of 250 or 500. Weight, 4.5mm: 7.28gn (MLV 861fs⁻¹). Length, 4.5mm: 0.250in.

TIPO MATCH
This is a typically German-style ribbed-skirt flathead (4.5 and 5.5mm), made of a very hard lead alloy and packed in tins of 250 or 500. Synonym: Tipo Alemaña. Weight: 7.55 and 12.26gn (MLV 845 and 663fs⁻¹). Length: 0.203 and 0.246in.

H&N

Haendler & Natermann GmbH of Hannover-Münden, West Germany (British distributor: Frank Dyke & Co. Ltd, 1-7 Ernest Avenue, West Norwood, London SE27 0DG), offers by far the largest range of airgun ammunition. Quality varies appreciably, according to price, though H&N Match pellets have helped to win many international honours: at the 1986 European Championships in Suhl, for example, all the airgun medallists used them.

BARRACUDA
This is the heaviest of all standard 5.5mm diabolo pellets; so heavy, in fact, that it taxes the average sporting gun appreciably. Velocity is greatly reduced and the trajectory is excessively parabolic, though the

Barracuda actually has excellent sectional density, a good ballistic coefficient and retains its velocity better than virtually any other airgun projectile. Similar design: Beeman Kodiak. Weight: 21.62gn (MLV 499fs⁻¹). Length: 0.339in. Note: a 4.5mm Kodiak weighing 10.62gn is also made.

COPPA POINT
The distinctive copper wash gives this plain-bodied cone-point pellet extra hardness and penetrative capability. 4.5 and 5.5mm; packed in tins of 250 and 500. Weight: 8.59 and 16.53gn (MLV 793 and 571fs⁻¹). Length: 0.274 and 0.334in. Note: one sample tin contained the output of two differing machines — one group of pellets weighed 8.10gn . . . the others, 9.07! These only grouped properly when individually selected by weight.

DIABOLO SPORT
Widely distributed in Britain, these sturdy flathead diabolos can be obtained with plain (glatt) or ribbed (geriffelt) skirts, the pattern being obvious from the tin seals. Synonyms: Browning Regular (ribbed skirt), H&N Wettkampfkugel, Mauser Wettkampf, Z&S Diabolo (q.v.). 4.5, 5.05 and 5.5mm; packed in tins of 250 and 500. Weight, ribbed versions: 7.25, 9.84 and 14.27gn (MLV 863, 740 and 615fs⁻¹). Length: 0.208, 0.233 and 0.249in.

'ENGLÄNDERMODELL'
This is essentially similar to the standard H&N Diabolo, but has an English style roundhead. The body is longer than most pellets made in Britain, enhancing accuracy. Synonym: Beeman Bearcub, Mauser Round Nose. 4.5, 5.05 and 5.5mm; packed in tins of 250 and 500. Weight, ribbed versions: 8.10, 10.74 and 14.16gn (MLV 816, 709 and 617fs⁻¹). Length: 0.231, 0.257 and 0.268in.

FIELD TARGET
Specially made for outdoor competitions, this is basically a lightened Silhouette (q.v.). Field Target pellets are specially selected and batched, quality being outstanding with scarcely any weight variation. 4.5 and 5.5mm; packed in tins of 500. Weight: 8.85 and 16.44gn (MLV 781 and 573fs⁻¹). Length: 0.269 and 0.303in.

MATCH
These number among the best of all diabolo pellets, having won countless medals at the highest levels. Unlike RWS rivals, which are plain-skirted, the H&N patterns can be obtained with plain (glatt) or ribbed (geriffelt) skirts. The 5.5mm

'H&N Match' version (14.67gn, 606fs⁻¹, 0.260in overall) offers neither the quality nor the performance of the 4.5mm pattern. Synonyms: Browning Match (plain skirt), Browning Record (ribbed skirt), Hy-Score Competition (or Match), Mauser Match. 4.5mm; packed in tins of 500, plastic multi-tray boxes of 500 or individual plastic trays of 100. Weight: High Speed 7.31gn (MLV 859fs⁻¹), standard 7.87gn (MLV 828fs⁻¹). Length: 0.208 and 0.210in respectively. Note: rifle and pistol-shooting variants are offered. Owing to the relatively less demanding 10m ISU air-pistol competition requirements, 'pistol' pellets may simply be rifle patterns that are marginally out of tolerance.

POINTED
H&N's equivalent of the RWS Superpoint has a strongly ribbed skirt and a slightly blunter cone point that may sometimes be sufficiently off-centre to compromise accuracy. Synonyms: Beeman Silver Sting, Browning Conic, Mauser Superpoint, Verminkiller, Z&S Pointed. 4.5, 5.05 and 5.5mm; packed in tins of 200, 250 or 500. Weight: 8.56, 10.86 and 16.00gn (MLV 794, 705 and 581fs⁻¹). Length: 0.281, 0.288 and 0.319in.

SILHOUETTE
Developed in America by Beeman, as the Ram Jet, this plain-bodied pellet has a very distinctive sub-diameter rounded head, appreciably greater weight than normal and better sectional density. 4.5mm; packed in tins of 500. Weight: 9.51gn (MLV 753fs⁻¹). Length: 0.280in. NB: one test tin contained the output of two different machines, the average of 9.40gn (MLV 757fs⁻¹) masking batches of light (8.92gn, MLV 778fs⁻¹) and heavy (9.88gn, MLV 739fs⁻¹) pellets. These pellets only grouped well if selected by weight.

SEMI-WADCUTTER
The hollowed nose of this Beeman design is supposed to expand on hitting an animate target. However, it contributes greatly to drag and the Semi-Wadcutter loses velocity at much the same rate as a flathead — though the effect is slightly masked by high initial velocity. Similar design: Beeman Silver Bear. Synonym: Mauser Hollow Point. 4.5, 5.05 and 5.5mm; packed in tins of 250 or 500. Weight: 6.82, 9.85 and 11.28gn (MLV 890, 740 and 692fs⁻¹). Length: 0.220, 0.241 and 0.246in.

Z&S RANGE
These fall marginally below the normal H&N acceptance tolerances

and are, therefore, slight seconds. Named after Zieh- & Stanzwerke Schedetal, a foundry acquired by Haendler & Natermann in 1927, Z&S pellets are usually cheaper than comparable H&N patterns. However, the best of them performs no differently to the standard Diabolo Sport.

SLUGS AND BALLS
H&N makes ball ammunition, from 3.30mm to 8.60mm (0.130-0.339in) in 0.05mm increments, as well as 4.5-6.25mm 'H&N Spitzkugeln' (slugs).

HASUIKE SEISAKUSHO

Osaka, Japan. British distributor: usually available through Webley & Scott Ltd. The products of this company were rarely seen in Britain until the late 1970s, when Beeman had begun marketing them in the USA and large quantities migrated across the Atlantic. Though some outrageous claims have been made for the Silver Jet — it is neither innovative nor especially 'high velocity' — there is no doubt that quality is unusually good.

JET
This multi-ring-seal roundhead offers similar construction, quality and performance to the Silver Jet (q.v.), though rather less penetration. Synonym: Mount Star Diabolo or Roundhead. 4.5 and 5.5mm; packed in boxes of 250 or 500. Weight: 8.12 and 15.01gn (MLV 815 and 599fs⁻¹). Length: 0.220 and 0.266in.

LASER
This ultra-lightweight roundhead was developed to legitimize high velocity claims though, ironically, the heavier Beeman Silver Bear (alias the H&N Semi-Wadcutter) may achieve comparable velocities in some guns. The Laser has a good head shape, but its low sectional density compromises retention of velocity. 4.5mm; packed in tins of 500. Weight: 6.17gn (MLV 935fs⁻¹). Length: 0.228in.

SILVER JET
This popular triple-ring-head pointed pellet is capable of excellent performance in the right gun. It is superbly made, but seats more on the head than the skirt and the extra friction may reduce velocity compared with conventional diabolos of similar weight. Synonyms: Jet Magnum, Lion Zet, Mount Star Pointed. 4.5, 5.05 and 5.5mm; packed in specially cushioned expanded polystyrene boxes containing 250, 375 or 500 pellets. Weight: 8.19, 11.22 and

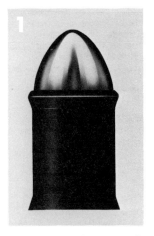

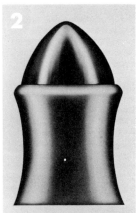

15.00gn (MLV 812, 693 and 600fs^{-1}). Length: 0.271, 0.287 and 0.306in.

JEFFRIES

The name of Lincoln Jeffries & Co. Ltd, Summer Lane, Birmingham B19 3TH, England, is renowned in airgun circles — though the company now makes little other than pellets, fishing weights and similar lead-based products.

MARKSMAN

Production of this conventional but inexpensive English-style roundheaded pellet began many years ago. Performance is satisfactory, though the Marksman is less effectual than the Eley Wasp. 0.177 and 0.22in; packed in boxes of 250 and 500, or tins of 500. Weight: 8.25 and 14.15gn (MLV 809 and 617fs^{-1}). Length: 0.220 and 0.243in. A 0.25-calibre version, weighing about 20.2gn, is made especially for John Knibbs (see Titan Black).

MARKSMAN POINTED

This is a variation of the standard Marksman, distinguished by its distinctive shallow-sided body, fine ribs and a low conical point. Packed as Marksman (q.v.).

JOLLY

Distributed in Britain by Scalemead Arms Company, 3 Medway Buildings, Lower Road, Forest Row, East Sussex RH18 5HE, the products of this Italian metal-foundry are best known in Britain under the Hustler banner.

HARRIER

This twin-ring roundhead, derived from the Hustler, offers acceptable performance at a highly competitive price — though the head diameter can be as small as 0.214in and accuracy suffers accordingly. Synonym: Hustler Harrier. 5.5mm;

packed in plastic tins of 500. Weight: 12.48gn (MLV 657fs^{-1}). Length: 0.264in.

HUSTLER

The pointed twin-ring seal Hustler usually displays a small-diameter head suited to German rather than British-type bores; performance is adequate at the price. 4.5 and 5.5mm; packed in tins of 500. Weight: 8.21 and 12.64gn (MLV 811 and 653fs^{-1}). Length: 0.280 and 0.287in.

STRIKE

A conventional derivative of the Hustler (q.v.), this features a particularly broad bearing surface that increases friction and lowers velocity compared with traditional designs. Synonym: American Strike. 4.5mm; packed in plastic boxes of 500. Weight: 7.21gn (MLV 865fs^{-1}). Length: 0.263in.

OTHERS

Jolly has also made the 5.5mm Hustler Jet (12.62gn, MLV 654fs^{-1}, 0.286in); the 4.5mm Hustler Match, which failed to offer true competition quality (7.21gn, MLV 865fs^{-1}, 0.216in); and the 4.5mm Hustler Tri-Jet (8.16gn, MLV 813fs^{-1}, 0.290in) based on the Silver Jet.

LANES

Lanes Pellets Ltd, Unit 76, Roding Road, London Industrial Park, London E6 4LS, England.

BULLDOG

This ribbed-body roundhead has been greatly improved since the recent reorganization of the company and now features among the best of the inexpensive English-style short body roundheads. Synonyms: (pre-1984) National Pellets, Precise Minuteman. 0.177 and 0.22in; packed in tins of 500. Weight: 7.81 and 13.43gn (MLV 831 and 634fs^{-1}). Length: 0.216 and 0.270in. The BSA Besa is essentially similar, but

lighter and somewhat shorter (7.76 and 12.44gn, 0.208 and 0.241in).

MILBRO

Milbro Caledonian Pellet Co. Ltd, Block 4, Unit 4G, Carfin Industrial Estate, Motherwell, Lanarkshire, Scotland ML1 4UL. The pellet-making rump of Milbro managed to survive the liquidation of the company in 1982, to be re-formed and achieve success as a separate enterprise.

CALEDONIAN

This standard English-style roundhead diabolo is generally regarded as the best of the British-made patterns, excepting the Eley Wasp. Synonyms: Kassnar, Webley. 0.177 and 0.22in; packed in tins of 500. Weight: 8.33 and 13.39gn (MLV 805 and 635fs^{-1}). Length: 0.204 and 0.243in.

RHINO

One of the very few extra-large pellets being mass-produced in Britain, this ribbed-body 0.25-calibre roundhead is especially suitable for high-power guns such as the Harper SS80K. It has a rather poorer sectional density than otherwise comparable 0.22 patterns, and retains velocity less efficiently. Packed in tins of 500. Weight: 20.77gn (MLV 509fs^{-1}). Length: 0.281in.

SELECT

This is a special form of the Caledonian (q.v.), batched by applying stricter control to tolerances.

TR

The Twin Ring ('TR') is primarily intended for field target shooting, but is still too new to have had much impact. 4.5mm; packed in tins of 500. Weight: about 7.8gn. Length: about 0.275in.

The Prometheus pellets — 0.177 (1) and 0.22in (2) — are the only wholly non-toxic synthetic skirt designs currently available. Semi-flathead field target derivatives are also made. By courtesy of Prometheus Pellets Ltd.

PROMETHEUS

Prometheus Pellets Ltd, 166 Archway Road, London N6 5BB, England, makes the only truly non-toxic synthetic-body design to achieve production status. The original polished steel head was replaced in 1981 by crushable zinc-alloy, which is less likely to ricochet than even particles from shattered lead pellet-heads. The principal disadvantage of Prometheus is light weight, which reduces sectional density and partly offsets the excellent head-shape; though initial velocity is prodigious, it is lost quite quickly and the advantages over some of the best lead pellets eventually disappear at long range. (See also 'Titan Black'.)

HUNTER

The standard pellet has a brightly-polished ogival head and a synthetic skirt (clear in the 0.22 version, black for the 0.177). Unlike most other pellets, the Prometheus seats on the skirt-bands and the head does not touch the bore at all. Performance in super-power guns may be poor — the skirts may melt — and Anschütz, M&G Diana, Weihrauch or other choke-barrel rifles may need counter-bored to assure immaculate performance with the Prometheus as well as lead pellets. Packed in plastic tubs of 100 (0.22, black) and 125 (0.177, red). Weight: 6.00 and 9.12gn (MLV 948 and 769fs^{-1}). Length: 0.345 and 0.350in.

FIELD TARGET

The truncated-head Prometheus is specifically intended for use against knock-down targets. As the ranges in field-target competitions are often quite short, the unusually high muzzle velocity — 120-150fs^{-1} greater than most other pellets — means a quicker travel up the bore and commensurately less effect from recoil or spring-surge. The velocity retention is marginally poorer than the standard Prometheus, but this is only evident at long range and sectional density remains much the same. Packed in plastic tubs of 100 (0.22in, blue) or 125 (0.177in, green). Weight: 6.00 and 8.75gn (MLV 948 and 785fs^{-1}). Length: 0.322 and 0.326in.

STIGA

Stiga AB, Tranås, Sweden

DOGG MATCH

This German-style flathead has a very distinctive skirt and outweighs even RWS Meisterkugeln. Together with the larger-than-normal head and skirt diameters, this excessive weight restricts velocity appreciably. 4.5mm; packed in tins of 250 and

500. Weight: 8.75gn (MLV 785fs^{-1}). Length: 0.217in.

TITAN PELLETS

John Knibbs International, 'Gillia', Blackfirs Lane, Birmingham B37 7JE, England, markets the officially licensed Titan Black. Unlike the light, fast-moving Prometheus pellets they outwardly resemble, Titan Blacks have a lead core. This increases weight markedly (reducing velocity commensurately), but the improved sectional density and ballistic coefficient enhance velocity retention and long-range performance. However, a powerful gun is needed to fire them. Data generally as 0.22

Prometheus Hunter except weight — 13.38gn (MLV 635fs^{-1}).

WESTHAVEN

Westhaven Marketing, Unit 3, Manor House Industrial Park, Millbrook Trading Estate, outhampton, England.

SABO

This comprises a sub-calibre boat-tailed coppered-lead bullet inside a plastic cage or 'sabot'. When the assembled Sabo emerges at the muzzle, air resistance drags the cage backwards and the bullet continues alone. Consequently, the sub-calibre projectile can have a greatly improved sectional density, a better

ballistic coefficient and an efficient aerodynamic shape. Maximum range and velocity retention are both greatly improved at the expense of unpredictable cage release and occasional fliers. The inconvenient 0.22 version has to be assembled in a loading tool before being inserted in the breech, though the smaller Sabo is supplied ready-assembled. Weight, 0.177 version: 7.53gn plus 0.48gn for the sabot (MLV 820fs^{-1} with the sabot attached, 846fs^{-1} without it). Weight, 0.22 version: 13.62gn plus 0.82gn for the sabot (MLV 611fs^{-1} or 629fs^{-1}, depending on sabot attachment). Length: 0.249 and 0.289in. Bullet diameter: 0.142 and 0.165in.

A selection of typical airgun projectiles. From left to right: RWS Diabolo, RWS Superpoint, Beeman Silver Bear, Hasuike Silver Jet, Bimoco Viper and a typical Sheridan slug. By courtesy of David Gibbons.

German-made 'Discofelt' cleaning pellets are a popular means of cleaning airgun barrels without the comparative inconvenience of assembling a cleaning rod or pull-through. Courtesy of Vereinigte Filzfabriken GmbH.

This is to be used in conjunction with the experiment.
The average velocity is found by dividing the total, 5764.4, by 25; the standard deviation is obtained by dividing the total of the d^2 column, 236.28, and square-rooting the answer.

	V_a	d	d^2	d$_{PS}$
1	228.0	−2.6	6.76	—
2	226.5	−4.1	16.81	1.5
3	227.0	−3.6	12.96	0.5
4	228.8	−1.8	3.24	1.8
5	235.2	+4.6	21.16	6.4
6	229.8	−0.8	0.64	5.4
7	233.8	+3.2	10.24	4.0
8	226.8	−3.8	14.44	7.0
9	228.3	−2.3	5.29	1.5
10	233.5	+2.9	8.41	5.2
11	229.6	−1.0	1.00	3.9
12	237.9	+7.3	53.29	8.3
13	230.6	0.0	0.00	7.3
14	231.7	+1.1	1.21	1.1
15	226.3	−4.3	18.49	5.4
16	230.4	−0.2	0.04	4.1
17	230.4	−0.2	0.04	0.0
18	230.4	−0.2	0.04	0.0
19	229.3	−1.3	1.69	1.1
20	228.6	−2.0	4.00	0.7
21	237.1	+6.5	42.25	8.5
22	229.3	−1.3	1.69	7.8
23	230.1	−0.5	0.25	0.8
24	230.9	+0.3	0.09	0.8
25	234.1	+3.5	12.25	3.2
Table I	5764.4		236.28	

Appendices

This information originally appeared in the British periodical *Guns Review* in 1981-2, and was then revised for the Third Edition of this book in 1984. Since then, no fundamental changes have been made other than those necessary to computerize the system. Changes have been made to the 'final expressions' by modifying the use of standard deviation, and these have had some effect on the figurework compared with the previous version. Further information may be found in John Walter, *Airgun Shooting A-Z*, available through Lyon Publishing International.

ASSESSING VELOCITY

* The minimum quantity necessary for mathematically-acceptable statistical analysis is 24 units. 25 is used here simply because it represents five 5-shot groups.

To be acceptable mathematically, the results of 25 shots* fired under identical conditions. As friction raises the temperature in the airgun cylinder during a rapid sequence of shots, causing the air pressure to vary, this ideal state is theoretically impossible to obtain; however, the effects of cylinder heating may be ignored provided that shots are not literally fired one after another, and assuming that ten 'warm-ups' have been fired to eliminate the first-shot dieselling that so often characterizes a spring-piston gun. Results obtained on a warm summer's day will usually be better than in midwinter, velocity being higher and consistency generally (but not always) improved.

Table One contains typical results. The *average velocity* (to be called V_x) may be calculated by totalling the *actual velocity* figures (V_a) and dividing by the number of shots (n) in the sequence. The average of the 25 velocities in Table One is about 230.6ms^{-1} (757fs^{-1}). There is a single high-velocity shot, the twelfth in the series, at 237.9ms^{-1} (781fs^{-1}); and a low one, the fifteenth, at 226.3ms^{-1} (742fs^{-1}). The difference between these extremes (GD) is 11.6ms^{-1} – which makes this particular 4.5mm Weihrauch HW35E a reasonably consistent performer with RWS Hobby pellets. 11.6ms^{-1} is 5.03 per cent of the average velocity: is it, therefore, an adequate index of performance? The answer is most definitely not: clearly, most of the individual shots were recorded between 228 and 233ms^{-1} and it is reasonable to conclude that this gun/pellet combination deserves a better rating than simply dividing the average velocity by the difference between the two extremes.

Consequently, the basic performance index of 5.03 per cent needs to be modified by using *standard deviation* (s), which will effect a desired improvement – but only if most of the shots group close to the average velocity. The value of s is obtained by finding the difference (d) between each value of V_a and the average velocity, V_x. This is calculated without worrying about whether V_a is greater or less than V_x. The d values are then squared (i.e., multiplied by themselves) and the resulting d^2 figures are totalled, divided by the number of shots (n) and square-rooted to provide the requisite value of s. Many modern scientific calculators will perform the task automatically, the key marked with the Greek letter delta (δ) and 'n-1' giving the correct interpretation.†

† There are two types of standard deviation, one using the entire data for a 'population' (i.e., any group of objects) to provide s and the other using data obtained from a sample of the population. The earlier editions of *The Airgun Book* incorrectly used the former; this edition relies on the latter, which gives perceptibly poorer-looking figures.

It will be noted how the extreme shots have a disproportionate effect on d^2: shots number 24 and 25 differ from the average by only 0.3 and 3.5ms^{-1} respectively – or, put another way, the deviation of the greater is about twelve times that of the smaller. The d^2 values increase this apparent difference more than elevenfold; however, as shot 24 is practically average, its adverse effect on the index of performance should be minimal.

Applying these calculations, using Table One, should give s a value of $3.14\,\mathrm{ms^{-1}}$, 1.36 per cent of the average velocity V_x. This clearly presents a good method of assessing performance. But is more progress possible? Thus far, the interpretation of the figures has provided a reasonable index for one particular combination of gun and pellet, undertaken on a specific occasion. Could it now be developed to apply to all trials undertaken by this rifle with the same pellets, assuming that the spring has not deteriorated? This can be done with the help of a second statistical term, *confidence limits* (**C**), which is an expression of probability. Here, a probability of 98 per cent (from which $C=2.33$) allows a small concession to unforeseen performance fluctuations.

A value for the average velocity of all RWS Hobby pellets fired by the trial Weihrauch HW35E can be derived from the the following expression: $\partial = V_x \pm \dfrac{Cs}{\sqrt{n}}$

In this it is simply necessary to substitute the average velocity (V_x), the confidence limit (C), the standard deviation (s) and the number of shots in the trial (n). The average has been found to be $230.58\,\mathrm{ms^{-1}}$, C is 2.33, s is 3.14 and n is 25. The equation, therefore, resolves to $230.58 \pm 1.46\,\mathrm{ms^{-1}}$. The $1.46\,\mathrm{ms^{-1}}$ value is known as the *velocity consistency limit* (**VCL**), and suggests that it is 98 per cent probable that the average velocity of all RWS Hobby pellets fired from this particular HW35E will lie between $230.57-1.46$ and $230.57+1.46\,\mathrm{ms^{-1}}$ — i.e., between 229.12 and $232.04\,\mathrm{ms^{-1}}$ (752 and $761\,\mathrm{fs^{-1}}$). The difference between these extremes, $2.92\,\mathrm{ms^{-1}}$, is called the *velocity consistency index* (**VCI**); in this case it represents a highly satisfactory 1.27 per cent of the average velocity V_x, and an acceptable final result.

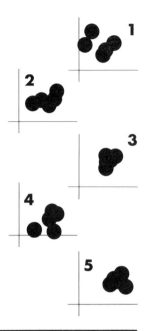

Table II. Summary of trials with an Ensign Magnum rifle.

ENSIGN ARMS COMPANY

	A	C	E	B	D	F	E+F	G
1	+ 2.7	- 10.2	104.04	+ 10.6	+ 1.3	1.69	105.73	10.28
2	+ 10.7	- 2.2	4.84	+ 6.5	- 2.8	7.84	12.68	3.56
3	+ 5.8	- 7.1	50.41	+ 16.5	+ 7.2	51.84	102.25	10.11
4	+ 15.1	+ 2.2	4.84	+ 11.4	+ 2.1	4.41	9.25	3.04
5	+ 11.8	- 1.1	1.21	+ 8.4	- 0.9	0.81	2.02	1.42
6	+ 9.9	- 3.0	9.00	+ 8.9	- 0.4	0.16	9.16	3.03
7	+ 13.5	+ 0.6	0.36	+ 7.0	- 2.3	5.29	5.65	2.38
8	+ 6.1	- 6.8	46.24	+ 7.8	- 1.5	2.25	48.49	6.96
9	+ 16.7	+ 3.8	14.44	+ 12.5	+ 3.2	10.24	24.68	4.97
10	+ 15.8	+ 2.9	8.41	+ 9.8	+ 0.5	0.25	8.66	2.94
11	+ 11.3	- 1.6	2.56	+ 7.8	- 1.5	2.25	4.81	2.19
12	+ 13.8	+ 0.9	0.81	+ 11.8	+ 2.5	6.25	7.06	2.66
13	+ 11.6	- 1.3	1.69	+ 10.5	+ 1.2	1.44	3.13	1.77
14	+ 11.3	- 1.6	2.56	+ 13.2	+ 3.9	15.21	17.77	4.22
15	+ 15.7	+ 2.8	7.84	+ 13.0	+ 3.7	13.69	21.53	4.64
16	+ 15.0	+ 2.1	4.41	+ 1.3	- 8.0	64.00	68.41	8.27
17	+ 6.6	- 6.3	39.69	+ 1.7	- 7.6	57.76	97.45	9.87
18	+ 14.3	+ 1.4	1.96	+ 9.8	+ 0.5	0.25	2.21	1.49
19	+ 13.1	+ 0.2	0.04	+ 6.6	- 2.7	7.29	7.33	2.71
20	+ 16.3	+ 3.4	11.56	+ 9.0	- 0.3	0.09	11.65	3.41
21	+ 16.1	+ 3.2	10.24	+ 10.8	+ 1.5	2.25	12.49	3.53
22	+ 13.3	+ 0.4	0.16	+ 8.1	- 1.2	1.44	1.60	1.26
23	+ 20.1	+ 7.2	51.84	+ 7.4	- 1.9	3.61	55.45	7.45
24	+ 18.6	+ 5.7	32.49	+ 12.9	+ 3.6	12.96	45.45	6.74
25	+ 16.6	+ 3.7	13.69	+ 9.4	+ 0.1	0.01	13.70	3.70
	+321.8			+232.7				112.6
								+ 25 = 4.50

The table of measurements plots the fall of the shots shown on the group diagrams above. 321.8 is the total of the horizontal (x-axis) displacement of the shots, while 232.7 is the result of similar addition of the vertical (y-axis) displacements. Columns C and D are the corrected displacements, taking the position of the true 25-shot group centre into account, while E and F are the squared values of C and D. G is the square root of E+F.

Totalling G and dividing by 25, the number of shots, gives the mean radius.

ACCURACY TRIALS

Airgun reviews stating that one hole accuracy was obtained from a three-shot group are potentially very misleading. It is rarely obvious how many groups were fired to obtain such perfection, nor whether the centres of individual groups were markedly displaced. To guard against these problems, it is necessary to fire 25 shots – five 5-shot groups are quite acceptable – and then assess the position of each and every shot individually.

Table Two is a typical trial of a British 0.22 Ensign Magnum rifle firing Eley Wasp pellets. Five 5-shot groups were obtained from targets on which a consistent aim-point was marked. Taking each of the groups in turn, the distance from the centre of each shot to the aim-point must be determined on the horizontal (x) and vertical (y) axes until a table of distances is obtained for all 25 shots.

Individual measurements are regarded as positive if the shots lie to the right of the aim point horizontally; if they strike to the left, they are regarded as negative. Similarly, they are positive above the aim-point and negative below.

Column A on Table Two lists the displacement of the shots horizontally. As all of them struck to the right of the aim-point (the sights must not be altered during the trial), their values range from +2.7 to +20.1mm. The 'positive' shots are added together, giving a total of +321.8mm.‡ It is already obvious that the centre of the 25-shot group lies to the right of the aim-point; however, if the sum of negative shots had exceeded that of the positives, the group centre would actually lie to the left. The actual displacement of the group centre is found by dividing the total, 321.8mm, by the number of shots (25): 12.87mm, or 12.9mm to the nearest tenth.

The horizontal position of the group centre has now been found, and the process is repeated vertically to discover whether it lies above or below the aim-point. In fact, all of the shots lie above the mark, and have positive values between +1.3mm and +16.5mm. The total is +232.7mm and after dividing this by 25, therefore, the group-centre is located 9.31mm above the point of aim.

Once the group centre has been established, there is still a minor problem; the distance each shot lies from the aim-point has already been determined from columns A and B, but these must be corrected in relation to the new group centre before proceeding further. Consequently, the value of +12.9 must be subtracted from all the figures in column A and +9.3 from those in column B. It is evident from the corrected figures in columns C and D that some previously positive shots, which lay to the right or above the aim-point, are negative in relation to the centre of the 25-shot group.

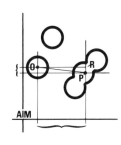

This diagram shows the aim-point, which was established before shooting began, and the relative position of the combined group centre (**P**). The distance the centre **O** of shot 1 lies from P is obtained by simple geometry – Pythagoras' Theorem – as the square of the displacement distance OP equals RO squared plus RP squared. RO is the relevant horizontal distance provided by column C on Table Two, while the vertical measurement RP may be found in column D. The values for the first shot are 10.2 and 1.3mm respectively, as it struck to the right and above the major group centre. $RO^2 + RP^2$ is found to be 105.73; $\sqrt{105.73}$, or 10.28mm, provides distance OP. Thus the first shot lies about 10.3mm away from the centre of the 'big group'. Column G indicates that the nearest shot was the 23rd, only 1.3mm distant.

There are several ways of expressing the overall result, including 'string total' (112.6mm in this case), but airgunners invariably refer to 'group diameter'. The easiest way to adapt to this is to obtain the average radial displacement (ARD) or *mean radius* (**MR**) by totalling column G and dividing the answer by the number of shots. The mean radius of this Ensign Magnum/Eley Wasp trial is 4.50mm. As diameter is twice radius, it is reasonable to claim a mean diameter (MD) – now renamed *mean grouping potential* (**MGP**) – of 9.0mm. This is actually lower than the average of the five separate group diameters (about 10.7mm), but has been obtained by differing means and will minimize the effects of a few fliers.

It now becomes possible to derive an acceptable prediction of the performance of the Ensign Magnum firing the same pellets on any other occasion, which makes it easy to predict if calamity is to befall the mechanism or whether some pellets shoot better than others despite offering comparable mean diameters. This involves the same statistical procedures outlined in the previous section, use of standard deviation (s) and con-

‡ In cases where there are positive and negative values to be assessed, it is advisable to total (i) the positives and then (ii) the negatives, after which the difference between the two can be found – remembering that the result may be negative or positive depending on the precise position of the group centre in relation to the aim-point.

fidence limits (C) allowing the variation of individual shots to be assessed. Following the principles that led to the determination of the velocity deviation limits can also give an *accuracy consistency limit* (**ACL**) by assessing the fluctuations in the individual shot displacement (column G on Table Two). For the Ensign/Wasp trial, the ACL is 2.63mm and the accuracy potential can be written as 4.50 ± 2.63mm. The *accuracy consistency index* (**ACI**), twice the ACL, is 117 per cent of the mean radius; a similar trial in which more pellets lay at the edge of the large group than the centre, for example, could have resulted in 4.50 ± 3.80mm and an ACI of 169.

Howa

Above: *the Howa 55G*

The final result, then, allows a claim that 98 per cent of all Eley Wasps fired from this Ensign rifle will lie within $4.50-2.63$ (1.87mm) and $4.50+2.63$mm (7.13mm) at a range of 15.5 metres. It is possible to correct the figures to a standard range and even to calculate average scores on standard targets. By applying a straightforward linear conversion to the Ensign/Wasp trial, accepting the attendant drawbacks, the MGP becomes 2.91mm at 10 metres – remarkably good shooting which, with a help of a micro-computer, can be shown to score 96×100 on a standard ISU 10m airrifle target.

GAS-POWERED GUNS

BENJAMIN
Sheridan Model F 0.20-calibre rifle (1976 to date)
Sheridan Model E or EB 0.20-calibre pistol (1978 to date)

CROSMAN
Crosman-Blaser 0.177 conversion kit for the 0.45-calibre Colt automatic pistol (1986 to date)
Mark 1 pistol, 0.177 pellet or BB (Ruger lookalike, discontinued in 1984)
Mark 2 pistol, 0.22 (larger-calibre version of Mark 1)
Model 38C, 0.177 S&W-based revolver (discontinued in 1983)
Model 38T, 0.177 S&W-based revolver (discontinued in 1984)
Model 73 Saddle Pal, 0.177 pellet or BB-firing pseudo Winchester (made 1975-84)
Model 84 Olympic, 4.5mm high-grade competition rifle (1984 to date)
Model 338 Auto, 0.175 BB-firing pistol based on the Walther P.38 (introduced in 1986)
Model 357, 0.177 Colt Python lookalike, but with a tipping barrel (357 Four and 357 Six introduced in 1983, 357 Eight in 1984)
Model 454 BB-Matic, 0.175 BB-firer (discontinued in 1984)
Model 1357 Six, BB-firing version of the 357 Six (1986 to date)
Model 1600 Powermatic, an 'economy' version of the 454 (1978 to date)
Model 1861 Shiloh, a short-lived (1981-4) Remington-like 0.177 revolver
Model 3357 Spot Marker, a 0.50-calibre paint ball firer based on the 357 (1986 to date)
Skanaker-Crosman 4.5mm competition pistol, prototypes made in 1985 and production expected to commence in 1987
Z-77, 0.175 BB-firing semi-automatic carbine based on the Uzi (1986 to date)

DAISY
Model 41 Magnum, a nickel-plated version of the Power Line 790, discontinued in 1984
Power Line 44, 0.177 revolver based on S&W lines (1986 to date)
Power Line 92, 0.177 pistol based on the Beretta M92 (1986 to date)
Power Line 780, Daisy's version of the 0.22 S&W Model 78G pistol (1980-2)
Power Line 790, Daisy's version of the 0.177 S&W Model 79G (1980-5)
Power Line 1200, a 0.175 BB-firing pistol based on the Browning Medalist
Model 8007 Quick Splotch, a 0.50-calibre paint-marking gun

FEINWERKBAU
LP2 and LP2 Junior 4.5mm competition pistols (Senfter/Idl system), introduced in 1981 and 1983 respectively

HEALTHWAYS
Model 9401 Plainsman, 0.175 BB-firing pistol (made 1956-83)
Model 9404 Plainsman Shorty, a short-barrelled 9401
Model 9405 Plainsmaster, 0.175 long-barrelled BB-firing pistol
Model 9406 Plainsmaster, 0.22 ball-firing variant of the 9405

HOWA
Model 55G, 0.22 rifle based on the Weatherby Mark V (production status uncertain)

MMM-MONDIAL
Model 4504 Roger, 0.175 BB-firing pistol

NATIONAL RIFLES LTD
Cadet, Hämmerli-based 0.177 rifle (produced since c.1969)

SHARP
current guns only
GR-75, 5mm-calibre Standard and Short, pump-loading rifles with vaguely Remington lines (introduced in 1975)
Mini-UD, 4.5mm carbine derived from the UD-2 (introduced in 1970)
UD-2, 4.5mm rifle (introduced in 1970?)
UD-2 Target, 4.5mm competition rifle derived from the UD-2
U-FP, 4.5mm pistol (introduced in 1972)
U-SL, 4.5mm 'Hand Rifle' or carbine prototype of U-FP (introduced in 1970)

SMITH & WESSON
Model 78G 0.22 pistol (made by S&W and then by Daisy in 1980-2)
Model 79G 0.177 pistol (made by S&W and then Daisy in 1980-5)
Model 80G 0.175 BB-firing rifle (discontinued in 1980)

STEYR-DAIMLER-PUCH
Competition rifle prototype, displayed at IWA in the Spring of 1987, is expected to reach production in 1988

WALTHER
CP1 4.5mm competition pistol (Senfter/Idl system, 1981-3)
CP2 4.5mm competition pistol (Senfter/Idl system, introduced in 1983)
CP2 Match 4.5mm competition pistol (as above, 1986)
CR1 match rifle prototype, expected to be announced in 1988